BRITIS

THE

OF YORKSHIRE

Metalliferous and associated minerals

by

M.C. GILL & R. BURT

**A
MONOGRAPH
OF THE
NORTHERN MINE RESEARCH SOCIETY
MAY 2003**

ISSN 0308 2199

ISBN 0 901450 56 1

Typeset in 10 point Times New Roman

by

N.M.R.S. Publications.

PRINTED

by

FRETWELL

PRINT AND DESIGN

Healey Works,
Goulbourne Street, Keighley,
Yorkshire, BD21 1PZ

for the publishers

THE NORTHERN MINE RESEARCH SOCIETY
SHEFFIELD, U.K.

Cover illustration: Composite picture: map of Yorkshire, High smelt mill at Marrick, the Octagon smelt mill at Langthwaite, Crushing machine at Museum of Yorkshire Dales Lead Mining, miners loading a waggon in Sun Level, Appletreewick. Spine: Drilling in Sun Level.

CONTENTS

PREFACE

In 1975, Roger Burt and his colleagues in the Department of Economic History at the University of Exeter began a project, supported by the Social Science Research Council, to analyse the mine-by-mine returns of production, ownership, management and employment that appeared in the annual *Mineral Statistics of the United Kingdom* (1845 to 1913). The data was assimilated and stored in what was probably one of the earliest computerised data-bases of historical information, and was also used to produce a series of county-based volumes of mineral statistics. The first of these, for Derbyshire, appeared in 1981 and was soon followed by others for the various Pennine counties, the Isle of Man, South-West England and, finally, central and north Wales. By 1990, ten county volumes had been published and the first stage of the project was drawing to a close. Work has not stopped, however, and it is intended to publish the *Irish Mineral Statistics*, also as part of the *British Mining* series, in 2003/4. Moreover, all of the published data, together with new material on Wales, will shortly be made freely available, in searchable form, on the world wide web. More importantly, a new generation of greatly expanded county data sets – of which this is the first – are planned to appear in the next few years. Mike Gill first proposed this latter extension project back in 1985 and this pilot on the pre-1974 county of Yorkshire has expanded progressively ever since. Clearly, further additions could continue almost indefinitely, but in 2002 it was decided that the data now provided a major new research tool and should be published.

There is over four times more data in this volume than in the original *Yorkshire Mineral Statistics*. Although it is presented in a broadly similar way, some changes have been made. Most significantly, there has been a far greater editorial input to exploit Mike Gill's extensive knowledge of the county's mining history and to give a clearer view of what is now a very much longer period. Similarly, whilst aware of Seneca's comment that "*anything that is divided into minute grains becomes confused*", entries have been made for the small mines which made up larger titles, such as the AD, Arkengarthdale and Grassington Mines. There are also new headings to include a wider range of data.

The successful progression of this project was achieved only with the active help and collaboration of a wide range of private and professional researchers, librarians and archivists. Many thanks are due to: Lawrence Barker (Swaledale), David and Margaret Carlisle (Arkengarthdale), Ray Fairbairn (Scargill), Dr Edmund Green (Swaledale, Wensleydale and Middleton Tyas), William Houston (post-war period), Alan King (Malham), Hazel Martell (Chatsworth Archive), Dr Jack Myers (Malham), Alasdair Neill (C20th returns), the late Dr Arthur Raistrick (Wharfedale), Dr Jim Rieuwerts (Calderdale), Ian Spensley (Swaledale and Wensleydale), Malcolm Street (Nidderdale) and Les Tyson (Swaledale, Arkengarthdale and Wensleydale). Thanks are also due to Professor Bernard Jennings for allowing the inclusion of data from his MA thesis (see bibliography). The late John Owen gave invaluable help with the Cleveland ironstone mining industry, including detailed comment on the author's interpretation and expansion of the first volume, the provision of new data on mining before 1858 and the National Grid references of mines.

Mike Gill would also like to acknowledge the great amount of assistance given to him by the Chatsworth Estate, in particular Mr J.M. Sheard, the Agent at Bolton Abbey, and Mr M. Pearman, the Archivist at Chatsworth. Thanks are also due to the staffs of the following institutions: Bradford City Archives and Library; British Geological Survey Library, Keyworth; British Library, Wetherby; Brotherton Library, University of Leeds; Cumbria County Record Office, Carlisle; Durham County Planning Department; Durham County Record Office; Gateshead City Library; Guild Hall Library, London; Institute of Historical Studies Library, London; Institute of Industrial Archaeology Library, Ironbridge; John Rylands Library, University of Manchester; Manchester Central Library; Norfolk Record Office; Northumberland County Record Office; North Yorkshire County Record Office; Public Record Office (Chancery Lane and Kew); Sheffield City Library; Sheffield Record Office; Warwickshire County Record Office and the West Yorkshire Archive Service, Leeds.

The compilation of this data, which was in widely varying forms was a daunting task and without a computer it would have been impossible. Financial assistance for the work was given by Miss Mary McTurk, Billiton U.K. Limited and the Kildwick Church Parochial Council.

Any mistakes are, of course, Mike Gill's responsibility.

INTRODUCTION

I

The Mineral Statistics

This volume brings together production and ownership data for metalliferous mining in Yorkshire, from the earliest origins of the industry to the present day. It undoubtedly does not capture everything – some further material will surely become available – and it does not cover every period of the industry's history, as many mines worked for centuries before the earliest data presented here, but it does encompass everything that long and detailed research could reveal. To give perspective to the scale of the industry, we have also included aggregate information on national production of the various metals, and Yorkshire's contribution to those totals, as well as comparative data for the production of coal in the county, which was far larger and more important than the other activities put together.

The sources from which this data has been derived can be roughly divided into two groups - *archival material*, mainly for the period before the mid-19th century, and *official government returns*, for the period thereafter. The *archival* sources consist mainly of material generated by the owners of the minerals (the 'mineral lords') and the various mining companies that leased the rights to work them. Their 'quality' in terms of reliability and coverage is patchy, their survival random, their distribution now widespread and uncertain, and their interpretation subject to considerable difficulties. In the latter context, there are particular difficulties with the interpretation of weights and measures, which varied between place and over time before the early 19th century. For example, in Swaledale and Arkengarthdale care must be taken when using the above accounts because most smelt mills and some mines had their own system of weights until the mid-19th century. In Swaledale and Arkengarthdale, ore was usually weighed in Bings (8 cwts) and Horse Loads (2 cwts) and lead was in Stockton fodders of 22 cwts (2464 lbs). A local fodder, which weighed 34 cwts or 17 horse, was sometimes used for ore. At the normal rate of produce achieved by an ore-hearth (about 65%) this would give one fodder of lead (22 cwts). This system of rough, ready-reckoning is also reflected in the practice of each smelt mill making pieces of different weights (each practically a full fraction of a fodder). Nevertheless, examination of accounts shows that the average weight of the pieces, from batch to batch, seldom varied by more than a few pounds. When cast, each batch of 400 pieces was stamped with the mineral lord's or company's logo and a letter, called a mill mark, to help identify it. The next batch got the next letter, and so on from A through to Z. Casting pieces in this way helped to keep track of progress during smelting, allowed the quick estimation of the weight of lead in stacks, and also allowed for the easy identification of any pieces with damaged mill marks. However, whilst output figures must always be treated with caution during this early period, and total output for the county certainly exceeds the figures produced here, some good and reliable long runs of data have been assembled for some of the larger mining operations, such as the AD, Grinton and Hurst Mines in Swaledale, and the Buckden, Hawkswick, Conistone, Grassington and Hebden mines in Wharfedale.

Regular and *official returns* from the mines to the government first began to be collected in 1845 and have continued, in changing formats, to the present day. Printed and regularly published, these formed the basis of our earlier volume, which looked only at the period from the 1840s to the First World War. Here we have extended that coverage to 2000. The first published series, relating to the output of copper and lead, principally in the years 1845 to 1847, appeared in *Memoirs of the Geological Survey of Great Britain and the Museum of Practical Geology in London* Vols. I and II (H.M.S.O. 1845 and 1847). The recently established Mining Record Office, in particular its Keeper of Mining Records, Robert Hunt, did the work. This was regarded as a limited exercise, with no commitment for the publication of further annual series. In 1853, however, Hunt updated and extended the earlier series in a volume published by the Geological Survey, under his name, entitled *Records of the School of Mines and of Science Applied to the Arts*, Vol. I Pt IV. In the same year, a Treasury Committee, enquiring into the working of the Geological Survey and Museum, reported favourably on the activities of the Mining Record Office and recommended that its activities should be placed on a more regular footing. This signalled the start of the regular collection and publication of a widening range of data on mineral extraction and related manufacturing and transportation.

The first of this annual series, for 1853, appeared in 1855 and was published under the title *Memoirs of the Geological Survey of Great Britain and of the Museum of Practical Geology: Mining Records: The Mineral Statistics of the United Kingdom of Great Britain and Ireland.* This continued the production data of lead and copper, from 1845, as an unbroken run. Thereafter, until 1882, the series was published by the Geological Survey in the autumn of the year following the recorded year. Robert Hunt retired after the preparation of the 1881 volume and the collection of a considerably extended range of data was rationalised. This was done by transferring the Mining Record Office from the Museum of Practical Geology to the Home Office, where the Mines Inspectors, established by the Coal Mine Inspection Act of 1850, had, for many years, been publishing similar output data in their annual reports.

In particular, the Coal and Metalliferous Regulation Act of 1872 required all active mines in the country to furnish the Mines Inspectorate with details of their output and employment and it was thought wasteful to continue the duplication of returns and computations by the Mining Record Office. Hunt's staff prepared the first of the new series, following the established format, which appeared in 1884 under the title *The Mining and Mineral Statistics of the United Kingdom of Great Britain and Ireland for 1882*. Unlike earlier versions, however, it appeared as a Parliamentary Paper. In the next year, the title became *Summaries of Her Majesty's Inspectors of Mines Reports to Her Majesty's Secretary of State, and the Mineral Statistics of the United Kingdom of Great Britain and Ireland, including Lists of Mines and Mineral Works*. From 1884 to 1887, they appeared annually as *The Mineral and Mining Statistics of the United Kingdom of Great Britain and Ireland, including Lists of Mines and Mineral Worked.* During these years, the volumes included returns of a) the quantity and value of all minerals wrought; b) the numbers of people employed in and about the mines and open works; c) the number of fatal accidents in the mines; d) a list of the mine owners, managers and agents; e) a list of the recorded plans of abandoned mines that had been deposited at the Home Office; f) an appendix showing the production of minerals in the British Colonies and Possessions.

From 1888 to 1896 the returns appeared as *The Mining Statistics of the United Kingdom of Great Britain and Ireland with the Isle of Man*, a change which was associated with important changes in content. The details of accidents in the mines, previously held over from the early annual reports of the Inspectors of Mines, were published separately, as was the *List of Mines*, a regular appendix of the names of the mine owners, agents, managers and the numbers employed, which had been included at the back of The Mineral Statistics since 1853 for coal mines, 1859 for most metalliferous mines and 1863 for ironstone mines.

In 1897, the annual returns became the *Mines and Quarries: General Report and Statistics*. Their content was changed to the format they kept until the First World War, being split into four sections with Part III giving details of output. The latter was subtitled *General Report and Statistics Relating to the Output and Value of the Mineral Raised in the United Kingdom, the Amount and Value of the Metals Produced and the Exports and Imports of Minerals*.

It is notable that until 1897 the 'Clerks of the Mineral Statistics', responsible for preparing the publications, were still largely the same men that had worked with Robert Hunt from the earliest days of the Mining Record Office. This continuity contributed to an unparalleled wealth of experience in collecting and editing the material. Following Hunt's retirement in 1882, the new Home Office department had been jointly run by Richard Meade and James B. Jordan. Meade was appointed by Hunt in 1841 and he was joined by Jordan in 1858. Meade retired from the Home Office in 1889 and Jordan continued until 1897, thereby consolidating more than half a century's data gathering under three close associates.

Publication of the annual *List of Mines* continued, with breaks in 1939, 46, 47 and 49, until 1950, when it was discontinued. The output of individual mines was not given from 1914 to 1919 but was resumed between 1920 and 1938.

Reliable data sets are more difficult to find after 1950. Nevertheless, the Cleveland ironstone mines were listed in the *Guide to the Coalfields*, an annual publication by the *Colliery Guardian*. After 1960, the Mines Inspectorate also published a *List of Miscellaneous Mines in Great Britain*, which gives details of ownership, location and type of mineral worked. More recently, the British Geological Survey has produced a similar list, thereby resuming the task it relinquished around one hundred years before.

As might be expected, various libraries hold incomplete runs of the *List of Mines* and the *Guide to the Coalfields* etc, but the British Geological Survey Library, at Keyworth, probably has the most complete set, plus a wide range of general statistical data.

II

Yorkshire Mineral Production

This volume focuses on the record of metalliferous mining – not because it was Yorkshire's most important extractive industry, but because it was the sector recorded in greatest and most regular detail. It was the only form of mining for which detailed mine-by-mine returns are available in long and continuous series. Coal returns were only ever published in round totals for the county and never included the same range of detail as those for metals. Similarly, the returns for stone quarrying (mainly limestone, sandstone, flagstone and aggregates) and evaporite production (such as gypsum, potash and rock salt) generally only appeared as county totals, though mine-by-mine breakdowns can be found for some short sub-periods. These have not been included here, however.

The regular collection and publication of *official* metalliferous mining data started in 1845 with series for **lead**, with details of its **silver** content (estimated by assay rather than commercial refining) being added in 1851. These were joined in the now annual *Mineral Statistics of the United Kingdom*, by **copper** in 1848, though it is difficult to separate out the Yorkshire data until 1854. Returns for **zinc**, **barytes** and **fluorspar** began in 1854, but it is unlikely that they were comprehensive before the 1870s. **Iron** production was first recorded in 1855, but many producers, especially those in the West Riding, refused the Mining Record Office permission to publish their detailed returns. As a result, the only mine-by-mine returns published for Yorkshire were those voluntarily provided by companies in the Cleveland district between 1858 and 1881. From 1872, however, the publication of output data for individual mines in the coal measures was expressly forbidden by the Coal Mines Regulation Act. Details of production from Cleveland ironstone mines, which worked stratified deposits and came under the latter Act, disappeared after the reorganisation of the publication of the *Mineral Statistics* in 1881.

The relative scale of output of the different minerals produced in Yorkshire, and their share of national production, is shown in Table 1. **Ironstone** was clearly the most important both by volume and by value and it employed more capital and labour than the other metals combined. With a remarkably steady level of output of between five and six million tons annually from the 1870s - see Table 2 - the county total for the period 1855-1914 fell a little short of 300 million tons and comprised more than a third of total national production. Nearly all this output was derived from the Cleveland district, where ironstone mining had a long history, but developed rapidly after a successful trial of the Main Seam at Eston in 1850. The total production of the West Riding was a comparatively insignificant 12 million tons, most of which was mined before 1880. Within the Cleveland field, a major part of the total output was controlled by a handful of large producers. During the period 1858 to 1881, just three companies, Pease & Co., Bolckow, Vaughan Co. and Bell Brothers, were responsible for around two-thirds of the district's production.

Even in 1880, when the orefield was fully developed, seven mines producing over a quarter of a million tons annually accounted for nearly 63 per cent of the total output, with the remainder coming from 37 smaller producers.

The output of Cleveland's mines and the numbers employed in them rose steadily between 1895 and 1914 but, at the same time, overall productivity fell by 25-30 per cent from about 850 tons per man year to 600 tons per man year. This was an inevitable consequence of the increased haulage distances, for ore and materials, as the maturing mines became more extensive. Moreover, as workings reached lease boundaries, production was also shifting to pillar extraction. To counter these effects, some mines introduced new technology, but, whilst they may have seen improvements, it was insufficient to reverse the decline.

The industry contracted at the outbreak of World War I, as mines closed or were merged, and the number of underground employees fell sharply and never recovered. The average annual output, which in the six years before the war was a little under six million tons, fell to 2.3 millions by the early 1920s. This process continued in the latter decade, when Dorman, Long & Co Ltd took over the mines of Bell Brothers Ltd (1923) and Bolckow, Vaughan & Co Ltd (1929). Other companies went out of business and by 1929 the industry was largely in the hands of two firms, Pease and Partners Ltd and Dorman, Long, the latter being the larger. This led to further rationalisation and the workforce shrank by a further 40 per cent. Nevertheless, output per man year was held at around 600 tons between 1922 and 1939, when some 31.3 million tons of ironstone were produced.

At the end of World War II, the industry had eight mines and the numbers employed had risen slightly. During the 1950s, mechanised loaders and diesel locomotives, for haulage, were introduced and new work systems adopted. Nevertheless, the mines could not compete with supplies of cheaper, higher quality, foreign ores and the last mine, North Skelton, closed in 1964.

Lead ore was the most important non-ferrous mineral produced in Yorkshire and its mining also has a long history. The principal areas of production, Swaledale, Arkengarthdale, Wensleydale and the Greenhow mining field, were established by the mediæval period. Although Wharfedale and Airedale also had earlier mines, they grew in prominence later. Production came mostly from fairly small mines until the late 18th century, when larger, more intensively capitalised mines, began to appear.

It is likely that for much of the early modern period Yorkshire's output was surpassed by, at least, Derbyshire, Durham, Cumberland and the Mendip. Precise comparisons are impossible, however, because county based tables are not available before 1845. Nevertheless, there is enough data to show that in 1750 Yorkshire's output was in the range of 1500-2000 tons of pig lead. John Taylor (*Records of Mining* Pt.1, 1829) estimated that in 1828 Yorkshire produced around 4700 tons of pig lead and had overtaken Derbyshire. Taylor's total was optimistic, however, and a likely figure was 500-1000 tons lower. Between 1845 and 1913, some 328,657 tons of lead ore were mined, which accounted for 7½ per cent of the total U.K. output. Even at its peak, in the late 1850s, Yorkshire was responsible for only around one-tenth of U.K. production, reaching a peak of 12.8 per cent in 1857 when 12,406 tons were mined. Most of this came from mines in Arkengarthdale and the north side of Swaledale and when these passed their best, the county's output declined. As shown in Table 5, this process began in 1870 and, in common with other U.K. lead producing districts, accelerated in the 1880s and 1890s.

By the eve of the First World War, the Yorkshire lead industry was practically dead and only survived as an adjunct to barytes and fluorspar working (Tables 9, 12 & 13). However, some small amounts of ore are still occasionally produced during limestone quarrying at Swinden and Coldstones.

Although Yorkshire's lead ores contained some **silver**, it was generally too little to repay the cost of separating it. With cupellation, the lower limit for the economic desilverisation of lead was around 8oz per ton and, after 1833, this was reduced to between 2 and 3 oz per ton with Pattinsonisation. In the late 16th and early 17th centuries, the Rimington and Brunghill Moor mines were claimed to be rich in silver, but the production of neither mine was sustained. Hunt's returns, which are supported by available assays, show that the silver content per ton of lead at the following mines was: Grassington 4½ oz; Old Gang 2½ oz; Arkengarthdale 2 oz and Appletreewick 1¾ oz per ton, all of them near the limit for economic extraction. Nevertheless, ore from the Braithwaite mine, in Wensleydale, assayed at around 7 oz per ton and was reputedly sent to Bollihope for smelting and, presumably, de-silvering. The New Rake at Grassington produced 611½ ounces of silver in 1860, but that was the only recorded silver from those mines. With these few exceptions, therefore, the county's mines were not silver producers and it is clear that even the less than half a per cent contribution to national output, suggested by Table 7, is far too generous. For these reasons, the expression 'silver producer', which was liberally scattered throughout Hunt's statistics, has been deleted from all but those mines known to have produced some silver.

Some mines supplemented dwindling receipts from lead ore by switching to the production of other minerals. **Zinc** ore (blende) is scarce in Yorkshire, but some was worked at Apedale, Elbolton and Skelhorn between 1872 and 1883. In the 18th century calamine, for the brass industry, was sought in various part of the Dales. Some was mined at Swinden and Cobscar, but the largest deposit, which filled caverns, was worked at Malham in the early 19th century. Small **copper** deposits were worked around Malham, Feldom, East Layton and Middleton Tyas in the 18th century. Copper was also worked at Merrybent in the 1860s and early 1870s, Kneeton in the 1890s and Billybanks from 1905 to 1912. The Merrybent mine reopened in 1910 and worked lead and copper ores until it closed in 1925. The total output of these mines, between 1863 and 1913, was 2588 tons of copper ore, but prices were depressed. A deposit of manganese was examined, but not worked, at Grassington in 1818.

Fluorspar from Gill Heads was bought for use as a flux at Grassington Cupola smelt mill in 1838 and a little was produced from Raygill barytes mine in the late 1870s. It became important after 1913 when the principal sources were the liberties of Appletreewick and Bewerley in the Greenhow mining field. Fluorspar has also been recovered from dumps at Wet Grooves, in Wensleydale, and in Arkengarthdale. Production from dumps and old lead workings tended to be small-scale and migrated across the area being worked, suggesting that few new reserves were found to replace those that were easily won. Yorkshire has never had the large, mechanised fluorspar mines found in Derbyshire and Durham and, with the exception of Dry Gill, most fluorspar has been produced by small groups of men since the mid 1930s.

Barytes was the most important secondary product. Nevertheless, its relatively low price meant that many mines with significant reserves could not exploit them profitably because working and transport costs were too high. Other deposits were often iron-stained. Small amounts of barytes were produced in the 1850s and early 1860s, but larger-scale working began in the 1870s. By the late 1880s county production, derived mainly from Lunehead and Raygill mines, with some from Rimington, was averaging over 3000 tons annually and accounted for around one-sixth of total UK output. Raygill was exhausted by 1900 and, except for two brief periods when the Glusburn mine was worked, Lunehead was left as the major producer. The latter, which also produced some lead, closed in 1938, but was reworked intermittently until the 1970s. During the 1940s, a new mine, Closehouse, also in Lunedale, took over as Yorkshire's main producer of barytes. In 1974, however, it became part of County Durham and closed during the 1990s. Between 1913 and 1990 barytes was recovered from dumps and shallow workings at Appletreewick, Cononley, Glusburn, Grassington, Old Gang and Arkengarthdale.

Coal was worked extensively throughout Yorkshire and has been by far its most important mineral product. The Coal Measures outcrop along the eastern edge of the Pennines, from Sheffield to Leeds, and have been worked for hundreds of years. The coal seams vary in thickness from almost nothing to 14 feet, with most falling between two and six feet. They generally dip eastwards and are covered by younger Permian and Triassic rocks to the east of a line approximating to that of the A1 road. Along that margin, thin coal seams were often associated with beds of fireclay, ganister or sideritic clayband and blackband ironstone, which combined to make their working viable. This led to an early iron industry as well as brickworks, pipeworks and refractory-ware works, as well as supporting rapid industrial growth from the 18th century onwards.

Apart from the Coal Measures, seams of poor quality coal were found in the Yoredale and Millstone Grit series in the Pennines and were worked extensively until the 1930s. Their output, which has never been quantified, was principally for local domestic use and lime burning.

The majority of the exposed coalfield, ie to the west of the A1, was developed by the end of the 19th century, whilst the deeper, concealed coalfield was developed in the early 20th century. Output from these mines peaked in the 1920s and averaged around 39 million tons annually until 1945, which was around 17 per cent of national output. After nationalisation, output steadily declined as mines closed or were merged, but productivity was increased through greater use of mechanisation. The National Coal Board sank a few new mines, such as Kellingley which began production in 1965, then in the 1970s it began to develop the virgin Selby coalfield. This involved sinking five mines, with ten shafts, and driving some 124 miles of roadways at a cost of about £1.3 billion. The output from each mine was brought to the surface at Gascoigne Wood for despatch to power stations.

A combination of Government policy, growing imports of coal in the 1980s and the increased use of gas by electricity generators in the 1990s led to the closure of many of Yorkshire's mines immediately prior to the industry's privatisation in 1993. This retrenchment has continued, with the Prince of Wales Colliery, at Pontefract, closing on August 30th 2002 and the whole Selby complex being scheduled for closure by 2004.

None of the above activity, which dwarfed that of lead mining many times over, is covered by this volume. A similar study covering Yorkshire's coal industry would be a major undertaking, with over 500 mines in the 1870s dwindling to seven in 2002. It would, however, be a significant addition to our knowledge.

Other extractive industries which do not feature here are stone quarrying and evaporite production. Yorkshire has been a major producer of **limestone**, **sandstone**, **flagstone** and **aggregates** for all purposes. **Gypsum** was formerly mined at Sherburn in Elmet near Leeds, and Boulby Mine, sunk on the site of an earlier ironstone mine, began work in 1973 and is still producing **potash** and **rock salt**. **Jet** and **alum** shale were also worked near Whitby.

III

The Mine Tables

The mine-by-mine returns reproduced in the following tables are those that appeared in the *Mineral Statistics* 1845 to 1913, its accompanying *List of Mines*, and the *List of Miscellaneous Mines*. They have been supplemented with miscellaneous additional material derived from mine accounts, smelting ledgers, and the *Colliery Yearbook*. The mine names are normally as they appear in the original returns, but editorial judgement has been used to ensure the proper allocation of data amongst sites. Where possible, location has been accurately specified by changing the original entry to the appropriate civil parish and adding Ordnance Survey National Grid references.

Four principal categories of information are listed for each mine, where available. **Production** data is given separately for each mineral and differs slightly between them. The absence of figures does not necessarily mean that the mine was not producing, because for some years its output might be subsumed in some other aggregate figures. See the *Comment* column for such details. In the earlier edition of the *Yorkshire Mineral Statistics*, the returns for iron were sometimes accompanied with the letters AC, to denote argillaceous carbonate ore. This is a redundant term for the Cleveland ironstone (which is an oolitic, chamositic, siderite mudstone) and has been deleted from this edition. The notation (P), to be found in the Merrybent mine copper returns, indicates that the data was derived from details of 'private contracts' with the smelters, rather than the more usual 'ticketing' auctions, of the type held in Cornwall or Swansea. Mine **Ownership and Management** returns are mainly drawn from the *List of Mines,* first published in 1859 for all non-ferrous workings and 1863 for non-coal measures iron mines. Although not entirely accurate, these returns give a guide to a mine's years of operation, as they purported to include the names and addresses of the owners and agents of all mines being worked that year. Careful examination of the earlier *Lists*, however, reveals periodic purges, when unusually large numbers of mines were removed. This suggests that the list was not edited for every annual edition. In a major change from the earlier edition of the *Yorkshire Mineral Statistics* the headings for Ownership and Management have been replaced by a new ones for **Mineral Lord**, as the owner of the minerals; **Worked by**, the company or individual working the mine; **Agent**, the manager or under-manager; **Secretary**, company secretary; and **Barmaster**, for customary liberties like Buckden, Conistone, Grassington, Hebden and Kettlewell. Because the volume covers a period of around 500 years, the title of the person responsible for running a mine varies from, for example, Agent, to Manager, Steward or Surveyor. For simplicity, therefore, the general term Agent, sometimes qualified by an entry in parentheses, has been used. The **Employment** returns were also drawn from the *List of Mines* and provide a useful check as to whether a mine was operational and also its likely level of production if this is not otherwise available. The original decision to publish the detailed employment returns was left to the local Mines Inspector and some did not provide them until the end of the century. There is data for non-ferrous mines in Yorkshire, however, from 1877 to 1881 and from 1898 to 1950. The same detail for ironstone mines begins in 1894. Some employment statistics have been added from the evidence given to the Kinnaird Commission in 1862-3 and a few others from census returns. Together, all these series provide a simple and comprehensive view of where, when and what metallic and related minerals were being produced in Yorkshire and by whom.

TABLE 1

The production of metalliferous and principal related minerals in Yorkshire and their percentage share of total U.K. production 1850 to 1910.

	1850	1860	1870	1880	1890	1900	1910
Iron	-	1,727,019	4,380,605	6,773,353	5,695,006	5,550,667	6,205,825
%UK Prod	-	21.5	30.2	37.6	41.3	39.6	40.8
Lead	8,706	10,666	6,594	6,974	1,683	885	197
%UK Prod	9.4	12.0	6.7	9.6	3.7	2.8	0.7
Silver	-	3,387	620	7,105	-	-	49
%UK Prod	-	0.6	0.07	2.4	-	-	0.03
Zinc	-	-	-	-	-	-	-
%UK Prod	-	-	-	-	-	-	-
Fluorspar	-	-	-	84	-	-	-
%UK Prod	-	-	-	?	-	-	-
Barytes	-	1,750	-	2,739	1,572	2,332	1,882
%UK Prod	-	13.2	-	15.7	6.2	7.9	4.2
Copper	-	-	80	-	-	-	76
%UK Prod	-	-	0.07	-	-	-	1.82

Production is in tons of ore, except for Silver which is ounces of metal.
No zinc production for these particular years.

TABLE 2

Yorkshire ironstone production and its share of total U.K. output 1855-1914

Year	U.K. Total	N. Riding	E.& W.Ridings	Quarries	Total	% of U.K.
1855	9,553,741	970,300	255,000	-	1,225,300	12.83
1856	10,483,309	1,197,417	242,100	-	1,439,517	15.07
1857	9,372,781	1,414,155	207,500	-	1,621,655	17.30
1858	8,040,959	1,367,395	189,750	-	1,557,145	19.37
1859	7,876,582	1,520,343	175,000	-	1,695,343	21.52
1860	8,035,306	1,471,319	255,700	-	1,727,019	21.49
1861	7,215,518	1,130,761	235,500	-	1,366,261	18.94
1862	7,562,240	1,690,097	350,500	-	2,040,597	26.67
1863	8,613,951	2,078,806	475,000	-	2,553,806	29.65
1864	10,064,891	2,401,891	555,000	-	2,956,891	29.38
1865	9,910,046	2,762,359	575,000	-	3,337,359	33.68
1866	9,665,013	2,809,061	357,000	-	3,166,061	32.76
1867	10,021,058	2,739,039	579,000	-	3,318,039	33.11
1868	10,169,231	2,785,307	785,628	-	3,570,935	35.12
1869	11,508,526	3,094,678	230,905	-	3,325,583	28.90
1870	14,496,427	4,072,888	307,717	-	4,380,605	30.22
1871	16,470,010	4,581,901	407,997	-	4,989,898	30.30
1872	15,755,675	4,974,950	466,305	-	5,441,255	34.54
1873	15,583,669	5,617,014	407,388	-	6,024,402	38.66
1874	14,844,936	5,614,323	370,960	-	5,985,283	40.32
1875	15,821,060	6,121,794	353,582	-	6,475,376	40.93
1876	16,841,584	6,562,000	381,463	-	6,943,463	41.23
1877	16,692,802	6,284,545	402,746	-	6,687,291	40.06
1878	15,726,370	5,605,640	370,405	-	5,976,045	38.00
1879	14,379,735	4,750,000	321,789	-	5,071,789	35.27
1880	18,026,050	6,486,655	286,698	-	6,773,353	37.58
1881	17,446,065	6,538,471	320,981	-	6,859,452	39.32
1882	18,031,957	6,326,314	175,681	-	6,501,995	36.06
1883	17,383,046	6,756,055	170,832	-	6,926,887	39.85
1884	16,137,887	6,052,608	67,812	-	6,120,420	37.93
1885	15,417,982	5,932,244	126,596	-	6,058,840	39.30
1886	14,110,013	5,370,279	92,285	-	5,462,564	38.71
1887	13,098,041	4,980,421	81,868	-	5,062,289	38.65
1888	14,590,713	5,395,942	67,148	-	5,463,090	37.44

TABLE 2 (continued)

Yorkshire ironstone production and its share of total U.K. output 1855-1914

Year	U.K. Total	N. Riding	E.& W.Ridings	Quarries	Total	% of U.K.
1889	14,546,105	5,657,118	71,196	-	5,728,314	39.38
1890	13,780,767	5,617,573	77,433	-	5,695,006	41.33
1891	12,777,689	5,128,303	78,019	-	5,206,322	40.75
1892	11,312,675	3,411,400	81,816	-	3,493,216	30.88
1893	11,203,476	4,625,520	87,758	-	4,713,278	42.07
1894	12,367,308	5,048,956	67,191	-	5,116,147	41.37
1895	12,615,414	5,285,617	45,538	100	5,331,255	42.26
1896	13,700,764	5,678,368	56,474	50	5,734,892	41.86
1897	13,787,878	5,679,153	50,821	99	5,730,073	41.56
1898	14,176,936	5,730,413	54,696	479	5,785,588	40.81
1899	14,461,330	5,612,742	59,136	288	5,672,166	39.22
1900	14,028,208	5,493,733	56,688	256	5,550,677	39.57
1901	12,275,198	5,100,823	49,609	224	5,150,656	41.96
1902	13,426,004	5,402,164	41,688	5,494	5,449,346	40.59
1903	13,715,645	5,677,560	46,375	9,264	5,733,199	41.80
1904	13,774,282	5,727,696	38,903	8,089	5,774,688	41.92
1905	14,590,703	5,944,491	45,050	10,208	5,999,749	41.12
1906	15,500,406	6,113,426	49,454	11,203	6,174,083	39.83
1907	15,731,604	6,240,369	48,875	9,382	6,298,626	40.04
1908	15,031,025	6,081,329	44,404	8,396	6,134,129	40.81
1909	14,979,979	6,191,632	42,957	8,614	6,243,203	41.68
1910	15,226,015	6,160,241	38,170	7,418	6,205,825	40.76
1911	15,519,424	6,050,265	36,099	46,308	6,132,672	39.52
1912	13,790,391	5,158,860	31,831	40,673	5,231,364	37.93
1913	15,997,328	6,011,390	28,269	70,425	6,110,084	38.19
1914	14,867,582	5,654,287	24,229	79,499	5,758,015	38.73
Total	801,870,554	281,940,401	12,001,515	316,469	294,258,385	36.70

Notes a) North Riding includes the Cleveland orefield.

b) The appearance of quarried ore in 1895 does not mean that no ore was quarried before this, but simply that it was not separated until the Quarries Act of 1894.

TABLE 3

Cleveland ironstone production 1922-1939

Year	Total Output in tons.	Av. % Fe.	Total net selling value £	Av net selling value £/ton	Cleveland basic pig iron £/ton
1922	1,169,754	28.66	498,166	0.436	4.184
1923	2,079,964	28.00	788,142	0.379	4.428
1924	2,234,447	27.24	772,446	0.346	5.340
1925	2,284,186	27.47	724,668	0.317	3.679
1926	976,562	28.34	316,994	0.325	3.460
1927	2,529,894	27.51	797,275	0.315	0.000
1928	2,272,124	28.00	695,104	0.306	3.250
1929	2,673,903	28.00	801,712	0.300	3.304
1930	2,167,905	28.23	658,071	0.304	3.296
1931	1,496,748	27.18	445,817	0.298	0.000
1932	1,083,168	28.20	300,276	0.277	0.000
1933	1,012,753	28.40	291,413	0.288	2.994
1934	1,649,218	29.00	470,654	0.287	3.300
1935	1,640,093	28.00	481,973	0.294	3.447
1936	1,848,490	28.00	595,111	0.322	3.658
1937	2,036,671	28.77	731,404	0.359	4.697
1938	1,513,726	28.67	584,741	0.386	5.000
1939 (part)	686,413	29.00	275,883	0.402	4.625
	31,356,019	28.06	10,229,850	0.326	3.911

TABLE 4

Cleveland Ironstone Mines

Year	EMPLOYMENT U/G	Surface	Total	Working Mines	Year	EMPLOYMENT U/G	Surface	Total	Working Mines
1894	4585	1179	5764	26	1929	3437	896	4333	12
1895	5009	1259	6268	26	1930	3308	877	4185	11
1896	5327	1297	6624	29	1931	2504	585	3089	5
1897	5531	1379	6910	29	1932	1656	360	2016	5
1898	5573	1318	6891	29	1933	1863	460	2323	7
1899	5761	1406	7167	28	1934	1545	421	1966	5
1900	5665	1415	7080	28	1935	2051	453	2504	6
1901	5179	1318	6497	24	1936	2474	582	3056	9
1902	5548	1320	6868	25	1937	2657	668	3325	9
1903	5598	1469	7067	24	1938	2600	654	3254	6
1904	6070	1518	7588	26	1939	2258	568	2826	-
1905	6321	1515	7836	25	1940	2633	671	3304	8
1906	6491	1546	8037	22	1941	2745	755	3500	8
1907	6748	1634	8382	24	1942	2770	765	3535	8
1908	6911	1713	8624	24	1943	2658	758	3416	8
1909	7122	1792	8914	25	1944	2420	730	3150	8
1910	7349	1840	9189	26	1945	1924	532	2456	8
1911	7204	1805	9009	27	1946	-	-	-	8
1912	7064	1770	8834	25	1947	-	-	-	8
1913	7284	1793	9077	26	1948	1402	504	1906	8
1914	7419	1884	9303	28	1949	-	-	-	7
1915	5456	1646	7102	25	1950	1392	498	1890	7
1916	5379	1640	7019	25	1951	1344	427	1771	7
1917	5899	1785	7684	23	1952-53	-	-	-	7
1918	5647	1886	7533	26	1954	1226	457	1683	7
1919	6076	2034	8110	25	1955	706	300	1006	4
1920	6038	2007	8045	25	1956	559	212	771	4
1921	5208	1829	7037	24	1957	530	218	748	4
1922	2125	856	2981	22	1958	499	257	756	4
1923	3138	1280	4418	21	1959	394	192	586	3
1924	2942	1020	3962	18	1960	389	197	586	3
1925	3011	965	3976	17	1961	385	194	579	3
1926	2831	863	3694	15	1962	378	190	568	3
1927	3564	1061	4625	15	1963	201	112	313	2
1928	3007	905	3912	9	1964	111	56	167	1

TABLE 5

Yorkshire lead ore & metal production
and its share of total U.K. output 1845 to 1913

Year	Yorkshire Ore(tons)	U.K. Ore(tons)	% of U.K. Ore Prod	Yorkshire Metal(tons)	U.K. Metal(tons)	% of U.K. Lead Prod
1845	7,176	78,267	9.20	5,203	52,700	9.87
1846	7,119	74,551	9.50	5,164	50,200	10.28
1847	7,438	83,747	8.90	5,223	55,700	9.38
1848	6,848	78,944	8.70	4,793	53,400	8.98
1849	7,906	86,823	9.10	5,597	58,700	9.53
1850	8,706	92,958	9.40	5,952	64,400	9.24
1851	9,101	92,312	9.90	6,283	65,300	9.62
1852	8,472	91,198	9.30	5,720	65,000	8.80
1853	10,308	85,043	12.10	6,868	61,000	11.26
1854	9,245	90,554	10.20	6,476	64,000	10.12
1855	9,378	92,038	10.20	6,369	65,700	9.69
1856	12,174	101,998	11.90	8,986	73,100	12.29
1857	12,406	96,820	12.80	7,876	69,300	11.37
1858	11,481	95,856	12.00	7,606	68,300	11.14
1859	9,705	91,382	10.60	6,338	63,200	10.03
1860	10,666	88,791	12.00	7,100	63,300	11.22
1861	8,801	90,666	9.70	6,204	65,600	9.46
1862	9,255	95,312	9.70	6,313	69,000	9.15
1863	8,982	91,283	9.80	6,171	68,200	9.05
1864	8,678	94,463	9.20	6,085	68,100	8.94
1865	7,618	90,452	8.40	5,316	67,300	7.90
1866	9,735	91,048	10.70	7,013	67,400	10.41
1867	7,539	93,432	8.10	5,243	68,400	7.67
1868	7,694	94,236	8.10	5,655	71,000	7.96
1869	8,563	96,866	8.80	6,158	73,300	8.40
1870	6,594	98,177	6.70	4,774	73,400	6.50
1871	5,916	93,965	6.30	4,446	69,100	6.43
1872	5,311	81,619	6.50	3,954	60,500	6.54
1873	4,987	73,500	6.80	3,705	54,200	6.84
1874	4,901	76,202	6.40	3,492	58,800	5.94
1875	4,150	77,746	5.20	2,945	57,400	5.13
1876	4,199	79,096	5.30	2,969	58,700	5.06
1877	5,011	80,850	6.20	3,621	61,400	5.90
1878	5,918	77,351	7.60	4,307	58,000	7.43
1879	5,132	66,877	7.70	3,713	51,600	7.20
1880	6,974	72,245	9.60	5,241	57,000	9.19

TABLE 5 (continued)

Yorkshire lead ore & metal production
and its share of total U.K. output 1845 to 1913

Year	Yorkshire Ore(tons)	U.K. Ore(tons)	% of U.K. Ore Prod	Yorkshire Metal(tons)	U.K. Metal(tons)	% of U.K. Lead Prod
1881	4,171	64,702	6.40	3,040	48,600	6.26
1882	4,513	65,002	6.90	3,292	50,300	6.54
1883	3,264	50,980	6.40	2,432	39,200	6.20
1884	2,621	54,485	4.80	1,847	40,100	4.61
1885	3,129	51,302	6.10	2,229	37,700	5.91
1886	3,767	53,420	7.00	2,697	39,500	6.83
1887	3,170	51,563	6.10	2,258	37,900	5.96
1888	2,629	51,259	5.10	1,872	37,600	4.98
1889	2,056	48,465	4.20	1,439	35,600	4.04
1890	1,683	45,651	3.70	1,171	33,600	3.49
1891	1,499	43,859	3.40	1,022	32,200	3.17
1892	1,282	40,024	3.20	876	29,500	2.97
1893	1,293	40,808	3.20	851	29,700	2.87
1894	1,135	40,599	2.80	762	29,700	2.57
1895	675	38,412	1.80	451	29,000	1.56
1896	479	41,069	1.20	323	30,800	1.05
1897	716	35,338	2.00	482	26,600	1.81
1898	1,158	32,985	3.50	768	25,400	3.02
1899	1,059	30,999	3.40	725	23,600	3.07
1900	885	32,010	2.80	609	24,400	2.50
1901	681	27,976	2.40	452	20,000	2.26
1902	662	24,606	2.70	441	17,700	2.49
1903	738	26,567	2.80	489	20,000	2.45
1904	247	26,374	0.90	159	19,800	0.80
1905	110	27,649	0.40	72	20,700	0.35
1906	137	30,795	0.40	86	22,300	0.39
1907	139	32,533	0.40	93	24,500	0.39
1908	192	29,249	0.70	145	21,000	0.69
1909	240	29,744	0.80	182	22,400	0.81
1910	197	28,534	0.70	148	21,600	0.69
1911	100	23,910	0.40	74	18,000	0.41
1912	23	25,409	0.09	17	19,200	0.09
1913	20	24,282	0.08	12	18,100	0.07
Total	328,657	4,408,228	7.50	230,395	3,218,000	7.16

TABLE 6

Yorkshire lead ore production and its share of total U.K. output 1920 to 1939

Year	Yorkshire Ore(tons)	U.K. Ore(tons)	% of U.K. Ore	Total net selling value of U.K. Ore	Av net selling value of U.K. £/ton	Av price of lead £/ton
1920	32	-	-	-	-	-
1921	8	-	-	-	-	-
1922	10	11,079	0.09	151,422	13.668	23.771
1923	10	14,294	0.07	302,061	21.132	26.779
1924	21	12,499	0.17	207,171	16.575	34.077
1925	51	15,570	0.33	348,207	22.364	36.503
1926	36	19,076	0.19	368,052	19.294	31.050
1927	267	20,428	1.31	295,920	14.486	24.482
1928	1,029	18,771	5.48	230,151	12.261	21.060
1929	96	23,260	0.41	306,334	13.170	23.241
1930	16	25,380	0.06	258,470	10.184	18.089
1931	0	29,500	-	191,156	6.480	12.963
1932	10	40,589	0.02	240,940	5.936	11.900
1933	5	49,055	0.01	303,126	6.179	11.707
1934	7	68,122	0.01	396,582	5.822	10.944
1935	230	52,858	0.44	451,054	8.533	14.305
1936	56	39,094	0.14	423,465	10.832	17.651
1937	0	33,411	-	495,947	14.844	23.484
1938	7	38,134	0.02	354,718	9.302	15.238
1939	-	12,232	-	104,437	8.538	14.500

TABLE 7

Yorkshire silver production and its share of total U.K. output 1851 to 1913

Year	Yorkshire Metal(Oz)	U.K. Metal(Oz)	% of U.K. Prod	Year	Yorkshire Metal(Oz)	U.K. Metal(Oz)	% of U.K. Prod
1851	-	674,458	-	1884	-	325,718	-
1852	-	818,325	-	1885	-	320,520	-
1853	-	496,475	-	1886	-	325,427	-
1854	-	562,659	-	1887	-	320,345	-
1855	273	561,906	0.05	1888	-	321,425	-
1856	302	614,188	0.05	1889	-	306,149	-
1857	445	532,866	0.08	1890	-	291,724	-
1858	1,657	569,345	0.29	1891	-	279,792	-
1859	1,178	576,027	0.20	1892	-	271,259	-
1860	3,387	549,720	0.62	1893	-	274,100	-
1861	3,650	569,530	0.64	1894	-	275,696	-
1862	3,331	686,123	0.49	1895	-	280,434	-
1863	3,270	634,004	0.52	1896	-	283,826	-
1864	3,604	641,088	0.56	1897	-	249,156	-
1865	2,328	724,856	0.32	1898	-	211,403	-
1866	3,143	636,688	0.49	1899	-	106,149	-
1867	5,060	805,394	0.63	1900	-	191,724	-
1868	1,530	841,328	0.18	1901	-	178,324	-
1869	999	831,891	0.12	1902	-	145,873	-
1870	620	784,562	0.08	1903	-	152,855	-
1871	308	761,490	0.04	1904	-	141,592	-
1872	-	628,920	-	1905	-	163,399	-
1873	1,500	524,307	0.29	1906	-	147,647	-
1874	1,500	509,277	0.29	1907	-	150,521	-
1875	7,438	487,358	1.53	1908	-	135,154	-
1876	8,850	483,422	1.83	1909	-	142,006	-
1877	7,512	497,375	1.51	1910	49	136,192	0.04
1878	7,719	397,471	1.94	1911	-	118,395	-
1879	6,505	333,674	1.95	1912	-	118,540	-
1880	7,105	295,518	2.40	1913	-	128,154	-
1881	4,115	308,398	1.33				
1882	5,186	372,449	1.39	Total	96,228	25,630,540	0.38
1883	3,664	344,053	1.06				

TABLE 8

Yorkshire zinc ore production and its share of total U.K. output 1872 to 1883

Year	tons
1872	5.0
1876	3.5
1877	4.8
1878	5.7
1881	35.3
1882	109.0
1883	16.0
Total	179.3

Percentage of U.K. production 0.01

TABLE 9

Yorkshire fluorspar production and its share of total U.K. output 1878 to 1939

Year	Yorkshire Ore(tons)	UK output Ore(tons)	% of U.K. Ore Prod	Average % CaF_2	Av price per ton(£)
1878	23	-	-	-	-
1879	61	-	-	-	-
1880	84	-	-	-	-
1904	138	-	-	-	-
1920	1,020	-	-	-	-
1921	624	-	-	-	-
1922	4,972	33,343	14.91	79.52	0.997
1923	5,263	49,031	10.73	83.87	1.021
1924	2,520	49,492	5.09	81.74	1.099
1925	1,984	39,079	5.08	83.43	1.062
1926	406	35,883	1.13	84.23	1.106
1927	892	37,629	2.37	84.18	1.064
1928	2,588	46,862	5.52	82.73	0.997
1929	184	39,070	0.47	83.30	0.909
1930	0	29,788	-	85.13	0.911
1931	0	19,923	-	84.23	0.894
1932	0	13,218	-	81.79	0.755
1933	655	28,058	2.33	83.76	0.815
1934	3,232	33,080	9.77	82.80	0.828
1935	4,326	31,147	13.89	82.76	0.806
1936	5,171	32,962	15.69	79.75	0.773
1937	4,399	42,160	10.43	79.94	0.819
1938	1,952	32,570	5.99	80.18	1.080
1939	-	17,244	-	82.53	1.188

TABLE 10

Yorkshire calcite production 1925 to 1927

Year	tons
1925	156
1926	287
1927	277
Total	720

TABLE 11

Yorkshire copper ore production
and its share of total U.K. output 1863 to 1913

Year	Yorkshire Ore(tons)	U.K. Ore(tons)	% of U.K. Ore Prod	Year	Yorkshire Ore(tons)	U.K. Ore(tons)	% of U.K. Ore Prod
1863	463	-	-	1890	-	12,481	-
1864	76	-	-	1891	-	9,158	-
1865	80	198,298	0.04	1892	18	6,265	0.29
1866	-	180,378	-	1893	-	5,576	-
1867	-	158,544	-	1894	2	5,994	-
1868	-	157,335	-	1895	2	5,791	-
1869	-	129,953	-	1896	10	9,168	-
1870	80	106,698	0.07	1897	-	7,352	-
1871	-	97,129	-	1898	-	9,131	-
1872	137	91,893	0.15	1899	-	8,319	-
1873	72	80,189	0.09	1900	-	9,488	-
1874	129	78,521	0.16	1901	-	6,792	-
1875	-	71,528	-	1902	-	6,112	-
1876	-	79,252	-	1903	-	6,867	-
1877	-	73,141	-	1904	-	5,465	-
1878	-	56,094	-	1905	251	7,153	3.51
1879	-	51,032	-	1906	341	7,758	4.39
1880	-	52,128	-	1907	379	6,792	5.58
1881	-	52,556	-	1908	106	5,441	1.95
1882	-	52,237	-	1909	-	3,717	-
1883	-	46,820	-	1910	76	4,178	1.82
1884	-	42,149	-	1911	270	3,262	8.28
1885	-	36,379	-	1912	92	1,933	4.76
1886	-	18,617	-	1913	4	2,732	0.15
1887	-	9,359	-				
1888	-	15,550	-	Total	2,588	2,104,015	0.10
1889	-	9,310	-				

TABLE 12

Yorkshire barytes production and its share of total U.K. output 1854 to 1913

Year	Yorkshire Ore(tons)	U.K. Ore(tons)	% of U.K. Ore Prod
1854	-	3,303	-
1855	-	-	-
1856	1,000	11,810	8.5
1857	1,000	12,522	8.0
1858	450	13,337	3.4
1859	-	-	-
1860	1,750	13,354	13.1
1851	795	11,451	7.0
1852	500	9,967	5.0
1853	-	-	-
1864	-	500	-
1865	-	6,769	-
1866	-	-	-
1867	-	11,109	-
1868	-	14,224	-
1869	-	5,987	-
1870	-	6,515	-
1871	-	5,513	-
1872	-	9,798	-
1873	-	14,005	-
1874	-	14,373	-
1875	-	15,548	-
1876	2,057	22,106	9.3
1877	2,723	21,057	13.0
1878	2,786	22,437	12.4
1879	2,255	19,349	11.7
1880	2,739	17,476	15.7
1881	2,017	21,313	9.5
1882	3,586	23,308	15.4
1883	2,698	21,396	12.6
1884	2,656	20,062	13.2
1885	2,885	26,153	11.0
1886	4,527	25,142	18.0
1887	3,995	24,813	16.1
1888	3,182	25,191	12.6
1889	2,912	24,849	11.7
1890	1,572	25,353	6.2
1891	1,014	26,876	3.8
1892	1,204	24,247	5.0
1893	622	22,343	2.8
1894	436	20,656	2.1
1895	923	21,170	4.4
1896	684	23,737	2.9
1897	1,556	22,723	6.8
1898	2,390	22,225	10.8
1899	2,358	24,664	9.6
1900	2,332	29,456	7.9
1901	694	27,613	2.5
1902	1,619	23,608	6.9
1903	1,348	24,271	5.6
1904	234	26,327	0.9
1905	943	29,063	3.2
1906	1,370	35,745	3.8
1907	2,050	41,974	4.8
1908	2,778	38,947	7.1
1909	2,033	41,766	4.9
1910	1,882	44,667	4.2
1911	1,701	44,118	3.9
1912	1,592	45,377	3.5
1913	2,004	50,045	4.0
Total	81,852	1,231,708	6.6

TABLE 13

Yorkshire and U.K. barytes production 1920 to 1939

Year	Yorkshire Ore(tons)	UK output Unground (tons)	Av price £/ton	UK output Ground (tons)	1Av price £/ton	UK output bleached (tons)	Av price £/ton
1920	5,528	-	-	-	-	-	-
1921	2,098	-	-	-	-	-	-
1922	2,968	17,487	2.279	22,181	2.818	-	-
1923	1,473	12,501	2.126	30,996	2.818	-	-
1924	1,477	37,155	1.818	17,612	2.798	-	-
1925	1,357	36,336	1.647	10,467	2.448	1,878	4.881
1926	922	27,956	1.667	12,819	2.385	2,000	4.147
1927	771	31,677	1.461	13,254	2.233	1,922	3.870
1928	937	34,221	1.547	15,100	2.093	580	4.090
1929	1,158	38,398	1.582	16,907	2.332	1,192	3.792
1930	899	39,941	1.388	16,034	2.386	1,823	3.752
1931	806	31,863	1.474	12,640	2.366	1,077	3.752
1932	2,294	41,970	1.227	12,786	2.336	1,881	3.750
1933	1,179	43,227	1.163	13,942	2.206	7,623	3.571
1934	955	48,132	1.321	20,317	2.254	5,548	3.625
1935	1,412	51,290	1.350	20,553	2.261	6,088	3.744
1936	887	46,000	1.363	21,337	2.303	5,731	3.781
1937	214	48,537	1.419	19,344	2.406	5,427	4.033
1938	0	57,279	1.339	15,029	2.467	4,011	4.193
1939	-	32,335	1.229	8,577	2.417	2,300	4.308

TABLE 14

Yorkshire coal production (in tons) and its share of total U.K. output 1854-1941

Year	U.K. Total	Yorkshire	% of U.K.	Year	U.K. Total	Yorkshire	% of U.K.
1854	64,661,401	7,260,500	11.23	1898	202,054,516	25,639,021	12.69
1855	64,453,079	7,747,470	12.02	1899	220,094,781	26,907,132	12.23
1856	66,645,450	9,083,625	13.63	1900	225,181,300	28,250,679	12.55
1857	65,394,707	8,875,440	13.57	1901	219,046,945	26,975,460	12.31
1858	65,010,649	8,302,150	12.77	1902	227,095,042	27,966,148	12.31
1859	71,979,765	8,247,100	11.46	1903	230,334,469	28,532,362	12.39
1860	84,042,698	9,284,000	11.05	1904	232,428,272	28,840,506	12.41
1861	86,039,214	9,374,600	10.90	1905	236,128,936	29,930,184	12.68
1862	81,638,338	9,255,500	11.34	1906	251,067,688	32,556,102	12.97
1863	86,292,215	9,402,500	10.90	1907	267,830,962	35,181,229	13.14
1864	92,787,933	8,809,600	9.49	1908	261,528,795	34,936,302	13.36
1865	98,150,587	9,355,100	9.53	1909	263,774,312	35,900,046	13.61
1866	101,630,544	9,714,700	9.56	1910	264,433,088	38,304,088	14.49
1867	104,500,480	9,843,575	9.42	1911	271,991,899	39,137,115	14.39
1868	103,141,157	9,740,510	9.44	1912	260,416,338	38,298,080	14.71
1869	107,436,557	10,829,827	10.08	1913	287,430,478	43,680,016	15.20
1870	110,431,192	10,606,604	9.60	1914	265,684,383	39,556,450	14.89
1871	117,352,028	12,801,260	10.91	1915	258,206,081	40,357,917	15.63
1872	123,497,316	14,576,009	11.80	1916	256,375,366	40,222,255	15.69
1873	128,680,131	15,311,778	11.90	1917	248,499,240	40,888,903	16.45
1874	126,500,108	14,827,313	11.72	1918	237,748,654	35,666,514	15.00
1875	133,306,485	15,860,008	11.90	1919	229,779,517	32,854,307	14.30
1876	134,124,106	15,137,373	11.29	1920	229,532,081	36,182,855	15.76
1877	134,179,968	15,813,310	11.79	1921	163,251,131	28,482,202	17.45
1878	132,612,068	15,589,119	11.76	1922	249,606,364	42,119,138	16.87
1879	133,720,398	16,248,156	12.15	1923	276,000,500	46,466,855	16.84
1880	146,969,409	17,473,806	11.89	1924	267,118,167	46,568,688	17.43
1881	154,184,300	18,294,177	11.87	1925	243,176,231	45,273,399	18.62
1882	156,499,977	18,530,331	11.84	1926	126,278,521	21,603,465	17.11
1883	168,737,227	19,567,670	11.60	1927	251,222,336	45,938,719	18.29
1884	168,757,779	19,224,354	11.39	1928	237,471,931	43,367,966	18.26
1885	159,531,418	18,501,684	11.60	1929	257,906,803	46,406,074	17.99
1886	157,518,488	19,392,975	12.31	1930	243,881,824	44,560,741	18.27
1887	162,119,812	20,108,903	12.40	1931	219,458,951	40,589,644	18.50
1888	169,935,219	20,579,960	12.11	1932	208,733,140	38,075,279	18.24
1889	176,916,724	21,976,027	12.42	1933	207,112,243	37,252,125	17.99
1890	181,614,268	22,338,886	12.30	1934	220,726,298	39,852,601	18.06
1891	185,479,126	22,794,057	12.29	1935	222,248,822	40,657,048	18.29
1892	181,786,871	23,189,915	12.76	1936	228,448,356	42,476,133	18.59
1893	164,325,795	15,955,817	9.71	1937	240,409,436	45,115,121	18.77
1894	188,277,525	23,446,184	12.45	1938	227,015,308	42,374,285	18.67
1895	189,661,352	22,811,038	12.03	1939	231,300,000	44,400,000	19.20
1896	195,361,260	23,943,488	12.26	1940	224,300,000	45,200,000	20.15
1897	202,129,931	24,055,380	11.90	1941	206,340,000	44,440,000	21.54

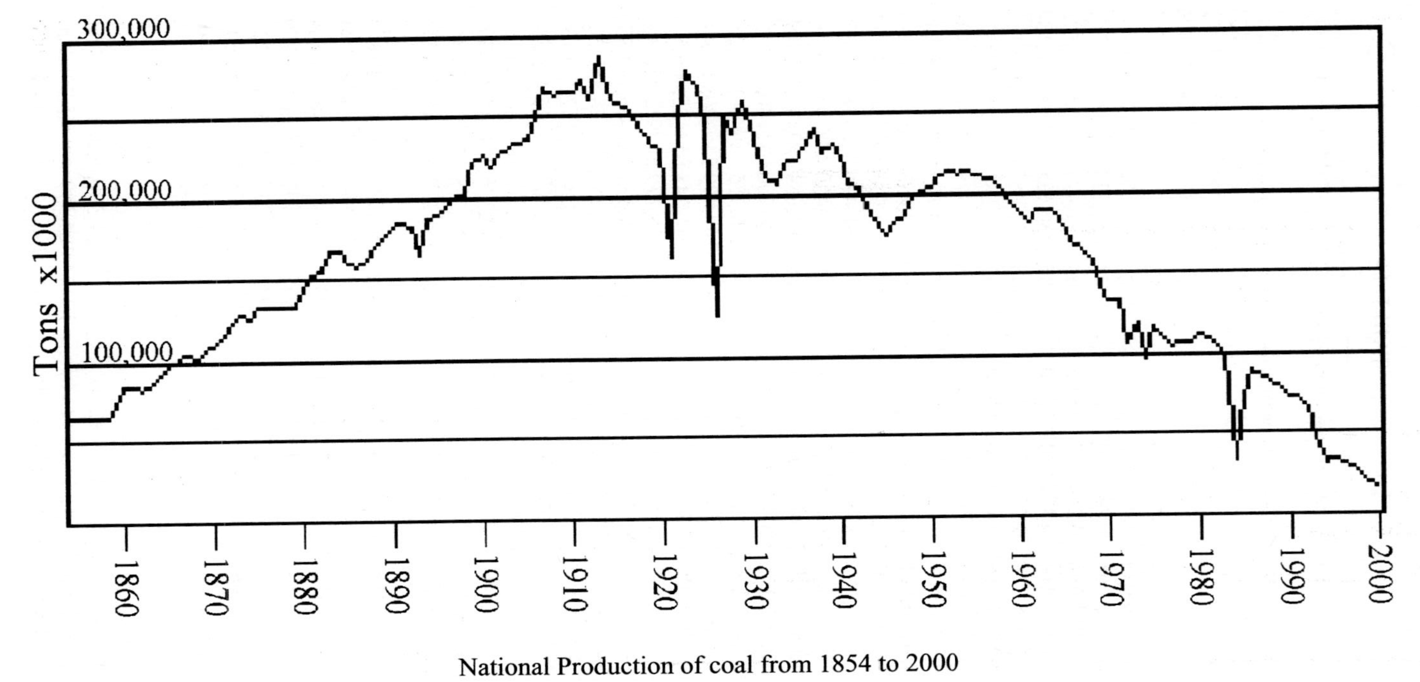
300,000
200,000
100,000
Tons x1000
1860
1870
1880
1890
1900
1910
1920
1930
1940
1950
1960
1970
1980
1990
2000
National Production of coal from 1854 to 2000

Figure 1

TABLE 15

Yorkshire coal production (in tons) and its share of total U.K. output 1942-2000

	Deep Mined Coal			**Opencast Coal**		
Year	U.K. Total	Yorkshire	% of U.K.	U.K. Total	Yorkshire	% of U.K.
1942	203,630,000	42,790,000	21.01	1,311,000	793,600	60.53
1943	194,490,000	40,320,000	20.73	4,427,000	1,662,700	37.56
1944	184,100,000	37,850,000	20.56	8,651,000	2,686,300	31.05
1945	174,660,000	36,700,000	21.01	8,118,000	2,491,500	30.69
1946	181,240,000	37,720,000	20.81	8,800,000	2,066,600	23.48
1947	187,201,050	38,217,000	20.41	10,245,190	2,166,000	21.14
1948	197,644,358	40,361,000	20.42	11,748,254	2,754,100	23.44
1949	202,687,381	42,085,000	20.76	12,439,652	2,539,900	20.42
1950	204,137,102	42,588,000	20.86	12,184,942	2,212,700	18.16
1951	211,880,760	44,376,000	20.94	10,985,699	1,929,300	17.56
1952	214,321,567	45,038,000	21.01	12,110,242	2,130,000	17.59
1953	212,500,803	44,657,000	21.01	11,697,962	2,124,700	18.16
1954	213,991,861	45,384,000	21.21	10,058,389	1,564,500	15.55
1955	210,257,820	43,540,000	20.71	11,365,599	1,703,500	14.99
1956	209,923,193	43,236,000	20.60	12,080,519	1,729,400	14.32
1957	210,057,044	43,340,000	20.63	13,568,821	1,807,000	13.32
1958	201,472,883	42,371,000	21.03	14,346,828	1,811,200	12.62
1959	195,271,461	41,917,000	21.47	10,832,952	1,700,600	15.70
1960	186,051,509	40,444,000	21.74	7,552,723	1,012,100	13.40
1961	181,936,583	39,377,000	21.64	8,528,062	961,200	11.27
1962	189,327,899	42,266,000	22.32	8,107,810	1,109,700	13.69
1963	189,656,620	43,158,000	22.76	6,138,433	668,400	10.89
1964	186,816,229	43,532,000	23.30	6,809,655	645,200	9.47
1965	180,166,014	42,465,000	23.57	7,332,263	814,800	11.11
1966	168,365,499	38,970,000	23.15	7,026,178	664,000	9.45
1967	165,058,599	40,261,000	24.39	7,085,230	584,000	8.24
1968	157,214,553	39,937,000	25.40	6,686,631	669,000	10.01
1969	144,240,876	35,918,000	24.90	6,319,525	537,000	8.50
1970	134,525,873	34,756,000	25.84	7,760,389	646,000	8.32
1971	134,321,160	29,608,000	22.04	10,497,439	989,000	9.42
1972	107,362,052	36,095,015	33.62	10,273,042		
1973	118,133,097	27,424,740	23.22	9,963,020		
1974	98,412,753	32,347,810	32.87	9,085,117		
1975	115,556,471	31,507,630	27.27	10,249,422		
1976	108,522,419	30,664,540	28.26	11,755,242		
1977	105,430,074	30,362,805	28.80	13,336,846		
1978	105,828,674	29,656,390	28.02	13,943,111		
1979	106,071,770	30,706,015	28.95	12,658,734		
1980	110,653,204	30,868,822	27.90	15,529,635		
1981	108,727,132	30,519,970	28.07	14,593,665		
1982	104,483,277	30,145,930	28.85	15,024,743		

TABLE 15 (continued)

Yorkshire coal production (in tons) and its share of total U.K. output 1942-2000

	Deep Mined Coal			Opencast Coal		
Year	U.K. Total	Yorkshire	% of U.K.	U.K. Total	Yorkshire	% of U.K.
1983	100,134,113	25,717,065	25.68	14,473,593		
1984	34,686,035	610,205	1.76	14,079,914		
1985	74,099,165	25,963,100	35.04	15,322,954		
1986	88,937,894	26,307,570	29.58	14,049,404		
1987	84,598,572	25,441,480	30.07	15,536,525		
1988	82,438,261	28,620,430	34.72	17,616,132		
1989	78,369,593	23,748,660	30.30	18,362,153		
1990	71,746,935	24,191,550	33.72	17,847,418		
1991	72,197,697	27,222,875	37.71	18,341,485		
1992	64,760,125	26,297,735	40.61	17,899,580		
1993	49,659,599	21,061,805	42.41	16,737,244		
1994	31,350,593	-	-	16,538,437		
1995	34,594,504	-	-	16,110,311		
1996	31,713,762	16,510,884	52.06	16,057,165	851,330	5.30
1997	29,802,452	14,121,250	47.38	16,436,080	1,041,280	6.34
1998	24,879,502	11,663,710	46.88	14,533,629	1,489,090	10.25
1999	20,557,895	11,496,400	55.92	14,693,100	1,790,250	12.18
2000	16,916,368	9,176,650	54.25	13,200,043	1,294,220	9.80

1873-1938 Figures from *Annual Report & Statistics* 1938 (App. A - table 6, pp.148-149)
1942 26 weeks ending December 30th
1947-onwards national figures converted from tonnes
1972 Miners' strike in first two months.
1974 Miners' strike in first three months.
1983-1984 Production was affected by a national overtime ban from November 1st 1983 and by wider industrial action from March 12th 1984.
1994-1995 Regional output figures unavailable after privatisation of the coal industry.

Sources: Meade, R. *The Coal and Iron Industries of the United Kingdom* (London: Crosby Lockwood & Co., 1882)
Annual Report & Statistics Table 6 - Output of Saleable coal in the principal districts of Great Britain 1873-1938 (Mines Dept., HMSO, 1938)
Mitchell, B.R. & Deane, P. *Abstracts of British Historical Statistics* (Cambridge: Cambridge University Press, 1962)
Ministry of Fuel and Power Statistical Digest, 1950 (HMSO, 1951)
Ministry of Power Statistical Digest, 1965 (HMSO, 1966)
Digest of United Kingdom Energy Statistics, 1972 (HMSO, 1972)
United Kingdom Mineral Yearbook, 1995 (Keyworth: BGS, 1996)
Digest of United Kingdom Energy Statistics, 1981 (Dept. of Energy, HMSO, 1981)
Office of National Statistics *Annual Abstract of Statistics* (London: The Stationery Office, 1997)

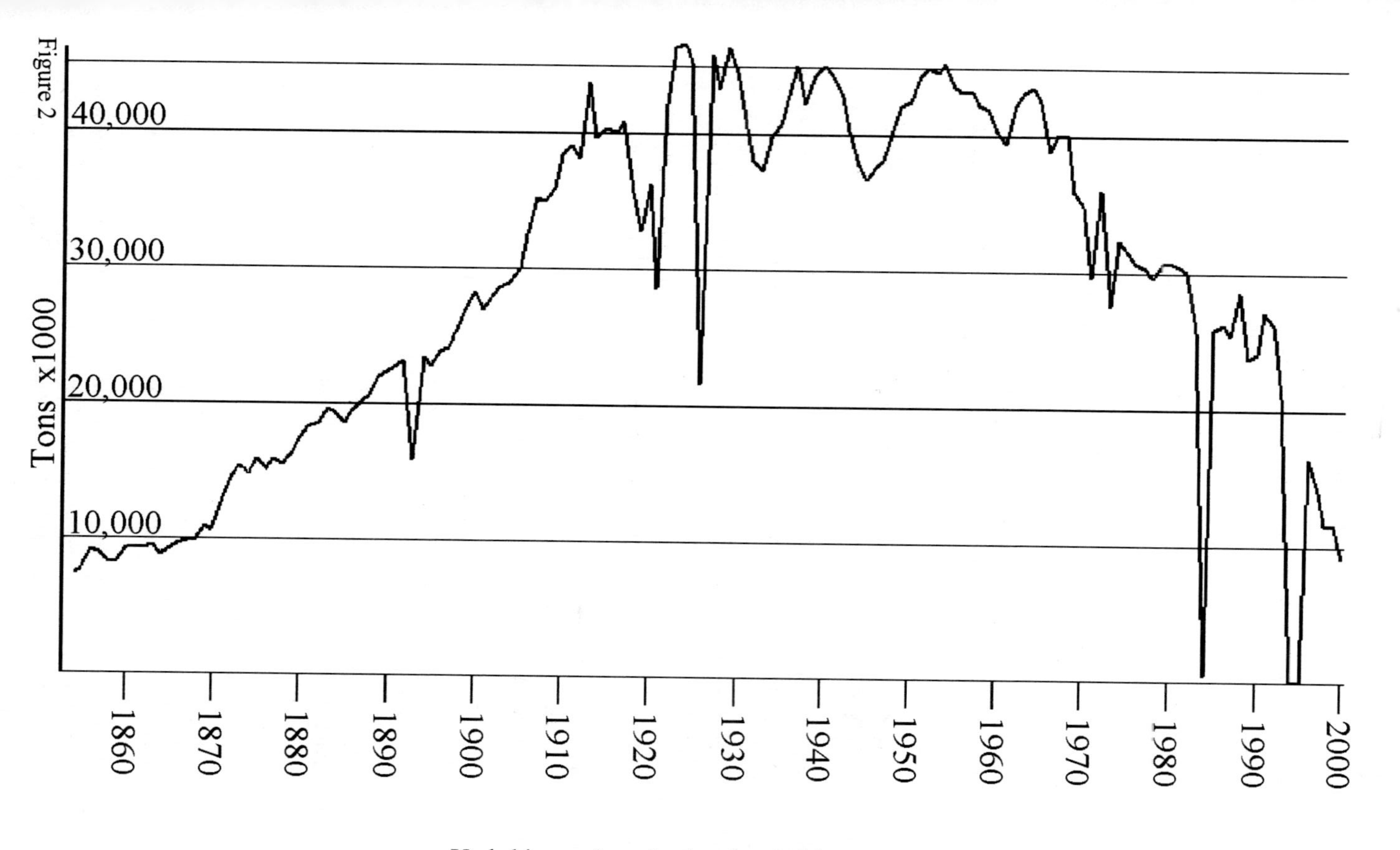

Yorkshire coal production from 1854 to 2000

BIBLIOGRAPHY

Ashcroft, M.Y. (Ed.) *Documents relating to the Swaledale Estates of Lord Wharton in the Sixteenth and Seventeenth Centuries* (Northallerton: North Yorkshire County Record Office, 1984).

Ashcroft, M.Y. *Papers of Sir William Chaytor* (1771-1847) (Northallerton: NYCRO, Publication No.50, 1993).

Barker, J.L. "The Mines of Downholme Moor and Thorpe Edge, Swaledale" *British Mining,* No.48 (1993), pp.22-30.

Barker, J.L. & White, R. "Early Smelting in Swaledale: A Further Look" pp.15-19, in Willies, L. & Cranstone, D. (Eds) *Boles and Smeltmills: Report of a Seminar on the History and Archæology of Lead Smelting* (Historical Metallurgy Society Ltd, 1992).

Berry, E.K. (Ed) *Swaledale Wills and Inventories 1522 – 1600* (Leeds: Yorkshire Archæological Society, Record Series Vol.CLII, 1998).

Burt, R. Waite, P. Atkinson, M. & Burnley, R. *The Yorkshire Mineral Statistics 1845-1913* (Exeter: Department of Economic History, University of Exeter, 1982).

Chapman, S. *Hope to Prosper A History of Ironstone Mining at North Skelton* (Guisborough: Cleveland Ironstone Series, 1997).

Chapman, S. *Whitecliffe Ironstone Mine* (Guisborough: Cleveland Ironstone Series, 1998).

Chapman, S. *Kirkleatham Ironstone Mine* (Guisborough: Cleveland Ironstone Series, 1999).

Chapman, S. *Kilton Ironstone Mine* (Guisborough: Cleveland Ironstone Series, 2000).

Chapman, S. *Guisborough District Mines* (Guisborough: Cleveland Ironstone Series, 2001).

Chapman, S.K. *Cleveland Ironstone* (Clapham: Dalesman Books, 1973)

Chapman, S.K. *Gazetteer of Cleveland Ironstone Mines* (Guisborough: Loughborough Museum Service Research Series, 1976. Second Edition)

Childs, W.R. (Ed) *The Customs Accounts of Hull 1453-1490* (The Yorkshire Archæological Society Records Series, Vol.CXLIV, 1984).

Clough, R.T. *Lead Smelting Mills of the Yorkshire Dales: Their Architectural Character, Construction and Place in the European Tradition* (Keighley: The Author, 1962).

Clough, R.T. *The Lead Smelting Mills of the Yorkshire Dales and Northern Pennines: Their Architectural Character, Construction and Place in the European Tradition* (Keighley: The author, 1980. Reprinted with Additional Material.)

Fieldhouse, R. & Jennings, B. *A History of Richmond and Swaledale* (London: Phillimore, 1978).

France, R.S. *The Thieveley Lead Mines, 1629-1635* (Lancashire and Cheshire Record Society, No.102, 1951).

Gill, M.C. *The Yorkshire and Lancashire Lead Mines: A Study of Lead Mining in the South Craven and Rossendale Districts* (Sheffield: Northern Mine Research Society, British Mining, No.33, 1987).

Gill, M.C. "The Wharton Lead Mines in Swaledale" *The Local Historian*, Vol.18 No.3 (1988), pp.112-118.

Gill, M.C. "Yorkshire Lead Mining - before 1700" *British Mining*, No.37 (1988), pp.46-62.

Gill, M.C. "Mining and Proto-industrialisation" *British Mining*, No.41 (1990), pp.99-110.

Gill, M.C. "Yorkshire Smelt Mills, Part 1: The Northern Dales" *British Mining*, No.45 (1992), pp.111-150.

Gill, M.C. *The Grassington Lead Mines* (Keighley: Northern Mine Research Society, British Mining, No.46, 1993).

Gill, M.C. "Yorkshire Smelting Mills, Part 2: The Southern Dales and Lancashire" *British Mining*, No.48 (1993), pp.132-151.

Gill, M.C. *The Wharfedale Mines* (Keighley: Northern Mine Research Society, British Mining, No.49, 1994).

Gill, M.C. "Harald Bruff and the Greenhaugh Mining Co. Ltd" *British Mining*, No.55 (1995), pp.139-152.

Gill, M.C. *The Greenhow Mines* (Keighley: Northern Mine Research Society, British Mining No.60, 1998).

Gill, M.C. "Yorkshire Smelting Mills, Part 3: Corrigenda" *British Mining* No.67 (2000), pp.108-119.

Gill, M.C. *Swaledale: its Mines and Smelt Mills* (Ashbourne: Landmark Press, 2001).

Gill, M.C. & Harvey, W.S. "Weights and Measures used in the lead industry" *British Mining* No.61 (1998), pp.129-140.

Goodchild, J. "The East Layton Copper Mine in Yorkshire and its Cost Book" *British Mining*, No.47 (1983), pp.

Hartley, M. & Ingilby, J. *Dales Heritage* (Clapham: Dalesman, 1982)

Hornshaw, T.R. *Copper Mining in Richmondshire in the Eighteenth and Nineteenth Centuries* (University of Durham MA Thesis, 1971/2).

Hornshaw, T.R. *Copper Mining in Middleton Tyas* (Northallerton: North Yorkshire County Council, 1975).

Jennings, B. *The Lead Mining Industry in Swaledale* (Univ. of Leeds MA Thesis, 1959).

Jennings, B. (Ed). *A History of Nidderdale* (Huddersfield: Advertiser Press Ltd, 1967).

McDonnell, J.G. "An Account of the Iron Industry in Upper Ryedale and Bilsdale c.1150-1650" *Ryedale Historian*, No.6 (1972), pp.23-52

Mitchell, B.R. & Deane, P. *Abstracts of British Historical Statistics* (Cambridge: Cambridge University Press, 1962)

Okey, S. "Ironstone in Cleveland" *Cleveland Industrial Archaeologist*, No.8 (1978), pp.31-32

Owen, J.S. "Geological Background to Ironstone Mining in Cleveland" Transactions of the Teesside Local History Group, Vol.1 No.1 (1967), pp.1-8

Owen, J.S. "Some Legal Aspects of Ironstone Mining in Cleveland" *Bulletin of the Cleveland and Teesside Local History Society*, No.3 (1968), pp.2-8

Owen, J.S. "Some Further Remarks on the Farndale Ironstone Mines" *Bulletin of the Cleveland and Teesside Local History Society*, No.5 (1969), pp.15-16

Owen, J.S. "Mining Failure in Cleveland. No.3 The Kildale Mines Part 1" *Bulletin of the Cleveland and Teesside Local History Society*, No.14 (Not Dated), pp.18-26

Owen, J.S. "Mining Failure in Cleveland. No.3 The Kildale Mines Part 2" *Bulletin of the Cleveland and Teesside Local History Society*, No.17 (Not Dated), pp.12-17

Owen, J.S. "Mining Failure in Cleveland. No.3 The Kildale Mines Part 3" *Bulletin of the Cleveland and Teesside Local History Society*, No.18 (Not Dated), pp.15-21

Owen, J.S. "Mining Failure in Cleveland. No.3 The Kildale Mines Part 4" *Bulletin of the Cleveland and Teesside Local History Society*, No.19 (Not Dated), pp.10-14

Owen, J.S. "Mining Failure in Cleveland. No.5 Tocketts Mine" *Bulletin of the Cleveland and Teesside Local History Society*, No.24 (1974), pp.10-27

Owen, J.S. "Early Days at the Rosedale Mines" *Bulletin of the Cleveland and Teesside Local History Society*, No.28 (1975), pp.1-11

Owen, J.S. "The Esk Valley Ironstone Mine: Part 1, Documented History" *Cleveland Industrial Archaeologist*, No.7 (1977), pp.1-10

Owen, J.S. "Pre-1865 Ironstone Mining Development at Skinningrove" *Cleveland Industrial Archaeologist*, No.8 (1978), pp.1-8

Owen, J.S. "The Esk Valley Ironstone Mine: Part 3, Excavations Completed" *Cleveland Industrial Archaeologist*, No.11 (1979), pp.13-24

Owen, J.S. "Excavation of the Esk Valley Ironstone Mine, North Yorkshire" *Industrial Archaeology Review*, Vol.IV No.1 (1979-80), pp.103-107

Owen, J.S. "Warren Moor Ironstone Mine, Kildale" *Cleveland Industrial Archaeologist*, No.13 (1981), pp.33-53

Owen, J.S. "Warren Moor Mine, North Yorkshire" *Industrial Archaeology Review*, Vol.V No.3 (1981), pp.260-263

Owen, J.S. "Lonsdale Ironstone Mines, Kildale" *Cleveland Industrial Archaeologist*, No.15 (1983), pp.31-48

Owen, J.S. *Cleveland Ironstone Mining* (Redcar: C. Books, 1986)

Owen, J.S. & Tuffs, P. "The Esk Valley Ironstone Mine: Part 2, Some Site Details" *Cleveland Industrial Archaeologist*, No.7 (1977), pp.11-15

Pepper, R. *Glimpses of Monument Mine Great Ayton 1908-1931* (Guisborough: Cleveland Ironstone Series, 1996).

Raistrick, A. *The Wharton Mines in Swaledale in the Seventeenth Century* (Northallerton: North Yorkshire County Council, 1982).

Raistrick, A. *Mines and Miners on Malham Moor* (Littleborough: Kelsall, 1983).

Raistrick, A. & Jennings, B. *A History of Lead Mining in the Pennines* (Longmans, 1965).

Robinson, P.C. "A Geological Guide to the Iron Deposits of the Scarborough District" *Transactions of the Scarborough and District Archaeological Society*, Vol.1 No.6 (1963), pp.30-34

Schmitz, C.J. *World non-ferrous metal production and prices 1700-1976* (London: Frank Cass, 1979)

Taylor, J. *Records of Mining Pt.1,* (London: John Murray, 1829).

Tuffs, P. "North Skelton Ironstone Mine, Cleveland" *Cleveland Industrial Archaeologist*, No.3 (1975), pp.23-30

Tuffs, P. "Kilton Ironstone Mine *Cleveland Industrial Archaeologist*, No.5 (1976), pp.21-34

Tuffs, P. "Lingdale Ironstone Mine" *Cleveland Industrial Archaeologist*, No.9 (1978), pp.11-22

Tuffs, P. *A Cleveland Ironstone Mining Era Ends* (Guisborough: Cleveland Ironstone Series, 1997).

Tuffs, P. *"Times" of the Past* (Guisborough: Cleveland Ironstone Series, 1997).

Tyson, L.O. *A History of the Manor and Lead Mines of Marrick, Swaledale* (Sheffield: Northern Mine Research Society, British Mining, No.38, 1989).

Tyson, L.O. "Mining and Smelting in the Marske Area, Swaledale" *British Mining*, No.50 (1994), pp.24-40.

Tyson, L.O. *The Arkengarthdale Mines* (Keighley: Northern Mine Research Society, British Mining, No.53, 1995).

Tyson, L.O. & Spensley, I. with White, R.F. *The Grinton Mines (Including Fremington & Ellerton)* (Keighley: Northern Mine Research Society, British Mining, No.51, 1995).

Tables of Mine Production, Ownership, Management and Employment

Please note:-

1. All dates prior to 1752 have been adjusted to begin on January 1st.

2. The traditional term 'ore' has been used throughout instead of concentrate.

3. In the tables for lead either from Grassington or "Smelted at Grassington", the figures for metallic lead up to, and including, 1849 are in smelt mill weight (i.e. 2460 lbs/ton). Thereafter, they are in tons of 2240 lbs. All figures for ore are in tons of 2240 lbs.

AD MINES Healaugh NY961017

Production:	Lead	Ore(tons)	Lead (tons)	Value (£)
	1684	305.60	177.19	
	1696		661.80	
	1697		490.02	
	1699		103.23	
	1700		462.18	
	1701		168.69	
	1736	250.50	193.72	
	1750	582.30	440.01	
	1751	1124.30	778.74	
	1752	1246.30	881.78	
	1753	616.50	413.95	
	1755	901.50	736.54	
	1756	861.00	621.28	
	1786		632.00	
	1787		689.00	
	1788		469.00	
	1789		544.00	
	1790		706.00	
	1791		839.00	
	1792		1183.00	
	1793		1100.00	
	1794		915.00	
	1796		1306.00	
	1797		1407.00	
	1798		1136.00	
	1799		1079.00	
	1800		1343.00	
	1801		3252.00	
	1802		2320.00	
	1803		1393.00	
	1804		1596.00	
	1805		736.36	
	1806		1510.82	
	1807		1468.26	
	1808		1142.14	
	1809		1196.59	
	1810		1196.59	
	1811		870.89	
	1812		389.42	
	1813		601.83	
	1814		339.86	
	1815		240.66	
	1816		575.34	
	1817		1600.05	
	1818		1834.02	

1819	1935.30
1820	2144.50
1821	1903.05
1822	1281.22
1823	1452.19
1824	1053.39
1825	1765.84
1826	2724.53
1827	1650.84
1828	1544.11
1829	1606.10
1830	1254.42
1831	1081.00
1832	1262.09
1833	1200.93
1834	1196.30
1835	1418.56
1836	1700.81
1837	1818.54
1838	1542.28
1839	2267.80
1840	3064.91
1841	2465.91
1842	2716.76
1843	3124.27
1844	2144.41
1845	2016.68
1846	1997.49
1847	1499.04
1848	1492.71
1849	1639.94
1850	1741.00
1851	1639.00
1852	1779.00
1853	1499.00
1854	1591.00
1855	1673.00
1856	3016.00
1857	2838.00
1858	2619.00
1859	1811.00
1860	1660.00
1861	1430.00
1862	1348.00
1863	1149.00
1864	1031.00
1865	1054.00

	1866	1338.00
	1867	2205.00
Comment:	1684	Data from NYCRO R/Q/R9/338
	1696-1699	Data from JLB MSS
	1736-1756	Data from PRO C114/145
	1786-1804	Data from Jennings Thesis
	1805-1816	Data from NYCRO ZLB 2/11
	1805-1816	Based on pieces weighing 158.601 Lbs
	1817-1849	Data from NYCRO ZLB 2/134
	1850-1867	Data from Jennings Thesis
	1684	December 1683 to July 1684
	1696	February to December 1696
	1699	September missing
	1700	December 1699 to September 1700
	1701	December 1700 to March 1701
	1364-1756	Smelted at High & Low Mills, Mill Gill
	1736	December 1735 to May 1736
	1750	June 1750 to December 1750
	1751	December 1750 to December 1751
	1752	December 1751 to December 1752
	1753	December 1752 to June 1753
	1755	June 1755 to December 1755
	1756	December 1755 to June 1756
	1750-1756	Inc. duty ore from: Spout Gill, Keldside
	1750-1756	Inc. duty ore from: Glovergill
	1801-1870	See Lane End, Keldside & Littlemoor
	1804-1912	See Swinnergill
	1806-1905	See Blakethwaite
	1811-1989	See Old Gang
	1818-1912	See Surrender
Mineral Lord:	-1548	Alice Staveley (1/4 share)
	1501-1561	Joan Neville (1/4 share)
	1548-1588	Edward Mollineux (1/4 share)
	1561-1588	John Mollineux (1/4 share)
	1588-1621	John Mollineux (1/2 share)
	1621-1635	Thomas Vachell (1/2 share)
	1515-1537	Francis Bigod (1/2 share)
	1537-1544	The Crown (Bigod's 1/2 share)
	1544-1568	Thomas Wharton (1st Lord) (1/2 share)
	1568-1572	Thomas Wharton (2nd Lord) (1/2 share)
	1572-1629	Philip Wharton (3rd Lord) (1/2 share)
	1629-1635	Philip Wharton (4th Lord) (1/2 share)
	1635-1696	Philip Wharton (4th Lord) (All shares)
	1696-1715	Thomas Wharton (5th Lord)
	1715-1722	Philip Duke of Wharton
	1722-1756	Trustees of the Duke of Wharton
	1764-1785	George Fermor (2nd Earl of Pomfret)

	1785-1787	George Fermor (3rd Earl of Pomfret)
	1787-1816	G. & T.W. Fermor, Charlotte Denys
	1816-1835	T.W. Fermor, Charlotte Denys, G.W. Denys
	1836-1857	G.W. Denys (1), Lady Pomfret, F. Shuckburgh
	1857-1876	G.W. Denys (2), Lady Pomfret, F. Shuckburgh
	1876-1880	G.W. Denys (2), Lady Pomfret, G. Shuckburgh
	1881-1884	F.C.E. Denys, Lady Pomfret, G. Shuckburgh
	1884-1889	F.C.E. Denys, Lady Pomfret, S.F.D. Shuckburgh
	1889-1917	F.C.E. Denys, T. Fermor-Hesketh, S.F.D. Shuckburgh
	1922-1924	J.F.E. Radcliffe, T. Fermor-Hesketh, G.F.S. Shuckburgh
	1924-1940	J.F.E. Radcliffe, T. Fermor-Hesketh, C. Shuckburgh
	1940-1944	Louise M. Pearson (nee Radcliffe), Fermor-Hesketh, C. Shuckburgh
	1944-1955	L.M. Pearson, F. Fermor-Hesketh, Shuckburgh
	1955-1980	L.M. Pearson, T. Fermor-Hesketh, Shuckburgh
Comment:	1635	Manor of Healaugh united
	1530-1544	See Muker
Worked by:	1679	Philip Swale and Robert Barker
	1736-1756	Alexander Denton - Principal Trustee
	1764-1808	Pomfret & Denys
Agent:	1715	Joseph Etherington
	1722-1735	Mr Etherington
	1735-1754	James Close
	1735-1736	Anthony Pratt & William Clarkson
	1749-1753	John Guy (Grove Steward)
	1749-1756	Thomas Stodart (Grove Steward)
	1755-1756	Thomas Hutchinson
	1765-1768	Jeremiah Hutchinson
	1769-1772	John Metcalfe
	1802-1822	John Davies
	1822-1861	James Littlefair
	1861-1883	Thomas Raw
	1884-1900	Simon Cherry
	1901-1928	Edward Cherry

AGNES Arkengarthdale NY954042

Production:	Lead	Ore(tons)	Lead (tons)	Value (£)
	1907-1916	No detailed returns		
Comment:	1907-1909	Inc. Little Punchard and Routh		
	1910-1916	Standing		
Mineral Lord:	1907-1916	See Arkengarthdale		
Worked by:	1907-1916	"CB", Lead Mines Ltd		
Agent:	1907-1916	Thomas Harker		

Employment:		Underground	Surface	Total
	1907	6	4	10
	1908	4	2	6
	1909	2	0	2

AILESBURY Whorlton NZ494008

Production:	Iron	Ore(tons)	Value (£)
	1872	No detailed return	
	1873	87968.00	26390.40
	1874	94829.00	28448.70
	1875	89174.00	
	1876	76546.00	
	1877	63918.00	
	1878	59150.00	
	1879	45446.40	
	1880	66042.00	
	1881	60910.00	
	1882-1887	No detailed returns	
Comment:	1887	Abandoned April	
Mineral Lord:	1872-1887	Marquis of Ailesbury	
Worked by:	1872-1875	North of England Ind. Iron & Coal Co.	
	1876	North of England Ind. Iron & Coal Co. Ltd	
	1877-1887	Carlton Iron Co. Ltd	
Secretary:	1873-1875	H. Jackson	
	1876-1885	Robert Bell	

Employment:		Underground	Surface	Total
	1883	-	-	39

AITHWAITE END Carperby Cum Thoresby SD982903

Production:	Lead	Ore(tons)	Lead (tons)	Value (£)
	1864	4.00	2.40	
	1865-1867	No detailed returns		
Comment:	1868-1876	Suspended		
Mineral Lord:	1862-1876	Lightfoot's Devisees		
Worked by:	1862-1867	Messrs Winn		

Employment:		Underground	Surface	Total
	1862	11	-	-

ANGLEZARKE LIBERTY SD631164

Production:	Lead	Ore(tons)	Lead (tons)	Value (£)
	1689-1830	No detailed returns		
Comment:	1781-1790	Witherite Producer		
Mineral Lord:	1689-1694	Sir Richard Standish		
	1721-1756	Sir Thomas Standish		
	1781-1812	Sir Frank Standish		
	1812-1841	Frank Hall Standish		
Worked by:	1689	Sir Richard Standish & Co.		
	1721-1732	Sir Henry Houghton		
	1781-1790	Sir Frank Standish		
	1824-1830	John Thompson & Co.		

APEDALE		Castle Bolton		SE015946
Production:	Lead	Ore(tons)	Lead (tons)	Value (£)
	1853		3.20	
	1854		2.60	
	1855		3.85	
	1856		12.20	
	1857		4.80	
	1858		6.90	
	1859		20.80	
	1860		9.65	
	1861		34.10	
	1862		22.25	
	1863		37.50	
	1864		37.10	
	1865		21.25	
	1866		14.45	
	1867		6.30	
	1868-1876	No detailed returns		
	1877		73.85	
	1878		23.40	
	1853-1878	Data from Lord Bolton's Lead Book		
	1864-1865	No detailed returns		
	1866	8.00	5.50	
	1867	No detailed return		
	1876	50.00	37.50	
	1877	113.00	65.00	1278.20
	1878	100.00	60.00	1000.00
	1879	50.00	20.00	382.60
	1880	45.80	34.00	756.80
	1881	70.70	56.50	777.00
	1882	68.60	56.10	652.00
	1883	23.80	18.80	258.00
	1884	No detailed return		
	1889	18.00	12.00	144.00
	1890	7.00	4.00	60.00
	1892	12.00	9.00	87.00
	1893	No detailed return		
	1896	13.00	9.00	80.00
	1897	No detailed return		
	1864-1865	See Keld Heads		
	1881	35.30	15.90	118.80
	1882	109.00	50.00	368.00
	1883	16.00	4.40	134.00
	1884	No detailed return		
	1864-1897	Data from Hunt's statistics		
Comment:	1868-1876	Standing		
	1883	Standing		

	1884	Abandoned: April
	1902	Abandoned
Mineral Lord:	1766-1902	See under Keld Heads
Worked by:	1759-1768	Chauncy Townsend
	1850-1867	Richard Willis & Co.
	1876-1883	Apedale Lead Mining Co.
	1886-1897	Apedale Mining Co.
	1898-1902	Joseph Cradock & Thomas Cradock
Agent:	1862	G.A. Robinson
	1873-1879	John Tattersall
	1880-1883	John Cain
	1886-1893	John Ascough Rodwell
	1894	F. Rodwell
	1895-1902	Thomas Cradock
Secretary:	1860-1861	Tattersall, Willis & Co.

Employment:		Underground	Surface	Total
	1877	15	8	23
	1878	12	6	18
	1879	8	4	12
	1880	17	7	24
	1898-1902	2	-	2

APEDALE GREETS Castle Bolton SE030954

Production:	Lead	Ore(tons)	Lead (tons)	Value (£)
	1854		2.90	
	1855		9.45	
	1856		7.85	
	1857		1.00	

Comment:	1859	See Apedale Head & Golden Groves
Mineral Lord:	1854-1859	See under Keld Heads
Worked by:	1854-1859	Wyvill & Co.

APEDALE HEAD Castle Bolton SE003953

Production:	Lead	Ore(tons)	Lead (tons)	Value (£)
	1850		3.20	
	1851		17.60	
	1852		18.85	
	1856		0.20	
	1860		0.30	

Comment:	1859	Inc. Apedale Greets (Part)
Mineral Lord:	1850-1860	See under Keld Heads
Worked by:	1850-1858	John Coats & Co.
	1858-1860	Apedale Head Mining Co.

APPLETREEWICK Appletreewick SE054607

Production:	Lead	Ore(tons)	Lead (tons)	Value (£)
	1861	146.00	94.90	
	1862	307.70	200.00	
	1863	234.80	152.60	
	1864	239.90	155.90	
	1865	528.60	343.60	
	1866	1026.50	667.20	
	1867	584.00	380.00	
	1868	469.10	304.90	
	1869	367.50	275.20	
	1870	182.60	118.80	
	1871	494.60	370.50	
	1872	45.00	33.30	
	1875	18.00	13.50	
	1876	137.70	97.00	1941.00
	1877	401.50	292.40	5703.00
	1878	412.00	254.40	6592.00
	1879	78.80	52.30	829.50
	1880	1880.00	1410.00	19740.00
	1881	153.10	107.80	1371.30
	1882	233.60	175.00	2103.00
	1883	83.00	56.40	640.00
	1884-1885	No detailed returns		
	1890-1891	No detailed returns		
	1861-1883	Data from Hunt's statistics		
	1873	Suspended		
	1874	Advertised for sale		
	1880-1893	Not working		
	1878		28.25	
	1880		0.20	
	1878 Smelted at Kettlewell			
	1880 Smelted at Grassington			
Production:	Calcite	Ore(tons)		Value (£)
	1925	156.00		
	1926	287.00		
	1927	277.00		
	1928	Standing		
Mineral Lord:	1857-1928	See Appletreewick Liberty		
Worked by:	1857-1870	Appletreewick Lead Mining Co.		
	1870-1873	Appletreewick Lead Mining Co. Ltd		
	1875-1883	New Appletreewick Mining Co. Ltd		
	1923-1928	Greenhaugh Mining Co. Ltd		
Agent:	1862-1871	Thomas Wiseman		
	1867	Thomas Dalton		
	1873	William Newbould		
	1875-1881	Edwin Dunkin		

	1878-1880	A. Hargreaves
Secretary:	1862-1866	John Blackburn
	1867	A.W. Blackburn
	1868	Thomas Dalton
	1869-1873	Thomas Marshall
	1877-1880	James Leith

Employment:		Underground	Surface	Total
	1862	32	-	-
	1868	-	-	73
	1877	50	21	71
	1878	45	15	60
	1879	6	2	8
	1881	18	7	25
	1882	18	6	24
	1926	8	20	28
	1927	13	22	35
	1925 Included with Gill Heads			

APPLETREEWICK LIBERTY SE079624

Production:	Lead	Ore(tons)	Lead (tons)	Value (£)
	1300-1538	No detailed returns		
	1620-1638	No detailed returns		
	1965	15.18		
	1638	Smelted at Heathfield		
	Fluorspar	Ore(tons)		Value (£)
	1938	342.26		
	1939	874.38		
	1940	323.84		
	1941	163.75		
	1942	207.08		
	1943	459.90		
	1944	1228.70		
	1945	2325.35		
	1946	2277.45		
	1947	2067.05		
	1948	1400.10		
	1965	1672.30		

Comment:	1965	July to December
	1938-1967	Inc. Burhill, Craven Moor & Gill Heads
	1938-1967	See Blackhill & Dry Gill
Mineral Lord:	1300-1539	Canons of Bolton
	1539	Thomas Proctor
	1539-1549	Sir Arthur D'Arcy
	1549-1568	Sir John Yorke
	1568-1589	Peter Yorke
	1589-1630	Sir John Yorke

	1630-1635 John Yorke
	1635-1663 John Yorke
	1663-1716 Thomas Yorke
	1716-1757 John Yorke
	1757-1768 Thomas Yorke
	1768-1813 John Yorke
	1813-1857 John Yorke
	1857-1883 John Yorke
	1883-1915 Thomas Edward Yorke
	1915-1996 John Edward Evelyn Yorke
Worked by:	1538-1544 Ingram Clifford
	1620-1638 John Yorke
	1930-1949 James Harold Clay
	1950-1963 Fred C. Walker
	1964-1967 Clay Cross Company Ltd
	1968-1971 Fred C. Walker

APPLETREEWICK MOOR Appletreewick SE072634

Production:	Lead	Ore(tons)	Lead (tons)	Value (£)
	1782	No detailed return		
Comment:	1782	WYAS Yorke MSS DB151		
Worked by:	1782	John Thornhill & Co.		

ARKENGARTHDALE Arkengarthdale NY996025

Production:	Lead	Ore(tons)	Lead (tons)	Value (£)
	1657	18.15		
	1658	30.20		
	1748	196.80		
	1749	474.20		
	1750	183.60		
	1783	596.00	365.00	
	1784	739.90	609.00	
	1785	1140.00	810.00	
	1786	729.30	953.00	
	1787	781.70	614.00	
	1788	657.60	563.00	
	1789	735.40	596.00	
	1790	725.50	599.00	
	1791	369.70	294.00	
	1794	1003.80	829.91	
	1795	1371.90	1142.45	
	1796	1160.10	1011.13	
	1797	733.40	592.23	
	1798	762.60	644.76	
	1799	337.80	261.97	
	1657-1658	Smelted at Clints Mills		
	1657-1558	Data from John Bathurst's accounts		

	1657	August to December		
	1658	January to October		
	1748-1799	Smelted at Moulds Mills		
	1748-1750	Data from ore accounts		
	1748	July to December		
	1750	January to June		
	1783-1799	Data from Charles Sleigh & Ptrs accounts		
	1783	November 1782 to December 1783		
	1784-1790	December to November		
	1791	December 1790 to June 1791		
	1794-1796	December to November		
	1797	December 1796 to November 1797		
	1798	December to November		
	1799	November to April		

Production:	Lead	Ore(tons)	Lead (tons)	Value (£)
	1871	896.40	671.18	
	1872	670.50	491.98	
	1873	873.35	664.84	
	1874	1204.80	907.62	
	1875	1502.10	1126.58	
	1876	1295.20	995.69	
	1877	1378.80	1082.36	
	1878	2190.80	1717.04	
	1879	1756.60	1396.50	
	1880	1653.30	1295.08	
	1881	1665.05	1273.76	
	1882	2387.20	1850.08	
	1883	1927.80	1497.26	
	1884	1773.05	1358.60	
	1885	1897.05	1465.47	
	1886	2237.95	1731.61	
	1887	1801.65	1369.25	
	1888	1426.70	1066.46	
	1889	1025.00	776.44	
	1890	803.30	614.52	
	1891	598.50	457.85	
Comments:	1871-1891	Data from George Gilpin Brown's accounts		
	1891	January to May		

Production:	Lead	Ore(tons)	Lead (tons)	Value (£)
	1868	1596.20	1257.00	
	1869	1617.00	1230.00	
	1870	935.00	700.00	
	1871	800.00	629.50	
	1872	601.00	450.70	
	1873	601.60	451.20	
	1874	1265.40	790.80	
	1875	1479.00	1037.00	

1876	1259.90	882.00	1007.00
1877	1974.60	1482.00	24678.10
1878	2459.00	1967.00	29508.00
1879	1623.30	1217.10	17041.50
1880	1659.20	1244.70	17419.00
1881	1959.60	1469.10	18500.00
1882	2334.80	1751.10	21597.00
1883	1879.10	1409.20	15032.00
1884	1764.00	1323.00	12898.00
1885	1966.00	1474.50	12779.00
1886	2220.00	1582.00	18304.00
1887	1536.00		
1888	1197.00	897.60	10236.00
1889	946.00	674.00	8514.00
1890	673.00	480.00	6220.00
1891	656.00	467.00	5597.00
1892	486.00	346.00	3405.00
1893	431.00	307.00	3011.00
1894	352.00	251.00	2464.00
1895	305.00	217.00	2440.00
1896	268.00	190.00	2412.00
1897	327.00	233.00	2695.00
1898	225.00	160.00	1850.00
1899	149.00	106.00	1937.00
1900	118.00	84.00	1593.00
1901	80.00	57.00	760.00
1902	72.00	51.00	648.00

Comment: 1868-1902 Data from Hunt's statistics
1898-1905 Arkendale C.B.
1906 Not working
1907-1909 Prospecting
1909-1915 Standing
1915-1916 In liquidation
Fluorspar
1955-1970 No detailed returns
1955-1970 No detailed returns

Mineral Lord: 1200-1628 The Crown
1628-1654 The Citizens of London
1654-1659 Dr John Bathurst
1659-1697 Theodore Bathurst
1697-1724 Charles Bathurst
1724-1743 Charles Bathurst Jnr
1743-1747 Frances Bathurst
1747-1771 Charles Turner
1771-1781 Charles Turner and Partners
1782-1783 Charles Turner, Charles Sleigh, Charles Foster
1784-1791 Charles Sleigh, William Hoar & Charles Foster

	1792-1799	Charles Sleigh and Partners
	1800-1812	Charles Sleigh, Charles Turner, Charles Foster
	1812-1821	George Brown
	1821-1854	John Gilpin
	1860-1889	George Gilpin Brown
	1889-1918	George Thomas Gilpin Brown
	1918-1942	Guy Greville Wilson
	1942-1975	Thomas Sopwith
	1975-2000	Duke of Norfolk & Ptrs
Worked by:	1531	William Conyers
	1532	James Metcalfe
	1544	Christopher Metcalfe
	1566	James Phillips
	1580	Robert Stapleton & John Mallory
	1602	Ambrose Appleby
	1654-1659	Dr John Bathurst
	1659-1697	Theodore Bathurst
	1697-1724	Charles Bathurst
	1724-1743	Charles Bathurst Jnr
	1743-1747	Frances Bathurst
	1747-1771	Charles Turner
	1771-1781	Charles Turner and Partners
	1782-1783	Charles Turner, Charles Sleigh, Charles Foster
	1784-1791	Charles Sleigh, William Hoar & Charles Foster
	1792-1801	Charles Sleigh and Partners
	1801-1811	Easterby, Hall & Co.
	1812-1817	The Arkindale & Derwent Mines Co.
	1817-1821	Hall & Puller
	1821-1860	Robert Jaques & Co.
	1860-1868	Arkendale Co.
	1869	William Whitwell & Co.
	1870-1890	Arkendale Mining Co.
	1891-1906	George Thomas Gilpin Brown
	1907-1916	"CB", Lead Mines, Ltd
	1955-1970	Lessee: Horace Taylor (Minerals) Co.
	1955-1970	Ernest Shevels on tribute to Taylor
Agent:	1657-1658	Benjamin Purchas
	1724-1735	Thomas Smailes
	1777-1780	James Alderson
	1797-1800	George Alderson
	1802-1821	Frederick Hall
	1862-1863	Thomas Coates
	1864-1867	Thomas Raw
	1868	George Alderson
	1868	Lancelot Wharton
	1869-1871	Robert Wharton
	1870-1878	Mathew Woodward

	1872-1873	Joseph Craig
	1877-1894	William Peacock
	1869-1880	William Whitwell
	1882	James Blenkiron
	1895-1905	Thomas Harker
	1906	R.T. Hammond
Secretary:	1860-1863	Jacques, Roper & Co.
	1874-1881	Joseph Carter
	1880-1882	William Whitwell
	1907-1908	Edmund Jones
	1908-1915	Walter Pickering

Employment:		Underground	Surface	Total
	1783	139	-	-
	1784	126	-	-
	1785	139	-	-
	1786	123	-	-
	1787	113	-	-
	1788	111	-	-
	1789	115	-	-
	1790	117	-	-
	1791	106	-	-
	1862	188	-	-
	1877	189	45	234
	1878	210	50	260
	1879	189	50	239
	1880	249	51	300
	1898	47	10	57
	1899	37	10	47
	1900	35	10	45
	1901	32	9	41
	1902	26	4	30
	1903	9	-	9
	1904-1905	4	-	4
	1783-1791 Includes waste workers			

ARNCLIFFE CLOWDER Arncliffe SD925698

Production:	Lead	Ore(tons)	Lead (tons)	Value (£)
	1779		1.14	
	1780		0.13	
	1785		0.09	
	1787		0.44	
	1788		1.18	
	1790		0.84	
	1792		0.24	
	1787-1792 George Tennant			
	1787		0.06	

	1788		0.30	
	1789		0.30	
	1790		0.50	
	1787	Robert Higgs		
	1788-1790	James Slater		
	1787		0.35	
	1787	C. Shackleton		
	1779-1792	Smelted at Grassington		
	1701-1847	See Darsey Rake		
	1791-1798	See Merrybotton		
Mineral Lord:	1779-1792	See under Grassington		

ARNGILL		Muker		SD912994
Production:	Lead	Ore(tons)	Lead (tons)	Value (£)
	1751	1.20		
	1756	2.00		
	1835		2.68	
	1836		3.33	
	1920	10.00		
	1921	12.75		
Comment:	1751-1756	Smelted at High & Low Mills in Mill Gill		
	1751-1756	See entry for AD Mines		
	1812-1832	Included with Swinnergill		
	1919	Prospecting		
	1918-1920	Inc. East Arngill		
Mineral Lord:	1751-1921	See AD Mines		
Worked by:	1811	Robert Metcalfe & Co.		
	1812-1832	Hopper & Co.		
	1835-1836	George Guy & Co.		
	1873-1883	AD Lead Mining Company Ltd		
	1919-1921	E.R. Fawcett & J.R. Pickup		

ARNGILL		Lunedale		NY853227
Production:	Lead	Ore(tons)	Lead (tons)	Value (£)
	1741	2.60		
	1746	9.20		
	1757	7.90		
Mineral Lord:	1741-1831	See Lunehead		
Worked by:	1771	London Lead Company		
	1831	James Ainsly & Co.		

ARNGILL HEAD		Lunedale		NY835238
Production:	Lead	Ore(tons)	Lead (tons)	Value (£)
	1831	No detailed return		
Mineral Lord:	1831	See Lunehead		
Worked by:	1831	Mathew Collison & Co.		

ASHNOTT		Newton		SD692481
Production:	Lead	Ore(tons)	Lead (tons)	Value (£)
	1814-1835	No detailed returns		
Comment:	1814-1835	Smelted at Newton Fell Mill		
	1835	Abandoned		
Mineral Lord:	1814	Duchess of Buccleauch		

ASKRIGG MOOR		Askrigg		SD946943
Production:	Lead	Ore(tons)	Lead (tons)	Value (£)
	1722-1768	No detailed returns		
	1769		12.10	
	1770-1771	No detailed returns		
	1771		0.90	
	1772		0.89	
	1773	No detailed return		
	1774		6.88	
	1775		8.19	
	1776		1.95	
	1777		29.05	
	1778		15.79	
	1779	No detailed return		
	1780		6.82	
	1811		0.22	
	1812		0.74	
	1821		3.21	
	1829		5.13	
	1861-1863	No detailed returns		
	1864	11.50	8.30	
	1865	4.40	3.10	
	1866	2.70	1.90	
	1867	37.00	25.90	
	1868	12.10	8.00	
Comment:	1722-1829	Data from PRO L.R.R.O. 3/84		
	1769-1781	Michaelmas to Michaelmas		
	1864-1871	Data from Hunt's statistics		
	1861-1875	See Beezy		
Mineral Lord:	1722-1875	The Crown		
Worked by:	1722-1732	Henry Metcalfe		
	1732-1758	Thomas Metcalfe		
	1758-1762	Richard Weddell		
	1762-1782	William Weddell		
	1774	John Park and George Dinsdale		
	1799-1829	Lord Grantham		
	1862-1864	Thomas Mason		
	1864-1871	Joshua Byers & Son		
Agent:	1756-1782	Alexander Fothergill (Steward)		
	1799	Thomas Bernard (Steward)		
	1866-1875	Thomas Mason		

AYGILL Bowes NY904110

Production:	Lead	Ore(tons)	Lead (tons)	Value (£)
	1732-1859	No detailed return		
Comment:	1755	Prospecting		
	1767-1859	See Bowes Moor		
Mineral Lord:	1732	Christopher Alderson		
	1755-1756	Wingate Pulleine		
	1766-1767	Winifred Pulleine		
Worked by:	1732	Wingate Pulleine		
	1755	Mathias Hanby & Co.		
	1756	Thomas Bowman & Co.		
	1766	Thomas Walker & Thomas Butson		

AYSDALEGATE Lockwood NZ652149

Production:	Iron	Ore(tons)	Value (£)
	1863-1876	No detailed returns	
Comment:	1877-1902	Standing	
	1902	Absorbed into Spa Wood	
Worked by:	1863-1865	Messrs Barningham	
	1877-1881	William Barningham	
	1881-1902	Exors of William Barningham	

AYSGARTH Aysgarth SE001884

Production:	Lead	Ore(tons)	Lead (tons)	Value (£)
	1862-1865	No detailed returns		
Worked by:	1862-1865	John Tattersall & Co.		

AYSGARTH MOOR Aysgarth SD970870

Production:	Lead	Ore(tons)	Lead (tons)	Value (£)
	1863-1877	No detailed returns		
Comment:	1863-1877	Data from Hunt's statistics		
	1863	0.55		
	1864	1.15		
Comment:	1863-1864	Smelted at Kettlewell		
Mineral Lord:	1862-1877	Henry Thomas Robinson		
Worked by:	1862-1877	Costobadie & Co.		
	1863-1864	Aysgarth Moor Company		
Agent:	1863-1864	William B. Briscoe		

AYTON Great Ayton NZ585103

Production:	Iron	Ore(tons)	Value (£)
	1908-1931	No detailed returns	
	1926	Standing	
	1928-1930	Standing	
	1931	Abandoned	
Mineral Lord:	1908-1931	Proctor's Trustees; Headlam; Crown	
Worked by:	1908-1931	Pease and Partners Ltd	

Agent:	1908-1910	W.B. Coxon		
	1911-1912	Christopher Heslop		
	1913-1929	George C. Heslop		
	1930	T. Mayes		
Employment:		Underground	Surface	Total
	1909	19	22	41
	1910	27	23	50
	1911	43	21	64
	1912	83	19	102
	1913	58	19	77
	1914	57	21	78
	1915	68	19	87
	1916	74	22	96
	1917	102	30	132
	1918	106	40	146
	1919	124	44	168
	1920	120	54	174
	1921	113	56	169
	1922	71	39	110
	1923	94	42	136
	1924	118	45	163
	1925	116	43	159
	1926	3	7	10
	1927	120	41	161
	1928	107	35	142
	1929	2	5	7
	1930	6	8	14
	1908	Included with Lingdale		

AYTON BANKS Great Ayton NZ588110

Production:	Iron	Ore(tons)			Value (£)
	1910-1929	No detailed returns			
Comment:	1910-1912	Opening			
	1922-1928	Standing			
	1929	Abandoned July			
Worked by:	1910-1921	Tees Furnace Co. Ltd			
	1922-1925	Burton & Son			
	1926	Gribdale Mining Co. Ltd			
Agent:	1912	T. Eato			
	1913	A.H. Askew			
	1913-1929	George C. Heslop			
	1914-1917	James White			
	1919-1924	D. Oakley			
Employment:		Underground	Surface	Total	
	1912	3	0	3	
	1913	11	10	21	
	1914	226	500	276	

	1915	50	160	66
	1916	56	180	74
	1917	64	230	87
	1918	59	290	88
	1919	71	330	104
	1920	69	300	99
	1921	53	260	79

BACCO RAKE Grassington SE024669

Production:	Lead	Ore(tons)	Lead (tons)	Value (£)
	1755		0.96	
	1765		5.60	

Comment: 1764-1813 Part of New Ripon
Mineral Lord: 1755-1813 See under Grassington
Worked by: 1755-1765 Mr Shackleton

BAGNALL & Co. MINES Eskdaleside Cum Ugglebarnby NZ829056

Production:	Iron	Ore(tons)	Value (£)
	1862	500.00	75.00
	1864	52500.00	

Comment: 1862-1864 See Grosmont

BALDERSDALE Lunedale

Production:	Lead	Ore(tons)	Lead (tons)	Value (£)

1877-1883 No detailed returns
Comment: 1877-1883 Standing
Worked by: 1877-1883 London Lead Co.
Agent: 1879-1883 Robert W. Bainbridge

BALE BANK Bewerley SE137653

Production:	Lead	Ore(tons)	Lead (tons)	Value (£)

1784-1785 No detailed returns
Mineral Lord: 1784-1785 See Bewerley Liberty
Worked by: 1784-1785 Sir John Ingilby

BAND Arkengarthdale NY997031

Production:	Lead	Ore(tons)	Lead (tons)	Value (£)
	1782	41.70		
	1783	304.50		
	1784	66.70		
	1785	9.60		
	1786	4.60		
	1787	0.50		
	1788	1.50		
	1789	8.50		
	1790	0.60		
	1879	7.35		

	1880	16.65		
	1881	0.45		
	1882	0.05		

Comment: 1782 November 1782 to November 1783 Inclusive
1783-1790 December to November Inclusive
1790 December 1790 to May 1791 Inclusive
Mineral Lord: 1782-1882 See Arkengarthdale
Worked by: 1782-1791 Charles Sleigh, William Hoar & Charles Foster
1862 Arkendale Co.
1879-1882 Arkendale Mining Co.

Employment:		Underground	Surface	Total
	1782-1783	13		
	1783-1784	35		
	1784-1785	22		
	1785-1786	6		
	1786-1787	2		
	1787-1788	1		
	1788-1789	1		
	1789-1790	3		
	1790-1791	1		
	1862	12		

BARROWS (BARRAS) PASTURE Grassington SE006667

Production:	Lead	Ore(tons)	Lead (tons)	Value (£)
	1749		2.93	
	1750		2.66	
	1751		11.32	
	1752		1.51	
	1753		2.53	
	1757		0.33	
	1758		0.62	
	1783		0.25	
	1787		0.27	
	1788		0.95	
	1789		2.76	
	1790		0.90	
	1791		0.13	
	1797		0.25	
	1798		0.50	
	1828	18.65	12.25	

Mineral Lord: 1749-1828 See under Grassington

BAXENDEN Haslingden SD775255

Production:	Lead	Ore(tons)	Lead (tons)	Value (£)
	1754	No detailed return		

Worked by: 1754 Clitheroe Mine Adventurers Co.

BECKHOLE		Egton		NZ821019
Production:	Iron	Ore(tons)		Value (£)
	1857-1864	No detailed returns		
Mineral Lord:	1857-1864	Top Seam		
	1857-1864	Trustees of Robert Cary Elwes		
Worked by:	1857-1864	Whitby Iron Co.		

BEEVER		Grassington		SE021657
Production:	Lead	Ore(tons)	Lead (tons)	Value (£)
	1848	4.20	2.15	
	1849	0.80	0.45	
Production:	Barytes	Ore(tons)		Value (£)
	1965	No detailed returns		
Mineral Lord:	1848-1989	See under Grassington		
Worked by:	1965	William Houston & T.C. Brammall		

BEEZY		Askrigg		SD946943
Production:	Lead	Ore(tons)	Lead (tons)	Value (£)
	1861-1875	No detailed returns		
Mineral Lord:	1861-1875	See Askrigg Moor		
Worked by:	1861	Ralph Milner		
	1862-1875	Thomas Mason		

BELDI HILL		Muker		NY908011
Production:	Lead	Ore(tons)	Lead (tons)	Value (£)
	1742-1766	No detailed returns		
	1767	70.00		
	1768	218.40	158.23	2186.58
	1769		114.16	1933.11
	1770		248.56	3276.51
	1771		316.05	4319.60
	1852		15.95	289.01
	1853		7.89	147.96
	1854			467.71
	1855			677.15
	1856			95.60
	1857			337.55
	1858			767.78
	1859			277.88
	1860			161.93
	1882	3.00	2.10	24.00
	1883	3.00	2.20	24.00
	1884	No detailed return		
Comment:	1767-1771	Data from NYCRO ZCC		
	1852-1860	Data from Durham R.O: Hanby Holmes MSS		
	1882-1884	Data from Hunt's Statistics		
	1738-1771	Also called Hall Moor Lead Mine		

	1768-1771	In dispute (Pomfret vs Smith)
	1877	Standing
	1883-1885	Standing
Mineral Lord:	1544-1738	See AD Mines
	1738-1773	Thomas Smith (1)
	1773-1817	Thomas Smith (2)
	1817-1868	Rev. Thomas Smith
	1868-1879	Eleanor Sillery
	1879-1927	Francis Horner Lyell
Worked by:	1738	Thomas Clarkson & Co.
	1742-1771	Leonard Hartley, John Parke & Ralph Parke
	1766-1772	John Scott, Richard Metcalfe (Sub-lease)
	1808	Hopper-Monkhouse & Co.
	1838-1849	Henry Alderson Thompson & Co.
	1849-1860	Isaac Fisher & Co.
	1860-1875	Beldi Hill Co.
	1878-1885	Beldi Hill Mining Co.
Agent:	1795-1796	James Grime
	1796	Thomas Butson
	1860-1870	Ralph Milner
	1871-1882	James A. Clarkson
Secretary:	1860-1863	John Knowles

Employment:		Underground	Surface	Total
	1862	36		
	1878	6	1	7
	1879	4	1	5
	1880	4	0	4

BELDI HILL 10 MEERS Muker NY906010

Production:	Lead	Ore(tons)	Lead (tons)	Value (£)
	1766		25.28	364.85
	1767		13.97	200.02
	1768		105.03	1461.98

Mineral Lord:	1768	See Beldi Hill
Worked by:	1766-1768	Richard Metcalfe & Co. (Sub-lessees)

BELMONT Guisborough NZ617144

Production:	Iron	Ore(tons)	Value (£)
	1856	73164.00	
	1857	No detailed return	
	1858	101425.00	16223.70
	1860	45000.00	6000.00
	1865	175894.30	43973.50
	1866	172620.00	43155.00
	1867	84629.10	23272.90
	1868	60394.00	15098.50

	1869	170945.00	42736.20
	1870	227553.50	56888.40
	1871	213525.50	53381.20
	1872	181068.40	
	1873	134964.80	40489.20
	1874	172805.00	51841.50
	1875	161188.00	
	1876	117600.00	
	1877	57301.20	
	1878	8966.90	
	1879	34352.30	
	1880	110148.70	
	1881	116944.40	
	1882-1885	No detailed returns	
	1907-1928	No detailed returns	
Comment:	1858	Includes 4 other mines	
	1858	Includes 1859	
	1859-1861	Includes Port Mulgrave & Staithes	
	1860	Includes 1861	
	1869	Includes Spawood	
	1873-1874	Includes Spawood	
	1877	Standing	
	1883	Standing	
	1885	Abandoned	
	1907	Opening	
	1929-1932	Standing	
	1933	Abandoned February	
Mineral Lord:	1858-1933	Chaloner Family	
Worked by:	1853-1866	Towlaw Coal & Iron Co.	
	1867-1871	Weardale Coal & Iron Co.	
	1872-1874	Weardale Iron & Coal Co.	
	1875-1887	Weardale Iron & Coal Co. Ltd	
	1907-1928	Bolckow, Vaughan & Co. Ltd	
	1929-1933	Dorman, Long & Co. Ltd	
Agent:	1863-1871	Thomas Allison	
	1872	T. Coulthard	
	1873-1881	Thomas Allison	
	1878-1882	W. Robinson	
	1883-1885	J. Robinson	
	1907	A.G. Thomson	
	1908-1910	Frank Robinson	
	1911-1912	A.M. Hedley	
	1913-1917	H. Palmer	
	1919-1920	C.H. Steavenson	
	1921	J.G. Hunter	
	1922-1925	W.G. Grace	
	1926-1929	T.E. Slater	

1930-1932 M. Hadley
1933 R. Metcalfe

Employment:

	Underground	Surface	Total
1883			157
1908	16	2	18
1909	137	44	181
1910	22	48	268
1911	258	41	299
1912	300	42	342
1913	344	48	392
1914	354	52	406
1915	246	49	295
1916	249	52	301
1917	313	74	387
1918	316	86	402
1919	374	105	479
1920	374	97	471
1921	376	87	463
1922	5	2	7
1923	11	0	11
1924	6	1	7
1925	10	0	10
1926	7	0	7
1927	8	0	8
1928	3	0	3
1929	4	0	4
1930	7	0	7
1931	6	0	6
1932	14	0	14
1933	4	4	8

BELMONT (SOUTH) Guisborough NZ638157

Production: Iron

	Ore(tons)	Value (£)
1865	54952.00	13738.00
1866	32700.00	8175.00
1867	33734.70	8443.70
1868	69672.00	17418.00
1869	No detailed returns	
1870	57376.00	19344.00
1871	35871.80	8967.90
1872	No detailed returns	
1873	125830.00	37749.00
1874	69385.00	20815.50
1875	35009.30	

Mineral Lord: 1863-1875 Admiral Chaloner
Worked by: 1863-1866 H.K. Spark

	1867-1868	H.K. Spark & Co.		
	1869-1875	The North of England Iron & Coal Co. Ltd		
Agent:	1863-1868	D.W. Dixon		
	1869-1871	Thomas R. Reed		
	1872	John Stone		
	1873-1875	H. Jackson		

BENTHAM		Grassington		SE031669
Production:	Lead	Ore(tons)	Lead (tons)	Value (£)
	1783		0.16	
	1786		0.54	
	1787		0.27	
	1790		63.15	
	1791		43.67	
	1792		36.30	
	1793		4.55	
	1794		22.70	
	1795		11.00	
	1796		3.20	
	1797		0.55	
	1798		3.80	
	1799		4.15	
	1800		6.25	
	1801		3.35	
	1802		3.30	
	1803		2.10	
	1804		3.85	
	1808		0.20	
	1809	0.98	0.50	
	1812	0.68	0.35	
Mineral Lord:	1783-1812	See under Grassington		
Worked by:	1783-1801	Peter Wilson Overend		
	1801-1803	Christopher Lawson		
	1802	William Coats		
	1804	Stephen Joy		
	1808	Elizabeth Daykin		
	1809	Emanual Ashton		
	1812	Jonathan Parmerley		

BEWERLEY No.1		Bewerley		SE112643
Production:	Fluorspar	Ore(tons)	Lead (tons)	Value (£)
	1922-1928	No detailed returns		
Comment:	1922-1928	See also Cockhill		
	1925	Standing		
	1928	Standing		
Mineral Lord:	1922-1928	See Bewerley Liberty		
Worked by:	1922-1925	Bewerley Mining Co.		

	1926-1928	Bewerley Mines Ltd			
Agent:	1922-1928	Arthur Kingham			

Employment:		Underground	Surface	Total
	1923	4	3	7
	1924	4	2	6
	1926	5	4	9
	1927	6	14	20

BEWERLEY No.2		Bewerley		SE122663
Production:	Lead	Ore(tons)	Lead (tons)	Value (£)
	1970-1975	No production		
Comment:	1970	Prospecting		
	1971-1975	Standing		
Mineral Lord:	1970-1975	See Bewerley Liberty		
Worked by:	1970	Bewerley Mines Ltd		
	1971	Stibbard, Gibson & Co.		
	1972-1975	Bewerley Mines Ltd		

BEWERLEY LIBERTY		Bewerley		SE117638
Production:	Lead	Ore(tons)	Lead (tons)	Value (£)
	1692		474.00	
	1693		326.05	
	1694		388.00	
	1695		454.85	
	1696		526.40	
	1697		263.55	
	1698		111.50	
	1699		102.90	
	1705		295.00	
	1706		243.00	
	1707		412.00	
	1708		310.00	
	1709		300.00	
	1710		176.00	
	1711		133.00	
	1712		112.00	
	1713		129.00	
	1714		160.00	
	1715		102.00	
	1716		137.00	
	1717		71.00	
	1718		83.00	
	1719		75.00	
	1720		51.00	
	1721		50.00	
	1722		64.00	

	1723	48.00
	1724	37.00
	1725	28.00
	1726	33.00
	1727	43.00
	1728	39.00
	1729	3.00
	1730	18.00
	1731	26.00
	1839	464.18
	1840	401.35
	1841	405.52
	1842	395.60
	1843	402.01
	1844	288.52
Comment:	1704-1732	Weights in fothers (Probably 2460 Lbs)
	1704-1732	Including Coldstones, Cockhill, Lumb
	1704-1732	Including Galloway and Stoney Grooves
	1839-1844	Including Sunside- Cockhill, Stoney Grooves,
	1839-1844	Including Eagle, Prosperous & Providence
Mineral Lord:	1066-1110	Gospatric
	1110-1175	Mowbray family
	1175-1539	Fountains Abbey
	1540	Sir Richard Gresham
	1552	Sir William Gresham
	1552-1573	Sir Arthur Darcy
	1573-1597	Thomas Benson
	1597-1618	Sir Stephen Proctor
	1698	Richard Taylor
	1699-1730	Thomas White
	1730-1769	John White
	1769-1772	Taylor White Snr
	1772-1795	Taylor White Jnr
	1795-1817	Thomas Woolaston White (1st Bart)
	1817-1861	Thomas Woolaston White (2nd Bart)
	1861-1893	T.F.A. Burnaby and Hanley Hutchinson
	1893-1900	T.F. Burnaby and Hanley Hutchinson
	1920	Hilton Hutchinson
	1926-2000	Bewerley Mines Ltd (metals)
	1970-2000	Viscount Mountgarret (Non-metals)
Worked by:	1585	John Wood
	1692-1732	The White family
	1733-2000	See individual mines

BILLYBANKS Richmond NZ164006

Production:	Copper	Ore(tons)	Copper (tons)	Value (£)
	1905	251.00	21.00	319.00
	1906	341.00	25.00	702.00
	1907	379.00	20.00	778.00
	1908	106.00	3.00	114.00
	1910	76.00	5.00	216.00
	1911	270.00	14.00	700.00
	1912	92.00	4.00	190.00

Comment: 1908-1909 Standing
1913-1918 Standing
Mineral Lord: 1905-1912 Richard Henry Prior-Wandesforde
Worked by: 1905-1909 Boulder Flint Co.
1910-1912 Yorkshire Minerals Ltd
1913-1914 Boulder Flint Co.
1915-1918 A.F. Springett
Agent: 1905-1914 John Wagstaff
Secretary: 1910-1912 Arthur Charles Bryant

Employment:		Underground	Surface	Total
	1905	7	1	8
	1906	15	0	15
	1907	12	1	13
	1908	8	1	9
	1910	12	2	14
	1911	14	0	14
	1912	6	0	6

BIRDS Eskdaleside Cum Ugglebarnby NZ833057

Production:	Iron	Ore(tons)	Value (£)
	1858	No detailed returns	
	1859	2062.00	355.00
	1860	24861.00	3314.00
	1861	8868.00	1034.90
	1862	15000.00	2250.00
	1863	17540.00	
	1864	12559.20	
	1865	13347.00	2002.00
	1866	8887.00	1333.00

Comment: 1858-1866 Avicular & Pecten Seams
1858 Includes Grosmont
1858-1866 Includes Birtley
1863-1864 Birds & Birtley Eskdale Mine
1865 Suspended Eskdale Mine
Mineral Lord: 1858-1866 Mrs Clark

BIRKDALE		Muker		NY875015
Production:	Lead	Ore(tons)	Lead (tons)	Value (£)
	1753-1767	No detailed returns		
Comment:	1753-1767	See Keld Side and Littlemoor Foot		
Mineral Lord:	1753-1767	See Beldi Hill		
Worked by:	1753-1767	George Tissington & Co.		

BIRKDALE		Lunedale		NY817274
Production:	Lead	Ore(tons)	Lead (tons)	Value (£)
	1736	3.75		
	1757	43.55		
	1758	10.95		
	1762	1.65		
	1845	No detailed returns		
Mineral Lord:	1736-1845	See Lunehead		
Worked by:	1845	London Lead Company		

BIRKS		Grinton		SE007969
Production:	Lead	Ore(tons)	Lead (tons)	Value (£)
	1785-1788	No detailed returns		
Comment:	1785-1788	See Mason Rake		
Mineral Lord:	1785-1788	See under Grinton		

BIRTLE		Lunedale		NY818271
Production:	Lead	Ore(tons)	Lead (tons)	Value (£)
	1833	0.52		
	1834	1.93		
	1835	14.00		
	1837	16.80		
	1838	24.00		
	1839	5.01		
	1841	0.83		
	1842	4.65		
	1844	18.65		
	1845	1.70		
Comment:	1835	Includes Green		
	1837	Includes Maizebeck		
	1844	Includes Maizebeck		
Mineral Lord:	1831-1845	See Lunehead		
Worked by:	1831	John Coatsworth & Co.		
	1834-1835	Lunehead Mining Company		
	1836	John Smith & Co.		
	1844	London Lead Company		

BIRTLEY Eskdaleside Cum Ugglebarnby NZ836058

Production:	Iron	Ore(tons)	Value (£)
	1858-1859	No detailed returns	
	1860	20975.00	3000.00
	1861-1866	No detailed returns	
	1867	8332.00	1310.90
	1871	5518.00	1379.50
	1874-1876	No detailed returns	
	1878	No detailed returns	
Comment:	1847-1878	Avicular Seam	
	1858-1866	See Birds	
	1865	Part of Eskdale Mine	
	1874-1878	See Grosmont	
Worked by:	1878	Birtley Iron Co.	
Agent:	1865	George Waddington	

BISHOPDALE GAVEL Newbiggin SD956801

Production:	Lead	Ore(tons)	Lead (tons)	Value (£)
	1850	3.48	1.50	
	1851	2.50	1.20	
	1852	4.60	2.35	
Comment:	1850-1852	Smelted at Grassington		
	1852	10.85	5.80	
	1854	10.20	5.10	
	1855	20.75	8.95	
	1856	4.85	2.50	
	1857	1.40	0.75	
	1861	1.90	1.00	
Comment:	1852-1861	Smelted at Starbotton Cupola		
	1861		3.40	
	1862		1.90	
	1863		1.40	
	1864		2.85	
	1865		2.60	
	1866		0.70	
Comment:	1861-1866	Smelted at Kettlewell		
	1863	6.30	4.40	
	1864	3.40	2.00	
	1865	100.00	70.00	
	1866	8.50	5.50	
	1867	12.70	6.60	
Comment:	1863-1867	Data from Hunt's Statistics		
Worked by:	1850	Joseph Wear		
	1851-1852	Thomas Joy		
	1852	Bains & Co.		
	1854-1866	William Sarginson & Co.		
	1855	Robert Hebden		

	1856-1857	Thomas Joy		
	1861	John Hillery & Co.		
	1862-1871	Sarginson & Co.		
	1862-1871	Ralph Lodge		

BISHOPDALE STAKE		Newbiggin		SD937827
Production:	Lead	Ore(tons)	Lead (tons)	Value (£)
	1869		0.80	
	1872		0.59	
	1876		0.15	
Comment:	1869-1876	Smelted at Kettlewell		
Worked by:	1869-1872	Arthur Sayer & Co.		
	1876	John Sayer & Co.		

BLACK ARK		Lunedale		NY845278
Production:	Lead	Ore(tons)	Lead (tons)	Value (£)
	1757	8.55		
Mineral Lord:	1757	See Lunehead		

BLACKHILL		Grassington		SE013659
Production:	Lead	Ore(tons)	Lead (tons)	Value (£)
	1745		1.16	
	1746		4.39	
	1747		17.50	
	1748		2.96	
	1749		2.38	
	1752		4.21	
	1753		2.59	
	1755		0.50	
	1770		0.35	
	1772		0.26	
Mineral Lord:	1745-1772	See under Grassington		
Worked by:	1745-1747	John Bownass		
	1747	Mr Alcock		
	1748	Robert Bownass		
	1749-1752	Thomas Wearing		
	1750	Joseph Natterass		
	1750-1751	James Rogers		
	1751-1755	Thomas Moorhouse		
	1753	Jacob Wrightson		
	1761	James Hodgson		
	1770-1772	Thomas Moorhouse & Company		

BLACKHILL Appletreewick SE079632

Production:	Lead	Ore(tons)	Lead (tons)	Value (£)
	1763-1782	No detailed returns		
	1894	7.00	5.00	49.00
	1895	No detailed return		
Comment:	1763	Raistrick MSS Blackhill Book		
	1872	WYAS Yorke MSS DB151		
	1967	See Dry Gill		
	1920-1921	See Gill Heads		
Mineral Lord:	1763-1949	See Appletreewick Liberty		
Worked by:	1763	George Storey		
	1782	Michael Lambert, Silvester Hebden & Co.		
	1854-1856	Craven Moor Mining Co. (Cost Book)		
	1856-1865	Craven Moor Mining Co. Ltd		
	1873-1884	West Craven Moor Lead Mining Co. Ltd		
	1890-1900	Reed & Williams		
	1920-1921	Greenhaugh Mining Company Ltd		
	1930-1949	James Harold Clay		
	1945-1949	Fred C. Walker on Tribute to J.H. Clay		

BLACKHILLS Arkengarthdale NY983030

Production:	Lead	Ore(tons)	Lead (tons)	Value (£)
	1871	13.60		
	1872	2.00		
	1873	2.30		
	1874	1.00		
	1875	2.30		
	1876	2.00		
	1877	5.20		
	1878	8.90		
	1879	6.45		
	1880	6.90		
	1886	0.15		
Comment:	1871	Year ending June		
	1881-1885	Standing		
Mineral Lord:	1871-1891	See Arkengarthdale		
Worked by:	1871-1891	Arkendale Mining Co.		

BLACK RAKE Grassington SE030672

Production:	Lead	Ore(tons)	Lead (tons)	Value (£)
	1754		13.29	
	1755		0.50	
	1761		6.15	
	1828	0.78	0.40	
	1845	0.38	0.25	
	1847	6.22	4.20	
	1848	2.68	1.40	
Mineral Lord:	1754-1848	See under Grassington		

BLACK RIGG		Bewerley		SE114633
Production:	Lead	Ore(tons)	Lead (tons)	Value (£)
	1781-1796	No detailed returns		
	1797		175.04	
	1798		19.80	
	1799		61.79	
	1800		57.83	
	1801		13.17	
	1802		33.63	
	1803	No detailed returns		
	1804		29.79	
	1805		9.75	
	1806		22.88	
	1807		55.04	
	1808		15.54	
	1809		18.50	
	1810	No detailed returns		
	1811		20.75	
	1812-1813	No detailed returns		
	1814		21.08	
	1815		8.17	

Comment: 1797-1815 Data from Black Rigg Book - Leeds University
1797-1815 Tons may be Fothers
Mineral Lord: 1781-1815 See Bewerley Liberty
Worked by: 1781 John Maxfield & Co.
1793-1815 George Bradley & Co.
1802-1815 Nathan Newbould

BLACK RIGG		Thornthwaite with Padside		SE108632
Production:	Lead	Ore(tons)	Lead (tons)	Value (£)
	1797		175.04	
	1764		86.00	
	1765		63.95	
	1766		34.90	
	1773		55.00	
	1774		15.00	
	1775		16.10	
	1776		5.90	
	1777		0.60	
	1778		20.90	
	1779		7.55	
	1780		10.15	
	1781		10.40	
	1782		7.85	
	1784		5.36	
	1782		3.15	
	1786		0.45	

	1787		5.40	
	1788		20.10	
	1789		128.20	
	1790		1.64	
	1791		147.00	
	1792		135.70	
	1793		6.70	
	1794		53.48	
	1795		33.60	
	1796		23.50	
	1797		0.60	
	1798		12.60	
	1799		6.85	
	1800		5.35	
	1801		0.30	
Comment:	1773-1789	Smelted at the Forest Mill (Hoodstorth)		
	1790-1801	Smelted at Grassington		
Mineral Lord:	1764-1801	See under Grassington		
Worked by:	1773-1801	Barker & Co.		
Agent:	1792-1801	William Marshall		
	1792	Jacob Bailey		

BLACK SIKE		Lunedale		NY823235
Production:	Lead	Ore(tons)	Lead (tons)	Value (£)
	1757	0.25		
Mineral Lord:	1757-1771	See Lunehead		
Worked by:	1771	London Lead Company		

BLAKETHWAITE		Melbecks		NY939029
Production:	Lead	Ore(tons)	Lead (tons)	Value (£)
	1797-1799	No detailed returns		
	1800		1.41	
	1801-1816	No detailed returns		
	1817		11.98	
	1818		8.34	
	1819		26.79	
	1820		622.15	
	1821		498.01	
	1822		511.37	
	1823		452.14	
	1824		583.23	
	1825		555.62	
	1826		470.11	
	1827		320.34	
	1828		188.50	
	1829		151.07	
	1830		122.45	

1831		122.18
1832		56.23
1833		46.83
1834		37.33
1835		9.36
1836		8.09
1837		37.56
1838		27.87
1839		267.94
1840		575.00
1841		551.99
1842		625.46
1843		605.58
1844		1060.37
1845		597.32
1846		631.83
1847		300.59
1848		243.69
1849		215.91
1850		138.27
1851		183.39
1852		223.85
1853		167.76
1854		123.63
1855		167.72
1856		71.65
1857		74.43
1858		144.10
1859		145.56
1860		137.12
1861		56.00
1862	94.80	58.50
1867	171.60	128.70
1868	155.00	114.00
1869	95.00	70.00
1870	148.90	111.60
1871	99.50	74.50
1872	16.50	12.30

Comment:
1801 Data from WRO CR1248/21/R16
1817-1860 Data from NYCRO ZLB 2/32 & 134
1861 Data from Jennings Thesis
1861-1872 Data from Hunt's Statistics
1797-1806 Part of Surrender Gound
1836-1872 Includes Lownathwaite
1848-1872 Includes Swinnergill
1862-1866 Includes Arngill and Ewe Scar
1873-1874 Suspended

	1873-1912	See Sun Hush		
	1876-1878	See Swinnergill		
	1894-1902	Standing		
	1903-1909	See Old Gang		
	1906	In liquidation		
	1910-1912	Abandoned		
Mineral Lord:	1797-1912	See AD Mines		
Worked by:	1797-1806	Chaytor & Co.		
	1806-1812	Thomas Chippindale & Co.		
	1813-1836	Robert Clarke & Co.		
	1836-1847	Ottiwell Tomlin & Co.		
	1848-1861	Thomas Bradley & Co.		
	1862-1866	Blakethwaite Mining Co.		
	1867-1872	Sir George Denys		
	1873-1883	AD Lead Mining Company Ltd		
	1888-1906	Old Gang Lead Mining Co. Ltd		
Agent:	1861	John Lowes, Robert Lowes		
	1862-1863	Thomas Coates		
	1862-1871	John Ralph Place		
	1872-1875	Thomas Raw		
	1880-1883	Frank Raw		
	1884-1896	John Reynoldson		
	1897-1900	Simon Cherry		
	1901-1912	Edward Cherry		
Employment:	1903-1909	See Old Gang		

BLAKEY		Farndale East		SE682976
Production:	Iron	Ore(tons)		Value (£)
	1875	21421.00		
	1876	720.00		
Comment:	1873-1879	Top Seam		
	1877-1879	Standing		
Mineral Lord:	1873-1897	Earl of Faversham		
Worked by:	1873-1879	Blakey Iron Co.		
	1880-1881	Farndale Iron Co.		
Agent:	1875-1881	William Martin		
Secretary:	1877	Robert B. Lavery		

BLAYSHAW GILL		Stonebeck Down		SE098728
Production:	Lead	Ore(tons)	Lead (tons)	Value (£)
	1876	12.10	9.00	138.20
	1883	9.30	7.40	70.00
	1884	No detailed returns		
	1885	2.00	1.40	12.00
	1887	0.50		
	1888	No detailed returns		

	1901	10.00	7.00	85.00
	1905	5.00	3.00	42.00
	1906	24.00	15.00	120.00
	1907	14.00	10.00	120.00
	1908	9.00	7.00	61.00

Comment: 1910-1911 Abandoned

Worked by:
1876-1887 Blayshaw Gill Lead Mining Co.
1888-1893 Blayshaw Gill Mining Co.
1894-1907 Joseph Cradock, John Appleby & Co.
1908-1911 Joseph Cradock & Co.

Agent:
1875-1881 John Appleby
1879-1881 James R. Peacock
1881 Robert Lobley
1894-1902 John Appleby

Secretary:
1876-1877 Robert Lotty
1878-1881 John Appleby
1903-1907 Joseph Cradock

Employment:		Underground	Surface	Total
	1877	4	2	6
	1878	7	0	7
	1879-1880	6	0	6
	1881	4	0	4
	1882	5	1	6
	1898-1899	4	0	4
	1900	6	0	6
	1901	12	2	14
	1902	2	2	4
	1904	2	2	4
	1905	5	2	7
	1906	8	0	8
	1907	6	0	6
	1908	5	1	6
	1909-1911	3	1	4

BLOW BECK Grassington SE038680

Production:	Lead	Ore(tons)	Lead (tons)	Value (£)
	1764		1.65	
	1765		26.63	
	1766		47.75	
	1767		15.30	
	1768		23.20	
	1769		39.15	
	1770		55.95	
	1771		11.50	
	1772		17.64	
	1773		16.15	

	1774		12.20
	1775		12.30
	1776		7.50
	1777		4.20
	1779		1.05
	1782		2.75
	1783		2.30
	1784		0.70
	1786		6.35
	1787		1.51
	1788		3.17
	1790		3.59
	1791		3.77
	1794		1.20
	1795		0.70
	1796		0.19
	1797		8.70
	1798		3.20
	1799		3.65
	1800		2.15
	1801		0.50
	1802		0.45
	1804		0.70
	1805		1.45
	1806		1.50
	1809	4.28	2.10
	1810	7.05	3.25
	1811	2.40	1.15
	1812	3.35	1.95
	1813	0.83	0.35
	1818	4.70	1.55
	1819	0.55	0.20
	1820	1.40	0.50
	1830	1.70	1.10
	1835	2.73	1.55
	1840	0.80	0.20
	1843	1.20	0.70
	1844	11.30	6.15
	1845	1.65	0.80
Mineral Lord:	1764-1845	See under Grassington	
Worked by:	1764-1768	Thomas Wearing	
	1769-1777	James Swale	
	1779	John Summers	
	1782-1787	Mr Swale	
	1784	Mr Brown	
	1788-1801	William Alcock	
	1800	Richard Lee	

	1801-1802	John Murton		
	1804-1806	William Wilkinson		
	1809-1811	John Ashbrook		
	1812	Stephen Joy		
	1813	Jonas Coats & Bridget Coats		
	1818	Thomas Rodwell & William Rodwell		

BLOW GROVES		Buckden		SD958794
Production:	Lead	Ore(tons)	Lead (tons)	Value (£)
	1699		83.76	
	1701		9.90	
Comment:	1699-1701	Smelted at Grassington		
	1699-1701	Weights in Fodders (2460 Lbs)		
Mineral Lord:	1699-1701	See under Grassington		
Worked by:	1698-1701	Robert Armistead & John Wass		

BLUBBERHOUSES		Blubberhouses		SE138554
Production:	Lead	Ore(tons)	Lead (tons)	Value (£)
	1787	No detailed returns		
	1866		0.48	
	1867-1877	No detailed returns		
Comment:	1787	Miners paid-off in early June		
	1866	Smelted at Cononley		
	1872-1877	See Perseverence		
Mineral Lord:	1787	Sir Thomas Frankland		
	1867-1871	Lady Frankland		
	1872-1875	Lord Walsingham		
Worked by:	1872-1873	Blubberhouse Mining Co.		
	1876-1877	Persevering Mining Co.		
Agent:	1787	George Hasleham		
	1866-1877	William Sigston Winn		
Secretary:	1867	Thomas Sykes		
	1872-1877	William Stead		

BLUE LEVEL		Grassington		SE026654
Production:	Lead	Ore(tons)	Lead (tons)	Value (£)
	1737		8.55	
	1738		1.50	
	1739		3.34	
	1740		2.35	
	1742		1.35	
	1744		0.75	
	1745		0.38	
	1746		1.03	
	1748		1.32	
	1749		3.03	
	1750		1.31	

	1754		1.38	
	1755		37.56	
	1764		6.50	
	1765		0.56	
	1766		2.30	
	1768		1.33	
	1770		0.79	
	1772		0.10	
	1773		1.06	
	1774		0.96	
	1775		0.10	
	1808		0.95	

Mineral Lord: 1737-1808 See under Grassington

Worked by:	1737	John Ripley
	1738-1739	William Broughton
	1740-1742	Mr Currer & Ptrs
	1742	George Wilson
	1744	Mr Coats
	1745-1750	Mr Alcock
	1746	Jacob Wrightson
	1748-1749	Thomas Birch
	1754-1755	Robert Pickles
	1755	William Birch
	1755-1764	Thomas Tennant
	1766-1775	William Brown
	1766	Edward Cunningham
	1772	William Cunningham
	1755	Thomas Nelson

BOLTON Bolton Abbey SE056555

Production:	Lead	Ore(tons)	Lead (tons)	Value (£)
	1808	0.75		
	1809	2.20	1.05	

Mineral Lord: 1808-1809 See under Grassington
Worked by: 1808-1809 Thomas Dickinson

BOLTON PARK Castle Bolton SE029930

Production:	Lead	Ore(tons)	Lead (tons)	Value (£)
	1856		7.65	
	1857		21.45	
	1858		83.65	
	1859		133.45	
	1860		123.45	
	1861		127.80	
	1862		19.90	
	1863		4.40	
	1864		92.80	

	1865		366.35
	1866		302.40
	1867		25.80
	1868		48.00
	1869		10.45
	1870		4.85
	1871		11.65
	1872		7.35
Comment:	1856-1872	Data from Lord Bolton's Lead Book	
	1866	475.60	356.70
	1867	46.00	34.00
	1868	15.00	10.80
	1870	20.00	15.00
	1871	No detailed returns	
	1866-1871	Data from Hunt's Statistics	
Mineral Lord:	1849-1872	See under Keld Heads	
Worked by:	1849-1862	Lambert & Co.	
	1862-1872	Bolton Park Mining Co.	
Agent:	1863-1871	George Spensley	
Secretary:	1863	Joseph Horner	
	1866-1871	Storey & Co.	

Employment:		Underground	Surface	Total
	1862	10		

BOOSBECK		Skelton	NZ658169
Production:	Iron	Ore(tons)	Value (£)
	1873	4785.00	1435.50
	1874	133316.00	39994.80
	1875	222637.00	
	1876	237978.00	
	1877	265870.50	
	1878	288210.00	
	1879	318659.70	
	1880	486695.60	
	1881	479623.00	
	1882-1886	No detailed returns	
	1891-1893	No detailed returns	
	1896-1901	No detailed returns	
Comment:	1887	Abandoned - Drowned Out	
	1891	Reopened	
	1894-1895	Standing	
	1901	Absorbed into South Skelton	
Mineral Lord:	1872-1887	Marley; Wharton	
Worked by:	1872-1888	Stevenson, Jacques & Co.	
	1891-1898	Clay Lane Iron Co. Ltd	
	1899-1901	Bolckow, Vaughan & Co. Ltd	

Agent:	1872	J. Holliday		
	1873-1877	John Bell Jnr.		
	1878-1884	William Walker		
	1891-1901	Abraham Gray		

Employment:		Underground	Surface	Total
	1883			383
	1893-1901	Included with South Skelton		

BOOZE Arkengarthdale NZ016024

Production:	Lead	Ore(tons)	Lead (tons)	Value (£)
	1748	3.90		
	1749	6.50		
	1782	2.90		
	1783	0.70		
	1788	10.60		
	1789	14.00		
	1790	53.10		

Comment:	1782-1783	November to November inclusive
	1783-1784	December to May inclusive
	1789	June to November inclusive
	1789-1790	December to November inclusive
	1790-1791	December to May inclusive
	1784-1789	Standing
Mineral Lord:	1748-1790	See Arkengarthdale
Worked by:	1748-1749	Charles Turner
	1782-1791	Charles Sleigh, William Hoar & Charles Foster

BOOZE WOOD Arkengarthdale NZ014020

Production:	Lead	Ore(tons)	Lead (tons)	Value (£)
	1873	27.45		
	1874	83.20		
	1875	190.55		
	1876	80.70		
	1877	90.05		
	1878	137.25		
	1879	55.60		
	1880	66.50		
	1881	35.00		
	1884	29.25		
	1885	10.90		
	1886	1.45		

Comment:	1873-1886	Booze Wood, Includes Cramer Rake
	1882-1883	Standing
Mineral Lord:	1748-1886	See Arkengarthdale
Worked by:	1873-1886	Arkendale Mining Co.

Employment:		Underground	Surface	Total
	1782-1783	3		
	1783-1784	2		
	1789	7		
	1789-1790	4		
	1790-1791	14		

BORDLEY LIBERTY Bordley SD934678

Production:	Lead	Ore(tons)	Lead (tons)	Value (£)
	1733		0.88	
	1747		1.08	
	1767		1.40	
	1769		0.25	
	1830	2.85	1.60	

Comment: 1733-1830 Smelted at Grassington
1767 From Bordley Mastile
1837-1853 See High Mark

Worked by: 1733 Henry Whittaker
1767 Mr Pulman & Mr Hartley
1769 Mr Hartley
1830 Robert Wiggin

BORING SHAFT Arkengarthdale NY979026

Production:	Lead	Ore(tons)	Lead (tons)	Value (£)
	1782	2.20		
	1783	10.20		
	1784	4.60		

Comment: 1782-1783 November to November inclusive
1783-1784 December to May inclusive
1784-1785 December to May inclusive

Mineral Lord: 1782-1785 See Arkengarthdale

Worked by: 1782-1785 Charles Sleigh, William Hoar & Charles Foster

Employment:		Underground	Surface	Total
	1782-1783	1		
	1783-1784	1		
	1784-1785	1		

BOULBY Easington NZ760181

Production:	Iron	Ore(tons)	Value (£)
	1903-1934	No detailed returns	

Comment: 1903-1904 Opening
1926 Standing
1928 Standing
1931-1933 Standing
1934 Abandoned July

Worked by: 1903-1921 Skinningrove Iron Co. Ltd

	1922-1932	Pease and Partners Ltd
	1933-1934	Skinningrove Iron Co. Ltd
Agent:	1903-1912	W. Walker
	1913-1930	A.H. Askew
	1931-1934	George C. Heslop

Employment:		Underground	Surface	Total
	1903	7	5	12
	1904	53	76	129
	1905	55	54	109
	1906	102	54	156
	1907	196	66	262
	1908	181	71	252
	1909	144	66	210
	1910	171	67	238
	1911	167	80	247
	1912	140	76	216
	1913	147	70	217
	1914	165	62	227
	1915	126	61	187
	1916	142	70	212
	1917	168	74	242
	1918	143	71	214
	1919	161	62	223
	1920	163	79	192
	1921	156	69	225
	1922	6	15	21
	1923	36	26	62
	1924	107	47	154
	1925	108	50	158
	1926	8	10	18
	1927	81	48	129
	1928	10	11	21
	1929	11	13	24
	1930	8	10	19
	1931	3	7	10
	1932	3	7	10
	1933	3	7	10
	1934	7	8	15

BOWDIN PASTURE Grassington

Production:	Lead	Ore(tons)	Lead (tons)	Value (£)
	1826	3.00	1.60	
	1827	2.20	1.15	

Mineral Lord: 1826-1827 See under Grassington

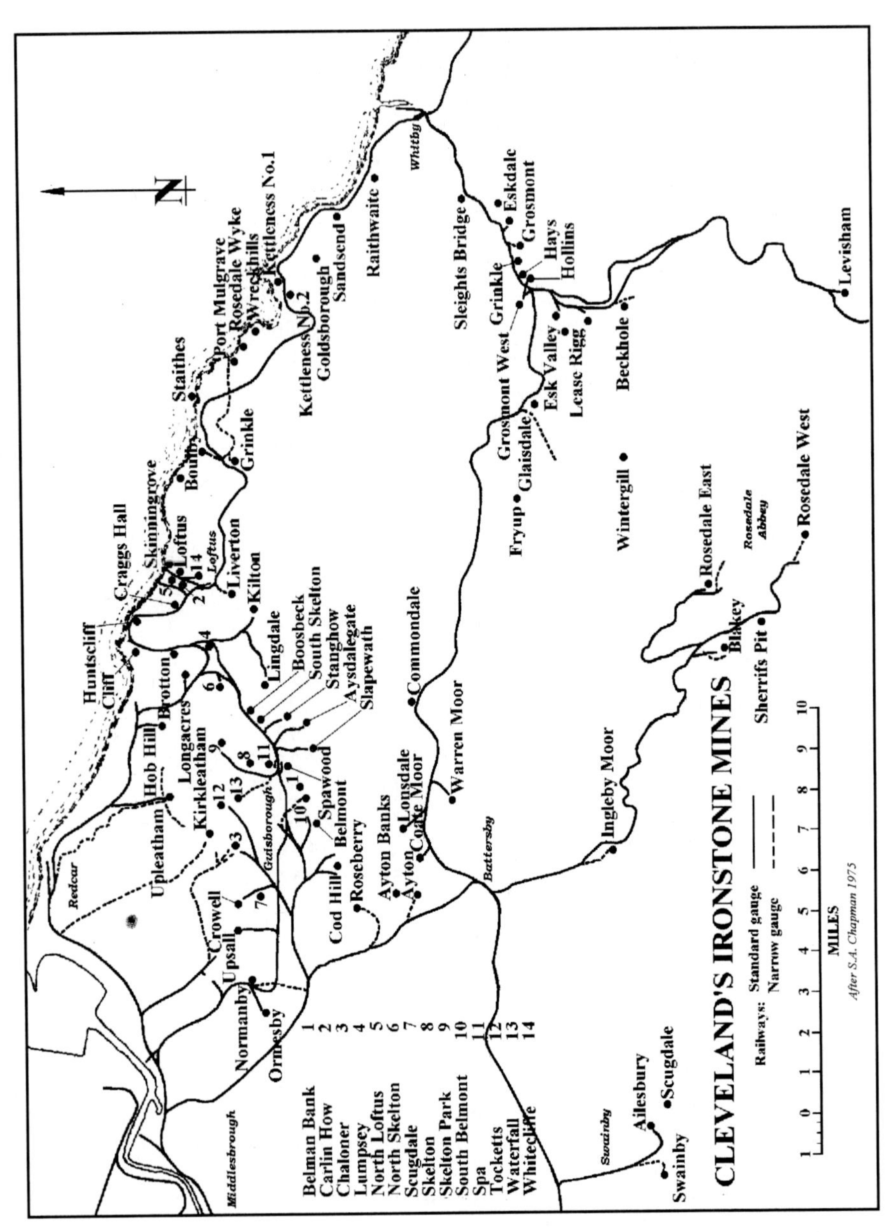

Map 1. Ironstone Mines in Cleveland.

BOWES LIBERTY		Bowes		NY958108
Production:	Lead	Ore(tons)	Lead (tons)	Value (£)
	1767-1859	No detailed returns		
Comment:	1767-1859	Including Aygill and Sleightholme		
Mineral Lord:	1767	Winifred Pulleine		
	1772-1789	Henry Pulleine		
	1859-1859	James Pulleine		
Worked by:	1767	John Chrishop		
	1780	Edward Halliday & Co.		
	1799	Christopher Wright & Co.		
	1858-1859	John Harns & Co.		
Agent:	1859-1859	Thomas Raw		

BOWES CROSS		Bowes		NZ029137
Production:	Lead	Ore(tons)	Lead (tons)	Value (£)
	1888	3.00		21.00
	1889	22.00	16.00	178.00
Comment:	1894-1896	Standing		
Worked by:	1888-1896	Bowes Cross Mining Co.		
Agent:	1888-1891	John J. Millican		
	1892-1896	Is. Walton		

BOWLAND LIBERTY		Bowland (Lancashire)		
Production:	Lead	Ore(tons)	Lead (tons)	Value (£)
	1743		1.35	
	1768		0.60	
	1808	1.55	0.75	
	1809	2.20	1.05	
	1810	0.50	0.15	
	1845	10.90	7.25	
Comment:	1743-1845	Smelted at Grassington		
Worked by:	1743	Mr Lawson		
	1768	James Swale (See: Sykes)		
	1810	James Watson (Slags)		
	1845	Cuthburt Shields		
	1849	Stephen Eddy (See: Moor End)		

BRACKENTHWAITE		Kettlewell		SD986734
Production:	Lead	Ore(tons)	Lead (tons)	Value (£)
	1863-1871	No detailed returns		
Comment:	1863-1871	See Silver Rake		

BRADLEY LIBERTY		Carlton Highdale		SE022817
Production:	Lead	Ore(tons)	Lead (tons)	Value (£)
	1873	2.53	1.65	
Comment:	1873	Smelted at Kettlewell		
Worked by:	1873	Arthur Sayer & Co.		

BRAITHWAITE East Witton SE119862

Production:	Lead & Silver	Ore(tons)	Lead (tons)	Silver (ozs)
	1683-1684	No detailed returns		
	1850-1853	No detailed returns		
	1854	96.40	70.00	
	1855	67.10	39.00	273.00
	1856	74.30	55.00	302.00
	1857	91.80	65.00	445.00
	1858	17.90	12.50	87.00
	1859	36.50	25.40	178.00
	1860	59.10	41.00	287.00
	1861	77.10	53.50	374.00
	1862	27.00	18.70	131.00
	1863	7.00	4.80	
	1865	16.20	11.70	81.00
	1866	15.60	10.80	75.00

Comment: 1873-1875 Suspended
Worked by: 1870-1877 Jos. Wighley & Co.
Agent: 1683-1684 Benjamin Purchas
1850-1869 John Bell
1870-1871 Jos. Wighley
1872-1877 Thomas Rumbold

BRASS CASTLE Grassington

Production:	Lead	Ore(tons)	Lead (tons)	Value (£)
	1795		1.65	
	1800		1.70	

Mineral Lord: 1794-1800 See under Grassington
Worked by: 1794 John Shaw
1800 Anthony Eccles

BRENNAND Bowland High Forest SD646543

Production:	Lead	Ore(tons)	Lead (tons)	Value (£)
	1814-1835	No detailed returns		

Comment: 1814-1835 Smelted at Newton Fell Mill
Mineral Lord: 1814 Duchess of Buccleauch
Worked by: 1814 Thomas Watson & Co.

BRIGILL BURN Arkengarthdale NY983027

Production:	Lead	Ore(tons)	Lead (tons)	Value (£)
	1748	25.00		
	1749	4.60		
	1786	9.40		
	1786	56.00		
	1787	13.30		
	1788	8.40		
	1790	4.80		

Comment: 1748 July to December
1786 June to November inclusive

	1786-1789	December to November inclusive			
	1789-1790	Standing - December to May inclusive			
	1790	June to November inclusive			
Mineral Lord:	1748-1790	See Arkengarthdale			
Worked by:	1748-1740	Charles Turner			
	1786-1790	Charles Sleigh, William Hoar & Charles Foster			

Employment:		Underground	Surface	Total
	1786	1		
	1786-1787	7		
	1787-1788	4		
	1788-1789	2		
	1790	1		

BROCKABANK		Winterburn		SD934569
Production:	Lead	Ore(tons)	Lead (tons)	Value (£)
	1705	No detailed returns		
Worked by:	1705	Emanuel Justice & John Blackburn		

BROTTON		Brotton	Value (£)
			NZ685200
Production:	Iron	Ore(tons)	Value (£)
	1865	113160.00	33948.00
	1866	164484.00	41121.00
	1870	414000.00	103500.00
	1872	392783.60	
	1873	375331.00	112599.30
	1874	337733.00	101319.90
	1875	384436.00	
	1876	403309.00	
	1877	458163.20	
	1878	481631.00	
	1879	416334.10	
	1880	510302.20	
	1881	428716.30	
Comment:	1870	Includes 1871	
	1921	Abandoned	
Mineral Lord:	1863-1921	Jackson; Stevenson	
Worked by:	1863-1921	Morrison & Co.	
Agent:	1863-1864	T. Charlton	
	1865-1871	William Hall	
	1872	Richard Hockells	
	1872	George Taylor	
	1873-1874	H. Ground	
	1875-1879	D.W. Dixon	
	1880-1884	Bartholomew Farrow	
	1885-1887	J. Farrow	
	1888-1896	C.H. Steavenson	
	1897-1921	P.J.H. Stanton	

Employment:		Underground	Surface	Total
	1883			557
	1894	299	24	323
	1895	290	37	327
	1896	291	32	323
	1897	289	33	322
	1898	255	33	288
	1899	242	30	272
	1900	226	33	259
	1901	219	32	251
	1902	216	34	250
	1903	218	39	257
	1904	209	34	243
	1905	174	36	210
	1906	155	36	191
	1907	136	36	172
	1908	125	43	168
	1909	115	40	155
	1910	99	36	135
	1911	93	32	125
	1912	84	34	118
	1913	88	30	118
	1914	80	30	110
	1915	65	30	95
	1916	64	29	93
	1917	64	29	93
	1918	62	31	93
	1919	62	28	90
	1920	49	29	78
	1921	42	26	68

BROWNA GILL		Grinton		SE010970
Production:	Lead	Ore(tons)	Lead (tons)	Value (£)
	1764-1786	No detailed returns		
Mineral Lord:	1764-1786	See under Grinton Liberty		
Worked by:	1764-1769	Park & Co.		
Agent:	1786	Anthony Harker		

BROWN BYCLIFFE		Grassington		SE025681
Production:	Lead	Ore(tons)	Lead (tons)	Value (£)
	1742		6.80	
	1743		0.20	
	1745		5.65	
	1746		30.40	
	1747		4.67	
	1748		44.77	
	1749		36.52	

1750		54.75
1751		17.96
1752		12.63
1753		6.85
1764		1.11
1765		0.75
1795		0.50
1799		3.99
1800		18.25
1801		7.75
1802		19.50
1803		21.65
1804		15.15
1805		16.10
1806		8.75
1807		7.60
1810	29.60	15.10
1811	48.70	21.10
1812	27.00	13.65
1813	18.45	8.70
1814	18.10	8.10
1815	18.60	8.75
1816	11.13	3.65
1817	18.78	6.70

Comment: 1756-1763 Data missing

Mineral Lord: 1742-1817 See under Grassington

Worked by:
1742 Robert Pickles & William Dawson
1743 Robert Pickles
1745-1746 Mr Close & Co.
1747 Mr Close & Leonard Marshall
1748-1753 Mr Morley & Co.
1764 Mr Simondson
1765 Leonard Marshall
1795 William Buck & James Ripley
1799-1803 Christopher Lawson & William Bell
1804-1807 Christopher Lawson & John Lambert
1810-1817 Various grantees

BROWNFIELD No.1 Carperby cum Thoresby SD978927

Production:	Lead	Ore(tons)	Lead (tons)	Value (£)
	1850		0.80	
	1856		0.75	

Comment: 1850-1856 Data from Lord Bolton's Lead Book

Mineral Lord: 1850-1856 See under Keld Heads

Worked by: 1850-1856 Anthony Robinson & Co.

BROWNFIELD No.2 Carperby cum Thoresby SD978927

Production:	Lead	Ore(tons)	Lead (tons)	Value (£)
	1850		1.15	
	1851		5.85	
	1852		8.55	
	1853		21.65	
	1854		11.20	
	1856		11.90	
	1857		4.50	
	1858		6.00	
	1859		4.40	
	1860		4.00	
	1862		6.90	
	1863		2.75	
	1866		3.60	
	1867		1.00	
	1868		4.85	
	1869		0.95	

1870-1878 No detailed returns

Comment: 1850-1869 Data from Lord Bolton's Lead Book
1870-1878 Data from Hunt's Statistics

Mineral Lord: 1850-1878 See under Keld Heads

Worked by: 1850-1862 Ralf Watson & Co.
1863-1869 John Tasker & Co.
1876-1878 Apedale Head Mining Co.
1862-1878 Dobson & Co.

BROWN PASTURE Grassington

Production:	Lead	Ore(tons)	Lead (tons)	Value (£)
	1824	2.20	0.75	
	1826	0.90	0.45	

Mineral Lord: 1737-1817 See under Grassington

BRUNGILL MOOR Newton SD689527

Production: Lead Ore(tons) Lead (tons) Value (£)
1575-1603 No detailed returns

Comment: 1575-1603 Silver producer

Mineral Lord: 1575-1603 The Crown

Worked by: 1575-1603 Bevis Bulmer

BUCKDEN GAVEL No.1 Buckden SD958794

Production:	Lead	Ore(tons)	Lead (tons)	Value (£)
	1704		40.20	
	1705		49.80	
	1706		75.00	
	1708		25.00	
	1709		60.00	

	1710	30.00
	1711	45.00
	1712	60.00
	1713	30.00
	1714	30.00
	1715	15.00
	1716	15.00
	1717	50.10
	1732	17.00
	1733	28.50
	1734	19.50
	1735	20.00
	1736	27.50
	1737	40.00
	1738	18.15
	1739	41.40
	1740	62.00
	1741	46.10
	1742	39.70
	1743	14.65
	1744	18.05
	1745	67.70
	1746-1803	No detailed returns
Comment:	1704-1745	Smelted at Buckden
	1704-1745	Weights in fodders (2460 Lbs)
	1698-1701	See Blow Groves
	1717	January to March 24th
	1732-1733	September to September
	1738	August to December
	1739	January to August
	1742-1743	September to September
	1744-1745	September to March 25th
	1745	March 25th to September
	1774-1775	Very little work being done
Mineral Lord:	1698-1803	See under Grassington
Worked by:	1704-1714	Emanuel Justice & Co.
	1762-1763	Stephen Peart & Co.
	1763-1788	Nathaniel Ward & Co.
	1788-1790	John Peart & Nathaniel Ward
Agent:	1738-1739	Thomas Garton (Overseer)

BUCKDEN GAVEL No.2 Buckden SD955781

Production:	Lead	Ore(tons)	Lead (tons)	Value (£)
	1803-1813	No detailed returns		
	1814	25.43	17.05	
	1815	240.40	153.80	
	1816	192.95	125.35	

	1817	221.25	145.25
	1818	274.35	169.00
	1819	252.90	161.70
	1820	22.93	9.40
	1821	8.00	5.10
	1822	16.45	9.70
	1823	2.00	1.20
	1824	2.35	1.15
	1827	19.00	10.50
	1828	8.85	4.10
	1835	0.83	0.20
	1842	2.95	1.10
	1844	1.68	0.70
	1849	52.10	0.90
	1851	0.90	0.25
	1876		16.80
	1877		28.00
	1879		0.96
	1880		3.35
Comment:	1803-1813 Smelted at Buckden		
	1814-1851 Smelted at Grassington		
	1817-1822 Including Starbotton Gill Head		
	1824		1.05
	1825		13.05
	1826		29.60
	1827		3.05
Comment:	1824-1827 Smelted at Kilnsey		
	1827		13.10
	1828		27.40
	1829		7.25
	1830		39.85
	1831		14.70
	1832		42.95
	1833		12.40
	1834		11.40
	1835		37.95
	1836		26.05
	1837		76.35
	1838		9.85
	1839		17.25
	1840		16.85
	1841		23.55
	1842		38.00
	1843		107.25
	1873		9.23
	1883		4.70
Comment:	1827-1883 Smelted at Kettlewell		
	1844		49.10

	1845		15.10
	1846		13.35
	1847		25.45
	1848		23.05
	1849		27.05
	1850	45.50	25.95
	1851	79.15	46.85
	1852	172.65	106.35
	1853	82.45	52.85
	1854	154.40	91.65
	1855	225.70	132.00
	1856	98.20	51.10
	1857	125.80	74.15
	1858	128.40	69.10
Comment:	1844-1858	Smelted at Starbotton Cupola	
	1859	182.00	128.50
	1860	128.10	73.50
	1861	104.10	60.10
	1863	120.50	73.00
	1864	152.00	137.70
	1865	115.20	67.20
	1866	62.80	40.00
	1867	63.60	39.90
	1868	19.20	12.20
	1869	12.10	6.20
	1870	21.50	18.50
	1872	12.10	6.50
	1873	19.80	13.70
	1874	No detailed returns	
Comment:	1859-1874	Data from Hunt's Statistics	
	1804	Driving Gavel Level	
	1874-1877	See Starbotton Cam	
	1879-1881	See Starbotton	
	1876-1884	See Starbotton Gavel	
Mineral Lord:	1803-1881	See under Grassington	
Worked by:	1803-1804	Robert Higgs & Co.	
	1812-1825	Bernard Lodge & Co.	
	1835-1850	Tennant & Co.	
	1849	John Harrison & John Hillery	
	1851	Francis Hargreaves	
	1851-1852	Lodge & Co.	
	1853-1858	Buckden Gavel Co.	
	1860-1872	Charles Lodge & Co.	
	1873	Bernard Lodge, Thomas Marshall & Bowdin	
	1873-1876	Gavel Mining Co.	
	1883	Lodge & Co.	
Agent:	1860-1871	Charles Lodge	
	1872-1876	Bernard Lodge	

Employment:		Underground	Surface	Total
	1862	10		

BUCKDEN LIBERTY Buckden SD942772

Mineral Lord:	1698-1990	See under Grassington
Barmaster:	1705-1708	Stephen Peart
	1708-1718	William Peart
	1718-1743	Christopher Falshaw
	1763-1800	Richard Falshaw
	1800-1824	Joseph Mason Snr

BUCKDEN LOW SMELT MILL Buckden SD933768

Production:	Lead	Ore(tons)	Lead (tons)	Value (£)
	1741		6.80	
	1744		0.60	
	1745		0.20	
Worked by:	1741	William Tailforth & Ptrs		
	1744	J. Tailforth		
	1745	William Tailforth		
	1741		0.10	
Worked by:	1741	John Coates & Ptrs		
	1741		0.40	
Comment:	1741-1744	From slags		
	1704	Mill built at a cost of £50.09		
	1814	Mill Closed		
	1741	George Pickersgill & Ptrs		
Mineral Lord:	1741-1814	See under Grassington		

BUFFET Grassington SE015676

Production:	Lead	Ore(tons)	Lead (tons)	Value (£)
	1804		0.55	
Mineral Lord:	1804	See under Grassington		
Worked by:	1804	Robert Summersgill		

BUNKERS HILL Grassington

Production:	Lead	Ore(tons)	Lead (tons)	Value (£)
	1822	1.15	0.65	
	1827	3.20	1.30	
	1841	0.78	0.45	
	1842	0.60	0.35	
Mineral Lord:	1822-1842	See under Grassington		

BURHILL Appletreewick SE072620

Production:	Lead	Ore(tons)	Lead (tons)	Value (£)
	1861	155.80	101.20	
	1862	116.90	76.00	
	1863	90.00	59.90	

1864	98.10	63.80	
1865	128.00	83.20	
1866	85.50	64.10	
1867	148.00	111.30	
1868	114.90	79.10	
1869	72.20	42.10	
1870	106.10	70.80	
1871	184.60	149.10	
1872	41.00	30.70	
1873	29.00	22.00	
1877	13.20	9.70	165.60
1878	12.00	8.00	162.00
1879	17.10	10.50	255.50
1880	14.00	10.50	133.00
1881	5.00	3.30	46.50

Production: Fluorspar Ore(tons) Value (£)
1943-1963 No detailed returns
1963-1967 No detailed returns
1968-1978 No detailed returns

Mineral Lord: 1861-1881 See Appletreewick Liberty
1938-1948 See Appletreewick Liberty

Worked by: 1857-1862 Burhill Mining Co. (Cost Book)
1862-1873 Burhill Mining Co. Ltd
1939-1949 James Harold Clay
1943-1949 Fred C. Walker on tribute to J.H. Clay
1950-1963 Fred C. Walker
1963-1967 Clay Cross Company
1967 Burhill Mines
1968-1973 Fred C. Walker

Agent: 1857-1862 William Buck & Co.
1862-1867 John Whitehead
1862-1867 Thomas Woodmas
1868-1879 George Demaine
1878-1881 Edward Press
1963-1967 Fred C. Walker

Secretary: 1863-1864 Edward Bolton
1867-1873 Charles E. Bolton
1878-1881 Benjamin Burrell

Employment:

	Underground	Surface	Total
1877	10	2	12
1878	6	2	8
1879	7	1	8
1880	8	1	9
1881	2		2

BURNT LING VEIN Grassington SE024670

Production: Lead	Ore(tons)	Lead (tons)	Value (£)
1737		55.98	
1738		25.14	
1739		1.90	
1740		69.39	
1741		69.92	
1742		78.03	
1743		98.00	
1744		63.80	
1745		54.46	
1746		70.23	
1747		27.39	
1748		19.58	
1749		40.48	
1750		27.40	
1751		37.48	
1752		17.29	
1753		13.78	
1754		4.90	
1755		5.45	
1759		18.10	
1765		171.49	
1766		19.85	
1767		3.11	
1768		10.48	
1769		12.82	
1770		5.76	
1771		4.84	
1772		3.80	
1773		1.36	
1774		1.98	
1775		1.48	
1777		2.84	
1778		0.30	
1780		0.94	
1781		58.18	
1782		15.00	
1783		0.16	
1784		28.60	
1785		32.50	
1786		14.90	
1787		2.04	
1788		5.63	
1789		4.36	
1790		4.53	
1791		0.87	

	1793		1.90
	1794		4.50
	1795		1.55
	1796		2.28
	1798		12.15
	1799		15.55
	1800		5.60
	1801		6.00
	1802		4.45
	1803		5.10
	1804		0.95
	1805		1.50
	1806		4.10
	1807		1.15
	1808		0.65
	1809	8.48	4.30
	1810	10.23	5.30
	1811	3.30	1.60
	1812	5.85	2.65
	1813	3.25	1.45
	1814	0.60	0.30
	1818	9.50	5.30
	1819	54.75	34.00
	1820	37.35	23.60
	1821	18.60	10.85
	1822	26.75	14.20
	1823	12.30	6.40
	1824	0.33	0.20
	1825	2.45	1.05
	1829	0.55	0.30
	1832	8.70	4.05
	1833	10.40	4.40
	1834	7.85	3.20
	1835	3.95	1.90
	1840	4.83	3.10
	1841	16.35	6.95
	1844	5.04	2.30
	1845	4.10	1.55
	1846	4.63	2.00
	1847	1.80	0.95
Mineral Lord:	1737-1847 See under Grassington		
Worked by:	1737-1752 Mr Tennant & Company		
	1738-1843 John Ripley		
	1744-1747 Mr Rushworth		
	1747-1748 Mr Stockdale		
	1750-1774 George Hasleham		
	1747-1748 Mr Stockdale		

BURNT LING SUN VEIN Grassington SE024669

Production:	Lead	Ore(tons)	Lead (tons)	Value (£)
	1737		2.03	
	1738		3.42	

Mineral Lord: 1737-1738 See under Grassington

BUSKHUL, HIGH Starbotton SD961744

Production:	Lead	Ore(tons)	Lead (tons)	Value (£)
	1782	No detailed returns		

Mineral Lord: 1782 See under Grassington
Worked by: 1782 Squire Holt

BYCLIFFE Grassington SE027681

Production:	Lead	Ore(tons)	Lead (tons)	Value (£)
	1808		14.80	
	1809	1.53	0.80	
	1810	47.05	18.05	
	1811	12.30	7.10	
	1813	6.55	2.65	
	1814	2.30	1.00	
	1815	4.65	1.60	
	1816	1.75	0.45	
	1817	1.25	0.40	
	1818	31.75	15.80	
	1819	3.40	1.10	
	1820	55.43	32.65	
	1821	47.35	24.30	
	1822	15.10	9.45	
	1823	16.30	9.35	
	1824	27.93	14.65	
	1825	43.88	24.10	
	1826	21.30	13.00	
	1827	8.03	4.85	
	1828	3.38	1.45	
	1829	1.43	0.70	
	1830	18.53	9.55	
	1831	29.75	15.05	
	1832	66.98	28.33	
	1833	37.33	15.45	
	1834	37.25	16.50	
	1835	35.45	15.55	
	1836	23.30	9.65	
	1837	8.03	4.85	
	1838	3.38	1.45	
	1839	13.20	7.00	
	1840	13.28	7.10	
	1841	3.53	2.05	

	1842	4.85	1.75
	1843	7.98	3.85
	1844	8.93	3.45
	1845	13.45	6.40
	1846	13.13	6.35
	1847	13.60	6.45
	1848	21.68	10.95
	1849	39.35	18.70
	1850	27.53	11.55
	1851	29.40	13.60
	1852	30.45	14.10
	1853	29.50	14.55

Mineral Lord: 1744-1853 See under Grassington
Worked by: 1808-1821 Various grantees
1822 Walter Hall & Co.

BYCLIFFE EAST 10 MEERS Grassington SE026680

Production:	Lead	Ore(tons)	Lead (tons)	Value (£)
	1808		14.80	
	1747		0.20	
	1748		43.00	
	1749		34.95	
	1740		82.50	
	1741		219.20	
	1742		100.05	
	1743		98.95	
	1744		117.43	
	1745		85.55	
	1746		98.53	
	1747		0.64	
	1748		100.76	
	1749		59.01	
	1750		29.25	
	1751		11.99	
	1752		14.62	
	1753		8.14	
	1754		14.11	
	1755		20.57	
	1764		1.65	
	1765		4.43	
	1766		2.99	
	1768		4.00	
	1769		2.40	
	1771		4.32	
	1772		0.95	
	1773		1.38	
	1774		3.73	

	1775		3.94	
	1776		1.11	
	1777		3.10	
	1778		3.36	
	1779		1.13	
	1782		0.25	
	1783		0.90	
	1784		0.21	
	1787		1.51	
	1788		0.34	
	1789		1.01	
	1790		0.56	
	1791		0.35	

Comment: 1756-1763 Data missing
Mineral Lord: 1737-1791 See under Grassington
Worked by: 1737-1745 Mr Windle
1746-1755 Mr Stansfield
1764-1779 James Swale
1782-1791 David Swale

BYCLIFFE TWO MEERS Grassington SE027680

Production:	Lead	Ore(tons)	Lead (tons)	Value (£)
	1744		5.25	
	1745		7.35	
	1746		10.27	
	1747		13.91	
	1748		4.31	
	1751		1.14	

Comment: 1752-1770 See Mexico
Mineral Lord: 1744-1751 See under Grassington
Worked by: 1744 Mr Martin
1745 Mr Windle
1746-1747 Mr Stansfield
1748 Richard Gilpin Sawry
1751 Mr Stansfield

BYCLIFFE WEST 10 MEERS Grassington SE023681

Production:	Lead	Ore(tons)	Lead (tons)	Value (£)
	1742		49.80	
	1743		58.00	
	1744		42.90	
	1745		19.15	
	1746		21.89	
	1747		0.20	
	1748		20.43	
	1749		4.19	
	1750		3.85	

	1753		1.14	
	1764		0.08	
Comment:	1742-1817	Also called Freeman Bycliffe		
Mineral Lord:	1742-1764	See under Grassington		
Worked by:	1742-1745	Mr Windle		
	1746-1750	Mr Stansfield		
	1747-1764	Leonard Marshall		
	1749-1753	Richard Gilpin Sawry		

CALF GARTH RAKE		Starbotton		SD961744
Production:	Lead	Ore(tons)	Lead (tons)	Value (£)
	1744		0.85	
Comment:	1744	Smelted at Buckden		
	1738-1877	See Starbotton Cam		
Mineral Lord:	1744	See under Grassington		
Worked by:	1744	Thomas Tatham		

CALIFORNIA		Eskdaleside Cum Ugglebarnby		NZ829053
Production:	Iron	Ore(tons)		Value (£)
	1863-1881	No detailed returns		
Comment:	1863-1881	Part of Eskdale Mine		
Worked by:	1863-1878	Birtley Iron Co.		
Agent:	1863-1878	George Waddington		

CAM NEW RAKE		Starbotton		SD961744
Production:	Lead	Ore(tons)	Lead (tons)	Value (£)
	1744		0.10	
Comment:	1744	Smelted at Buckden		
	1738-1877	See Starbotton Cam		
Mineral Lord:	1744	See under Grassington		
Worked by:	1744	John Barras & Thomas Calvert		

CAM OLD RAKE		Starbotton		SD961744
Production:	Lead	Ore(tons)	Lead (tons)	Value (£)
	1738		1.15	
	1739		1.70	
	1740		1.30	
	1741		1.10	
	1744		2.20	
Worked by:	1738-1744	John Barras		
	1740		2.60	
	1741		10.15	
	1744		7.80	
Worked by:	1740-1744	John Stott & Ptrs		
	1744		3.55	
Worked by:	1744	Ralph Harrison		
Comment:	1738-1744	Smelted at Buckden		

	1740		1.14	
Worked by:	1740	John Barras		
	1740		4.15	
Worked by:	1740	John Stott & Ptrs		
	1772		0.25	
Comment:	1740	Smelted at Grassington		
	1738-1877	See Starbotton Cam		
	1789	Old Cam Forefield		
Mineral Lord:	1738-1789	See under Grassington		
Worked by:	1772-1778	Joseph Airey		
	1778	Simon Harker & Co.		
	1789	Ralph Summers		

CAM PASTURE		Starbotton		SD961744
Production:	Lead	Ore(tons)	Lead (tons)	Value (£)
Comment:	1738-1877	See Starbotton Cam		

CAM SCAR		Kettlewell		SD969734
Production:	Lead	Ore(tons)	Lead (tons)	Value (£)
	1860		1.00	
	1865		2.35	
	1872		0.20	
Comment:	1860-1872	Smelted at Kettlewell		
	1860	Merged with Stoney Rake		
	1867-1868	Not trading		
Mineral Lord:	1860-1872	Trust Lords of Kettlewell		
Worked by:	1860	Cam Scar Mining Co.		
	1865	Henry Wiseman		
	1865	John Wiseman		
	1867-1868	United Cams Mining Co. Ltd		
Secretary:	1867-1868	Joseph Garton Briggs		

CAM SCAR & STONEY RAKE			Kettlewell	SD969734
Production:	Lead	Ore(tons)	Lead (tons)	Value (£)
	1860		0.60	
	1862		0.20	
Comment:	1860-1862	Smelted at Kettlewell		
Mineral Lord:	1860	Trust Lords of Kettlewell		
Worked by:	1860-1862	Cam Scar & Stoney Rake Mining Co.		
	1860	Robert Bell		
	1862	William Storey		

CARDEN		Cracoe		SD995605
Production:	Lead	Ore(tons)	Lead (tons)	Value (£)
	1838	10.80	4.30	
	1839	3.35	2.50	
	1840	2.53	1.45	

	1843	1.70	1.20
	1844	16.25	11.95
	1845	20.75	14.95
	1846	13.78	9.55
	1847	8.20	5.95
	1848	8.15	5.90
	1849	1.58	1.05
Worked by:	1845-1849	Thomas Atkinson	
	1838	4.03	2.85
	1840	3.45	2.35
Worked by:	1838-1840	Richard Pickles	
	1848	3.73	2.55
Worked by:	1848	James Brown	
	1850	3.28	2.30
	1851	1.60	1.05
	1852	2.93	2.00
	1853	7.78	4.15
Worked by:	1850-1853	Christopher Duckett & Co.	
	1851	4.00	2.80
Worked by:	1851	Emanuel Lupton	
	1851	0.90	0.65
Worked by:	1851	James Ibbotson	
Comment:	1838-1853	Smelted at Grassington	
	1788-1871	See Cracoe Liberty	
Mineral Lord:	1848	See under Grassington	

CARGO FLEET North Riding

Production:	Iron	Ore(tons)	Value (£)
	1871	11887.00	2972.00

CARLIN HOW Kilton NZ709191

Production:	Iron	Ore(tons)	Value (£)
	1873	4523.50	1356.70
	1874	32036.40	9615.70
	1875	53140.00	
	1876	64377.00	
	1877	107302.10	
	1878	30151.50	
	1880	115465.60	
	1881	135222.50	
	1882-1939	No detailed returns	
Comment:	1876-1877	See Loftus North	
	1925-1946	Part of Lumpsey	
Mineral Lord:	1873-1946	Wharton family	
Worked by:	1873-1873	Bell Brothers	
	1874-1923	Bell Brothers Ltd	
	1923-1946	Dorman, Long & Co. Ltd	

Agent:		
	1873-1874	Armstrong Varty
	1875-1881	Addison L. Steavenson
	1876-1878	Thomas Bell
	1878	W. Moore
	1879	John Harbottle
	1881	Armstrong Varty
	1882	L. Hill
	1883-1894	Armstrong Varty
	1897-1917	D.W. Dixon
	1919-1925	J. Chapman Jnr

Employment:		Underground	Surface	Total
	1883			164
	1894	109	26	135
	1895	111	30	142
	1896	116	30	146
	1897	122	27	149
	1898	121	18	139
	1899	145	14	159
	1900	150	15	165
	1901	176	13	189
	1902	194	15	209
	1903	212	19	231
	1904	222	15	237
	1905	240	14	254
	1906	237	15	252
	1907	236	15	251
	1908	235	15	250
	1909	242	20	262
	1910	249	23	272
	1911	247	23	270
	1912	254	23	277
	1913	253	26	279
	1914	234	25	259
	1915	220	23	243
	1916	218	24	242
	1917	224	23	247
	1918	212	25	237
	1919	209	27	236
	1920	173	26	199
	1921	190	28	218
	1922	21	14	35
	1923	18	13	31
	1924	248	86	334

Comment: 1925-1946 Included with Lumpsey

CARLTON LIBERTY Carlton SD765477

Production:	Lead	Ore(tons)	Lead (tons)	Value (£)
	1774		6.95	
	1775		4.65	

Comment: 1774-1775 Smelted at Grassington
1774-1775 See Parkhead
Mineral Lord: 1774-1775 See under Grassington

CARRIER PASTURE Starbotton SD950730

Production:	Lead	Ore(tons)	Lead (tons)	Value (£)
	1835		1.20	

Comment: 1835 Smelted at Kettlewell
1739-1851 See Hag End
1821-1828 See Moor End
1856-1857 See Providence, New
1857-1880 See Wharfedale
Mineral Lord: 1835 See under Grassington
Worked by: 1835 John Sunter

CASTAWAY Grassington SE024673

Production:	Lead	Ore(tons)	Lead (tons)	Value (£)
	1735		117.55	
	1736		153.52	
	1737		31.26	
	1738		22.39	
	1739		4.75	
	1740		9.75	
	1742		6.36	
	1743		0.45	
	1744		4.03	
	1745		3.62	
	1746		3.29	
	1747		0.73	
	1749		2.03	
	1750		92.75	
	1751		190.25	
	1752		182.59	
	1753		87.89	
	1754		22.35	
	1755		1.17	
	1765		2.36	
	1766		1.27	
	1767		4.86	
	1768		3.35	
	1769		2.54	
	1770		2.78	

1771		1.34
1772		3.01
1773		2.84
1774		0.74
1775		0.60
1777		2.28
1778		5.76
1779		3.73
1780		1.11
1781		4.53
1782		0.97
1783		2.36
1784		0.60
1786		1.57
1787		2.15
1788		2.40
1789		2.07
1790		0.65
1791		0.34
1792		0.65
1798		0.34
1800		1.45
1801		0.80
1802		0.15
1803		0.55
1806		2.40
1807		0.20
1808		1.25
1809	9.53	4.10
1810	10.20	4.65
1812	1.70	0.80
1813	5.83	2.90
1814	8.88	3.15
1818	1.00	0.45
1821	0.50	0.15
1822	4.50	1.95
1826	3.90	1.85
1827	9.68	4.15
1828	13.25	6.15
1829	2.35	1.00
1832	0.65	0.35
1833	1.33	0.65
1834	2.03	0.85
1835	9.03	4.05
1836	11.45	4.25
1837	17.03	7.30
1838	1.40	0.50

1840	14.30	7.70	
1841	1.00	0.35	
1842	0.75	0.35	
1843	2.00	0.95	
1846	6.30	2.25	
1847	3.20	1.95	
1848	10.23	5.55	
1849	5.50	2.80	
1850	4.20	1.80	
1851	2.80	1.40	
1852	1.70	0.80	

Comment: 1756-1764 Data missing
Mineral Lord: 1735-1852 See under Grassington
Worked by: 1838-1852 Duke of Devonshire

CAT HOLES Todmorden SD919264

Production: Lead Ore(tons) Lead (tons) Value (£)
1871-1877 No detailed returns
Comment: 1877-1879 In liquidation
Worked by: 1871-1877 Cat Holes Mine Co. Ltd
Secretary: 1871-1877 John Gledhill

CATSCAR Aysgarth SE008884

Production: Lead Ore(tons) Lead (tons) Value (£)
1862-1863 No detailed returns
Comment: 1862-1865 See Aysgarth
Worked by: 1862-1863 John Tattersall & Co.

CHALONER Guisborough NZ604174

Production: Iron	Ore(tons)	Value (£)
1872	15831.00	
1873	100513.40	30004.00
1874	150393.90	45118.20
1875	207694.00	
1876	207894.00	
1877	234995.00	
1878	322332.00	
1879	261005.80	
1880	260000.00	

1881-1939 No detailed returns
Comment: 1880-1881 See Eston
1881 Standing
1887-1895 Standing
1939 Abandoned - August
Mineral Lord: 1874-1939 Chaloner family
Worked by: 1872-1876 Bolckow, Vaughan & Co.
1877-1928 Bolckow, Vaughan & Co. Ltd
1929-1939 Dorman, Long & Co. Ltd

Agent:		
	1872	George Lee
	1873-1880	Thomas Lee
	1880-1910	John Thompson
	1911-1912	A.M. Hedley
	1913-1925	W.G. Grace
	1926-1932	T.E. Slater
	1933-1938	M. Hedley

Employment:		Underground	Surface	Total
Comment:	1883	Included with Eston		
	1902-1939	Included with Eston		

CHANCE Grassington SE031672

Production:	Lead	Ore(tons)	Lead (tons)	Value (£)
	1777		0.50	
	1778		1.10	
	1786		2.78	
	1787		0.87	
	1803		8.85	
	1804		5.75	
	1805		7.55	
	1806		9.15	
	1807		3.25	
	1808		7.30	
	1849	5.50	2.80	
	1809	4.60	1.95	
	1810	11.60	5.10	
	1811	1.75	0.55	
	1814	1.85	0.65	
	1815	9.50	5.30	
	1825	0.55	0.15	
	1827	0.48	0.20	
	1838	0.50	0.30	

Mineral Lord: 1777-1838 See under Grassington

CHATSWORTH Grassington SE025672

Production:	Lead	Ore(tons)	Lead (tons)	Value (£)
	1808		36.90	
	1809	41.33	25.55	
	1810	31.40	19.20	
	1811	3.48	1.65	
	1812	2.15	1.10	
	1815	0.43	0.20	
	1819	20.50	12.85	
	1820	47.48	30.45	
	1821	37.88	25.15	
	1822	0.65	0.30	
	1823	0.95	0.40	

	1826	0.60	0.20	
	1827	1.35	0.65	
	1828	38.58	25.85	
	1829	4.53	2.80	
	1830	23.98	16.85	
	1831	2.38	1.55	
	1839	0.80	0.35	
	1841	0.13	0.05	
	1847	2.95	1.25	

Mineral Lord: 1808-1847 See under Grassington
Worked by: 1808-1815 Duke of Devonshire
1820-1838 Robert Summerville & Co.
1838-1847 Duke of Devonshire
Agent: 1838-1847 Stephen Eddy

CHAYTOR'S RAKE Redmire SE062930

Production:	Lead	Ore(tons)	Lead (tons)	Value (£)
	1797	No detailed returns		

Mineral Lord: 1797 See under Keld Heads
Worked by: 1797 Chaytor & Co.

CHELSEA Grassington SE021675

Production:	Lead	Ore(tons)	Lead (tons)	Value (£)
	1793		28.15	
	1794		56.40	
	1795		18.65	
	1796		33.25	
	1797		8.50	
	1798		9.80	
	1799		1.00	
	1800		8.00	
	1801		11.55	
	1802		11.10	
	1803		9.20	
	1804		15.55	
	1805		12.15	
	1806		3.75	
	1807		0.50	
	1808		28.80	
	1809	46.58	22.35	
	1810	31.58	18.25	
	1811	6.13	3.55	
	1812	8.00	4.10	
	1819	12.00	7.45	
	1821	14.05	8.60	
	1822	16.25	9.65	
	1824	3.55	2.05	
	1825	0.55	0.20	
	1826	0.48	0.35	

	1827	5.30	3.70	
	1828	17.78	9.75	
	1829	3.70	2.35	
	1830	6.93	4.45	
	1831	3.08	2.10	
	1832	4.85	2.85	
	1833	0.65	0.35	
	1834	1.23	0.55	
	1836	1.40	0.55	
	1851	5.30	2.10	
	1852	1.80	1.00	
Mineral Lord:	1793-1852	See under Grassington		
Worked by:	1789	Simondson & Co.		
	1812	Jacob Ragg & Co.		
Agent:	1793	Christopher Lawson		

CHOICE		Grassington		SE035671
Production:	Lead	Ore(tons)	Lead (tons)	Value (£)
	1786		2.95	
	1787		1.11	
Mineral Lord:	1786-1787	See under Grassington		
Worked by:	1786-1787	P.W. Overend		

CLEAVER'S RAKE		Castle Bolton		SE015929
Production:	Lead	Ore(tons)	Lead (tons)	Value (£)
	1806	No detailed returns		
Mineral Lord:	1806	See under Keld Heads		
Worked by:	1806	Cleaver & Co.		
Agent:	1806	Nathan Newbould		

CLIFF		Brotton		NZ686212
Production:	Iron	Ore(tons)		Value (£)
	1866	10055.00		2513.70
	1867	No detailed return		
	1868	90417.00		22604.20
	1869	No detailed return		
	1870	208448.00		52112.00
	1871	266084.30		66521.00
	1872	111820.00		
	1873	85545.40		25663.50
	1874	75500.90		22650.00
	1875	73682.00		
	1876	60968.30		
	1880	58332.50		
	1881	33765.00		
Comment:	1867	See Normanby		
	1869	See Normanby		
	1870-1871	May include Huntcliffe		
	1877-1879	Standing		

	1882-1886	Standing
	1887	Abandoned
Mineral Lord:	1863-1887	J. Rigg
	1863-1873	Bell Bros.
	1874-1887	Bell Brothers Ltd
Agent:	1863-1881	Addison L. Steavenson
	1876-1878	Thomas Bell
	1878-1882	W. Anderson
	1880-1881	Thomas Bell

CLOSEHOUSE Lunedale NY840226

Production:	Lead	Ore(tons)	Lead (tons)	Value (£)
	1757	8.90		
	1758	33.30		
	1796	2.45		
	1797	4.40		
	1833	0.52		
	1834	1.64		
	1835	1.24		
	1837	6.61		
	1843	2.47		
	1844	2.71		
	1845	8.40		

Comments:	1844	Lease assigned to London Lead Company
Mineral Lord:	1757-1845	See Lunehead
Worked by:	1771	London Lead Company
	1831	James Ainsly & Co.
	1834-1835	James Beadle & Co.
	1844-1845	London Lead Company

CLOSEHOUSE Lunedale NY851228

Production:	Barytes	Ore(tons)	Value (£)
	1939-1990	No detailed returns	

Comments:	1940-1942	Standing
	1940-1990	Includes Arngill
	2001	Summer - closed
Mineral Lord:	1939-1990	See Lunehead
Worked by:	1939-1981	Athole G. Allen (Stockton) Ltd
	1981-1989	Fordamin Co. (Sales) Ltd
	1989-1993	Hopton Mining Co. Ltd
	1993-2001	Viaton Industries Ltd

Employment:		Underground	Surface	Total
	1943	2	14	16
	1944	6	11	17
	1945	2	12	14
	1948	13	23	36
	1950	16	24	40

COALGROVEBECK		Grassington		SE030667
Production:	Lead	Ore(tons)	Lead (tons)	Value (£)
	1752		13.50	
	1753		50.06	
	1754		68.95	
	1755		328.11	
	1765		65.00	
	1766		55.35	
	1767		65.55	
	1768		41.70	
	1769		19.90	
	1770		42.25	
	1771		39.01	
	1772		5.70	
	1773		18.20	
	1774		11.40	
	1775		11.45	
	1776		2.60	
	1777		1.95	
	1778		37.56	
	1779		50.01	
	1780		6.69	
	1781		13.61	
	1782		5.98	
	1783		4.27	
	1784		4.01	
	1785		6.71	
	1786		3.09	
	1787		4.19	
	1788		8.54	
	1789		4.62	
	1790		2.19	
	1791		7.88	
	1792		7.93	
	1793		0.30	
	1794		1.65	
	1795		2.20	
	1796		1.35	
	1797		4.70	
	1798		4.80	
	1800		4.00	
	1801		1.06	
	1804		1.55	
	1805		0.30	
	1806		6.00	
	1808		9.85	
	1809	1.45	0.50	

1810	2.13	0.80
1812	3.85	1.60
1813	4.90	1.90
1814	3.65	1.60
1816	1.85	0.70
1817	2.43	0.80
1819	4.05	1.80
1821	35.05	20.25
1822	217.45	120.85
1823	84.15	45.85
1824	27.90	15.55
1825	15.45	8.20
1826	3.69	1.32
1827	53.24	32.00
1828	175.91	113.10
1829	34.98	21.45
1830	57.50	36.65
1831	61.33	37.00
1832	113.30	69.00
1833	168.05	101.50
1834	300.73	193.70
1835	447.33	277.25
1836	451.00	280.15
1838	12.70	5.05
1839	5.98	2.25
1840	41.23	16.90
1841	22.50	8.10
1842	3.25	1.35
1843	7.25	3.25
1844	1.15	0.40
1846	0.23	0.10
1847	1.00	0.55
1848	1.00	0.80
1849	8.50	4.85
1850	15.40	7.45
1851	18.15	7.90
1852	7.85	3.25
1853	5.90	3.25

Comments:	1756-1764	Data missing
Mineral Lord:	1752-1853	See under Grassington
Worked by:	1753-1755	James Swale & Co.
	1765-1791	John Summers & Co.
	1821-1844	Duke of Devonshire
Agent:	1800	Christopher Lawson
	1821-1824	Joseph Mason Snr
	1825-1834	John Barratt
	1834-1844	Stephen Eddy

COALGROVEBECK & YARNBURY Grassington

Production:	Lead	Ore(tons)	Lead (tons)	Value (£)
	1828	121.99	75.15	
	1829	230.30	141.50	
	1836	78.00	48.20	
	1837	401.40	243.05	
	1838	575.20	344.45	
	1839	1022.20	641.10	
	1840	1095.75	701.95	
	1841	845.20	537.35	
	1842	952.85	597.15	
	1843	1279.55	770.75	
	1844	1124.10	681.90	
	1845	991.95	589.05	
	1846	1119.30	674.05	
	1847	1113.18	674.70	
	1848	898.70	578.50	
	1849	791.90	504.75	
	1850	1413.60	941.25	
	1851	1635.95	1109.50	
	1852	953.05	635.30	
	1853	1504.60	1009.35	

Mineral Lord: 1828-1853 See under Grassington
Worked by: 1828-1853 Duke of Devonshire
Agent: 1828-1834 John Barratt
1834-1853 Stephen Eddy

COALGROVEHEAD Grassington SE032670

Production:	Lead	Ore(tons)	Lead (tons)	Value (£)
	1751		38.14	
	1752		3.03	
	1753		28.79	
	1754		37.11	
	1765		263.00	
	1766		157.60	
	1767		134.92	
	1768		319.31	
	1769		269.25	
	1770		186.60	
	1771		298.83	
	1772		181.45	
	1773		237.15	
	1774		235.75	
	1775		227.45	
	1776		155.85	
	1777		117.60	
	1778		123.30	

1779		113.45
1780		106.50
1781		56.25
1782		66.08
1783		40.00
1784		142.00
1785		181.90
1786		120.75
1787		99.70
1788		80.80
1789		59.40
1790		61.50
1791		35.55
1792		6.97
1793		16.40
1794		20.90
1795		41.45
1796		60.40
1797		28.05
1798		32.35
1799		15.40
1800		30.95
1801		21.55
1802		42.25
1803		42.25
1804		44.95
1805		41.25
1806		41.90
1807		41.65
1808		56.10
1828	121.99	75.15
1809	111.03	58.70
1810	89.50	48.30
1811	99.15	53.85
1812	103.00	56.90
1813	125.43	72.90
1814	120.20	69.50
1815	62.45	36.15
1816	38.10	20.60
1817	37.75	19.50
1818	11.43	6.50
1819	7.63	4.35
1820	5.10	2.60
1821	14.63	6.20
1822	2.40	1.05
1823	12.65	6.45
1824	8.85	4.50

	1825	9.85	5.10
	1826	4.82	2.55
	1827	15.70	8.20
	1828	102.55	71.65
	1829	0.70	0.40
	1830	4.58	2.15
	1831	0.70	0.35
	1832	78.93	45.60
	1833	5.63	3.00
	1834	10.00	3.95
	1835	2.25	0.85
	1836		27.00
	1837	304.85	201.15
	1838	215.38	153.60
	1839	69.65	39.80
	1840	52.60	30.05
	1841	7.85	2.90
	1842	9.13	3.85
	1843	12.95	4.90
	1844	5.25	2.20
	1845	7.48	3.25
	1846	7.38	2.80
	1847	25.90	11.50
	1848	24.15	11.35
	1849	15.53	6.90
	1850	24.00	10.35
	1851	18.10	9.10
	1853	9.45	3.50

Comments: 1756-1764 Data missing
Mineral Lord: 1751-1853 See under Grassington
Worked by: 1737 Isaac Thornhill
1751-1768 Elias Thornhill
1769-1807 John Thornhill
1808-1817 Christopher Thornhill
1819-1840 Robert Fell & Co.
Agent: 1773-1774 John Summers

COATE MOOR Kildale NZ602099

Production:	Iron	Ore(tons)	Value (£)
	1873	9000.00	2700.00
	1874	1000.00	300.00

Comment: 1866 Opening
1866 See Lonsdale
1875 Standing
1876 Abandoned
Mineral Lord: 1866-1876 Trustees of Robert Bell Livesey
Worked by: 1866 Lonsdale Vale Iron Co.
1872 Downes & Co.

	1872-1876	Coate Moor Ironstone Co. Ltd		
Agent:	1872	John Hodgson		
	1873-1876	C. Campbell Downes		

COATEWORK		Starbotton		SD955770
Production:	Lead	Ore(tons)	Lead (tons)	Value (£)
	1738		0.50	
	1739		1.60	
	1740		1.05	
	1744		0.35	
	1745		0.65	
Worked by:	1738-1740	George Coates & George Sawley		
	1744-1745	George Sawley		
	1745		0.40	
Worked by:	1745	Robert Calvert		
	1745		0.25	
Worked by:	1745	J. Batersby		
Comment:	1738-1745	Smelted at Buckden		
	1744-1778	Coatnook		
	1778	Sidgwick & Southern's grants were adjacent		
	1800-1832	See Knucklebone		
Mineral Lord:	1738-1778	See under Grassington		
Worked by:	1774	John Mitton & Co.		
	1778	Thomas Southern & Co.		
	1778	Roger Sidgwick & Co.		

COBSCAR		Redmire		SE055930
Production:	Lead	Ore(tons)	Lead (tons)	Value (£)
	1762-1828	No detailed returns		
Comment:	1762	Calamine Producer		
Mineral Lord:	1760-1781	See under Keld Heads		
Worked by:	1762	James Plews & Co.		
	1760-1781	William Chaytor & Co.		
	1827	Messrs Hall & Co.		

COBSCAR SMELT MILL		Redmire		SE059930
Production:	Lead	Ore(tons)	Lead (tons)	Value (£)
	1853		1.10	
	1857		0.90	
	1859		2.35	
	1861		5.25	
	1863		2.60	
	1865		10.90	
	1866		7.60	
	1867		10.30	
	1868		0.15	
Comment:	1853-1860	From mill wastes and roasting furnace		
Worked by:	1853-1868	Lord Bolton		

COCKBUR		Grassington		SE026656
Production:	Lead	Ore(tons)	Lead (tons)	Value (£)
	1722		0.25	
	1736		0.63	
	1737		0.83	
	1738		1.10	
	1739		0.82	
	1741		3.91	
	1742		1.76	
	1743		2.37	
	1744		3.35	
	1745		2.63	
	1746		0.85	
	1747		1.64	
	1748		1.10	
	1749		0.96	
	1752		0.90	
	1753		0.51	
	1756		0.64	
	1760		0.44	
	1762		0.28	
	1766		0.13	
	1772		0.20	
	1773		0.66	
	1774		0.18	
	1775		0.13	
	1780		0.38	
	1781		0.22	
	1782		0.14	
	1788		0.26	
	1791		0.55	
	1798		0.30	
	1800		0.65	
	1801		0.15	
	1802		0.60	
	1804		2.95	
	1805		2.95	
	1806		4.80	
	1807		5.15	
	1808		8.15	
	1809	46.40	25.70	
	1810	28.28	16.05	
	1811	125.38	75.05	
	1812	100.65	58.90	
	1813	41.48	21.80	
	1814	28.45	13.90	
	1815	33.65	17.50	
	1816	23.85	10.75	

	1817	19.75	10.60
	1818	29.98	17.30
	1819	62.80	38.45
	1820	37.20	21.95
	1821	13.50	6.95
	1822	66.05	36.50
	1823	18.25	9.60
	1824	10.78	5.20
	1825	24.50	13.25
	1826	209.58	129.40
	1827	33.29	18.95
	1828	9.65	4.60
	1829	13.29	6.00
	1830	44.83	21.80
	1831	27.53	17.00
	1832	52.43	30.50
	1833	32.18	16.15
	1834	26.25	13.35
	1835	10.85	5.25
	1836	45.60	20.90
	1837	47.88	23.20
	1838	53.60	27.10
	1839	44.95	22.15
	1840	36.45	16.75
	1841	29.70	13.65
	1842	15.35	8.65
	1843	41.05	21.40
	1844	32.65	16.70
	1845	28.00	15.15
	1846	22.68	14.00
	1847	27.95	16.65
	1848	25.50	14.40
	1849	23.15	13.75
	1850	20.65	12.75
	1851	29.15	19.05
	1852	28.68	16.45
	1853	32.05	19.00

Comment: 1722 Smelted at Hebden
1757-1759 Data missing
Mineral Lord: 1722-1853 See under Grassington
Worked by: 1722 Mr Barker

COCKER Arkengarthdale NY954035

Production:	Lead	Ore(tons)	Lead (tons)	Value (£)
	1783	2.90		
	1784	12.20		
	1785	2.10		
	1786	35.40		
	1787	171.70		

	1788	120.00		
	1789	31.30		
	1790	14.40		

Comment: 1782-1783 November to May inclusive
1784-1795 December to November inclusive
1785-1796 December to May inclusive
1786-1790 December to November inclusive
1790-1791 December to May inclusive

Mineral Lord: 1782-1791 See Arkengarthdale

Worked by: 1782-1791 Charles Sleigh, William Hoar & Charles Foster

Employment:		Underground	Surface	Total
	1783-1784	1		
	1784-1785	1		
	1785-1786	1		
	1786-1787	7		
	1787-1788	19		
	1788-1789	14		
	1789-1790	9		
	1790-1791	7		

COCKHILL Bewerley SE112643

Production:	Lead	Ore(tons)	Lead (tons)	Value (£)
	1782-1814	No detailed returns		
	1935	230.00		2037.00
	1936	50.00		390.00

Production:	Fluorspar	Ore(tons)	Value (£)
	1933	655.00	
	1934	3232.00	
	1935	4326.00	
	1936	5171.00	
	1937	4399.00	
	1940-1946	No detailed returns	

Comment: 1782-1814 See Sunside- Cockhill
1782 Driving Cockhill Level
1845-1860 See Pateley District
1861-1883 See Sunside-Cockhill
1923-1928 See Gillfield & Cockhill
1933-1937 Including Gillfield
1944 Discontinued - September
1946 Abandoned - August 28th

Mineral Lord: 1782-1938 See Bewerley

Worked by: 1782-1814 Edward Cleaver & Co. - Lease expired 1814
1927-1928 Bewerley Mines Ltd
1931-1938 Caldbeck Company
1940-1946 George Boddy
1985 Crust Mining Co.

Employment:		Underground	Surface	Total
	1927	6	14	20
	1933	8	14	22
	1934	9	16	25
	1935	25	32	57
	1936	30	22	55
	1937	0	18	18
	1938	0	6	5
	1940	3	1	4
	1941	2	0	2
	1942	3	0	3
	1943	2	0	2
	1944	0	2	2
	1945	0	5	5

Comment: 1935-1938 See Craven Cross No.2

COCKLAKE Lunedale NY886226

Production:	Lead	Ore(tons)	Lead (tons)	Value (£)
	1771	No detailed returns		
Mineral Lord:	1771	See Lunehead		
Worked by:	1771	London Lead Company		

COD HILL Guisborough NZ604134

Production:	Iron	Ore(tons)	Value (£)
	1853-1865	No detailed returns	
Comment:	1863-1865	See Hutton Low Cross	
Worked by:	1853	Joseph Pease	

COLDSTONES ALLOTMENT Bewerley SE117638

Production:	Lead	Ore(tons)	Lead (tons)	Value (£)
	1800	No detailed returns		
Comment:	1800	See Also Sunside and North Coldstones		
Mineral Lord:	1800	See under Bewerley		
Worked by:	1800	Edward Cleaver & Co.		

COLDSTONES, NORTH Bewerley SE118644

Production:	Lead	Ore(tons)	Lead (tons)	Value (£)
	1782-1855	No detailed returns		
Comment:	1783	Driving Gillfield Level		
	1824	United with Sunside-Cockhill		
Mineral Lord:	1782-1824	The White family		
Worked by:	1760-1782	Mr Thornhill & Co.		
	1782-1790	Peter Wilson Overend		
	1802	H. Hardcastle & Co. Lease expired 1823		
	1824-1855	Thomas Hopper & Co. = Sunside Mining Co.		
Agent:	1776	William Bell		
	1776	Ralph Robinson		
	1784-1789	Alexander Wearing		
	1792	Mr Harker		

COLDSTONES, SOUTH Bewerley

Production:	Lead	Ore(tons)	Lead (tons)	Value (£)
	1828-1844	No detailed returns		
Comment:	1828-1844	See under Sunside-Cockhill		

COLLODEN Grassington

Production:	Lead	Ore(tons)	Lead (tons)	Value (£)
	1805		0.25	
Mineral Lord:	1805	See under Grassington		

COLOTAN Grassington

Production:	Lead	Ore(tons)	Lead (tons)	Value (£)
	1800	0.70	0.45	
Mineral Lord:	1800	See under Grassington		
Worked by:	1800	Richard Waddelove		

COLSTERDALE Colsterdale SE108803

Production:	Lead	Ore(tons)	Lead (tons)	Value (£)
	1709	2.35	1.64	
	1710	4.60	2.57	20.70
	1711-1722	No detailed returns		
Comment:	1709-1710	Smelted at Preston Mill		
Mineral Lord:	1709-1722	Sir Abstrupus Danby		
Worked by:	1710-1713	Sir Abstrupus Danby		
	1721	Christopher Simpson & Joseph Simpson		
	1722	Vincent Coates		

COMMONDALE Commondale NZ664102

Production:	Iron	Ore(tons)	Value (£)
	1863-1876	No detailed returns	
Mineral Lord:	1863-1876	J.S. Pratt	
Worked by:	1863-1876	Cleveland Iron Ore Co.	
Agent:	1863-1876	Thomas Watson	

CONISTONE LIBERTY Conistone with Kilnsey SE010702

Production:	Lead	Ore(tons)	Lead (tons)	Value (£)
	1746		0.16	
	1752		0.25	
	1753		0.05	
	1767		0.81	
	1768		1.54	
	1770		0.11	
	1772		1.10	
	1831	8.10	6.15	
	1835	0.50	0.33	
	1836	0.75	0.44	
	1838	0.20	0.16	
	1847	3.50	2.09	

	1849	41.40	26.91
	1850	1.80	0.88
	1851	0.80	0.27
	1852	5.30	3.02
	1853	5.98	4.00

Comment:	1746-1853	Smelted at Grassington
	1756-1764	Data missing
	1768	See Dreadnought
	1768	See Twenty Meers
	1772-1788	See North Mossdale 33 Meers
	1831-1838	See Royal Exchange
	1831-1871	See Fearnought
	1847-1868	See Conistone Moor Head
	1854-1872	See Mossdale
	1860-1872	See Conistone Out Moor
Mineral Lord:	1687-1872	Trust Lords of Conistone
Worked by:	1746	John Gill
	1752	John Calvert
	1753	Thomas Moorhouse
	1767-1768	James Cockburn
	1770	Francis Sigwick
	1772	Ralph Summers Jnr
	1835	Matthew Alderton
	1836	Robert Hudson
	1838	Robert Hancock
	1847	George Mangham
	1849	Joseph Pattinson & William Pattinson
	1850-1853	James Daykin
	1851	Joseph Pattinson
	1853	Edward Garnett & Robert Aldersley
Barmaster:	1687	Richard Wigglesworth
	1732-1733	Henry Constantine
	1733	John Constantine
	1745	Thomas Hebden
	1747-1748	Richard Bolland
	1749	Thomas Leyland
	1749-1750	William Wigglesworth
	1750	Richard Slinger
	1751	Mr Tennant
	1752	Giles Tennant
	1753	Jonathan Constantine
	1753	William Slinger
	1753-1761	John Whitaker
	1757	Henry Constantine
	1757-1758	John Constantine
	1758	Robert Constantine
	1759	Henry Leyland
	1761-1762	William Slinger
	1762	Henry Constantine

1763 Giles Tennant
1764-1765 Robert Slinger
1766 Luke Horner
1766-1767 John Whitaker
1767-1768 John Constantine
1768-1769 Michael Down
1769-1770 George Horner
1771-1772 John Mason
1772-1773 Giles Tennant
1774-1789 George Horner
1789-1790 Henry Constantine
1790-1791 Stephen Constantine
1791-1792 Stephen Wrathall
1792-1793 Henry Whitaker
1793-1794 John Cockson
1794-1795 Robert Wrathall
1795-1796 Anthony Downes
1796-1797 John Leyland
1797-1798 Luke Horner
1798-1800 John Leyland
1800-1801 William Wrathall
1801-1802 Stephen Wrathall
1802-1803 Henry Whitaker
1803-1804 Robert Wrathall
1804-1805 William Wrathall
1805-1806 Anthony Downes
1806-1807 John Leyland
1807-1808 Luke Horner
1808-1809 Leonard Sidgwick
1809-1810 Stephen Wrathall
1810-1811 Henry Whitaker
1811-1812 Thomas Cockson
1812-1813 Anthony Downes
1813-1814 John Leyland
1814-1815 Henry Whitaker
1815-1816 John Whitaker
1817-1818 Stephen Wrathall
1818-1819 Henry Whitaker
1819-1821 Leonard Sidgwick
1821-1823 Luke Horner
1823-1824 Leonard Sidgwick
1824-1825 William Wrathall
1825-1826 John Whitaker
1826-1832 Leonard Sidgwick
1832-1835 James Watson
1835-1837 William Wrathall
1838-1839 James Watson
1839-1848 William Wrathall
1877 George Horner

CONISTONE MOOR HEAD Conistone with Kilnsey SE000703

Production:	Lead	Ore(tons)	Lead (tons)	Value (£)
	1847	0.70	0.38	
	1848	0.75	0.38	
	1849	1.10	0.55	
	1850	0.68	0.38	
	1851	1.80	0.55	
	1852	1.90	0.66	
	1847-1852 Smelted at Grassington			
	1852	7.75	5.25	
	1857	1.80	0.95	
	1859	1.90	0.65	
	1852-1859 Smelted at Starbotton Cupola			
	1862		4.16	
	1863		6.40	
	1864		2.80	
	1868		0.30	
	1862-1868 Smelted at Kettlewell			
	1863	9.10	6.40	
	1864	4.60	2.80	
	1865-1867 No detailed returns			
	1868	0.50	0.30	

Comment: 1863-1868 Data from Hunt's Statistics
1870-1871 Not trading
Mineral Lord: 1847-1868 See Conistone Liberty
Worked by: 1847-1859 Thomas Rodgers & Co.
1862-1864 Conistone Moor Head Mining Co. (Cost Book)
1868-1869 Joseph Fallowfield Masser
1869-1870 Conistone Moor Head Mining Co. Ltd
1870-1871 New Grassington Mining Co. Ltd
Agent: 1862-1863 Joseph Craig
1864-1870 Ralph Place
Secretary: 1869-1870 William Stead

CONISTONE OUT MOOR Conistone with Kilnsey SE012703

Production:	Lead	Ore(tons)	Lead (tons)	Value (£)
	1860	51.60	35.80	
	1861	127.10	88.00	
	1862	184.50	128.40	
	1863	123.60	83.20	
	1864	7.90	2.80	
	1865	78.30	52.10	
	1866	28.00	18.70	
	1867	11.00	7.30	
	1868	21.70	13.50	
	1869	9.70	6.50	
	1870	90.80	62.70	
	1871	122.30	79.00	
	1872	10.50	8.10	

Comment: 1860-1872 Data from Hunt's Statistics
1862-1871 See Fearnought
Mineral Lord: 1860-1872 See Conistone Liberty
Worked by: 1862-1871 Conistone Out Moor Co.
Agent: 1862-1868 Robert Place
1869-1871 John Ralph Place

Employment:		Underground	Surface	Total
	1862	4		

CONJUROR RAKE Grassington

Production:	Lead	Ore(tons)	Lead (tons)	Value (£)
	1799		0.20	

Mineral Lord: 1799 See under Grassington

CONONLEY Cononley SD980461

Production:	Lead	Ore(tons)	Lead (tons)	Value (£)
	1744	No detailed returns		
	1820	9.25	5.55	
	1826	10.63	7.19	
	1827	26.30	14.22	
	1828	10.23	7.30	
	1838	0.53	0.35	
	1840	87.00	60.00	
	1841	574.00	396.00	
	1842	177.00	122.00	
	1843	95.00	65.70	
	1844	601.00	415.00	

Comment: 1744 Prospecting
1820-1838 Smelted at Grassington
1840-1844 Output estimated from lead sales

Production:	Lead	Ore(tons)	Lead (tons)	Value (£)
	1845	631.00	414.00	
	1846	663.00	436.00	
	1847	692.00	441.00	
	1848	699.00	437.00	
	1849	588.20	395.30	
	1850	804.00	556.00	
	1851	733.50	520.50	
	1852	554.00	381.60	
	1853	772.00	550.00	
	1854	606.00	463.00	
	1855	654.40	475.00	
	1856	596.00	441.30	
	1857	538.70	388.40	
	1858	555.40	387.20	
	1859	519.30	363.40	

	1860	494.90	345.00	
	1861	380.60	254.00	
	1862	485.20	329.20	
	1863	523.90	358.20	
	1864	409.30	287.00	
	1865	290.20	201.40	
	1866	268.70	190.60	
	1867	247.90	173.20	
	1868	170.80	188.70	
	1869	130.80	95.90	
	1870	54.10	37.50	
	1871	12.70	7.30	
	1872	5.10	3.10	
	1873	No detailed returns		
	1874	20.50	14.50	
	1875	26.40	18.50	
	1876	9.50	7.00	
	1881	12.70	9.00	118.00
Comment:	1845-1881	Data from Hunt's Statistics		
	1878	Advertised for sale December 1878		
	1882	Standing		
Production:	Lead	Ore(tons)	Lead (tons)	Value (£)
	1858	553.10	387.65	
	1859	521.80	363.65	
	1860	459.60	345.25	
	1861	386.60	246.70	
	1862	491.60	329.40	
	1863	524.60	358.00	
	1864	392.75	296.50	
	1865	284.90	195.55	
	1866	271.90	189.65	
	1867	217.15	172.25	
	1868	284.70	198.50	
	1869	128.65	95.90	
	1870	55.45	37.50	
	1871	8.65	5.85	
	1878	19.80		
	1881	26.44		
Comment:	1840-1871	Smelted at Cononley		
	1858-1871	Data from Cononley Smelting Ledger		
	1878-1881	Smelted at Grassington		
Production:	Barytes	Ore(tons)		Value (£)
	1919	763.77		
	1920	361.42		
	1921	212.79		
	1922	2389.87		
	1923	766.10		

Comment:	1919-1923 Barytes from the mine	
Production:	Barytes Ore(tons)	Value (£)
	1921 107.51	
	1922 3127.33	
	1923 2678.22	
	1924 784.94	
	1925 2782.89	
	1926 251.00	
	1927 105.25	
	1928-1931 No detailed returns	
	1948 No detailed returns	
	1928-1931 No detailed returns	
	1954-1958 No detailed returns	
Comment:	1921-1927 Barytes from the dumps	
	1919-1925 See Glusburn	
	1982 Prospecting	
Mineral Lord:	1744-2000 See under Grassington	
Worked by:	1820 James Garth	
	1825-1827 Walter Hall	
	1828 John Gill	
	1838 John Newbould	
	1836-1881 Duke of Devonshire	
	1919-1927 Edward Murgatroyd	
	1927-1931 James Harold Clay	
	1948 Ernest Gregory	
	1954-1957 Connonley Lead Mines	
	1957-1958 McKechnie Brothers	
	1982 Wharfedale Mining Co.	
	1990-2000 Friends of Cononley Mine	
Agent:	1836-1861 Stephen Eddy	
	1841 James Shummers	
	1842-1853 Josiah Remfrey	
	1853-1869 Thomas Ward	
	1861-1881 James Ray Eddy	
	1954-1957 Fred A. Smith	

Employment:		Underground	Surface	Total
	1841	31	3	34
	1851	74	31	105
	1861	59	22	81
	1862	56		
	1871	21	5	26
	1877	8	1	9
	1878	6	1	7
	1879	4	1	5
	1880-1881	2	0	2

COPPERTHWAITE		Marrick		NZ052000
Production:	Lead	Ore(tons)	Lead (tons)	Value (£)
	1660-1718	No detailed returns		
	1724		10.70	
	1725		23.28	
	1726		22.18	
	1727		8.95	
Comment:	1660-1727	See Hurst		
	1727	January to August		
Worked by:	1724-1727	Lord William Powlett		

COTTINGLEY		Grassington		SE034690
Production:	Lead	Ore(tons)	Lead (tons)	Value (£)
	1778		23.50	
	1779		6.00	
	1780		27.30	
	1786		12.87	
	1787		4.69	
	1790		0.08	
	1795		3.90	
	1796		0.19	
	1798		0.15	
	1800		0.60	
	1801		3.50	
	1802		4.20	
	1803		7.20	
	1804		7.25	
Mineral Lord:	1778-1804	See under Grassington		
Worked by:	1778	Colonel Henry Wickham		

COVERDALE LIBERTY		Carlton Highdale		SE003785
Production:	Lead	Ore(tons)	Lead (tons)	Value (£)
	1786		0.25	
	1840	2.00	1.25	
Comment:	1786-1840	Smelted at Grassington		
	1862		0.50	
	1866		1.50	
	1868		0.35	
Comment:	1868	Smelted at Kettlewell		
	1774	See: Huntersleets and Stonegill 10 Meers		
	1873	See: Bradley and Woodale		
Mineral Lord:	1699	John Lambert		
Worked by:	1699	William Pearson, Robert Armistead & John Wear		
	1840	Stott & Co.		
	1862	Simon Brown & Ptnr		
	1866-1868	John Brown		
Agent:	1786	Christopher Lawson		

COVES ENCLOSURE VEIN Grassington SE000650

Production:	Lead	Ore(tons)	Lead (tons)	Value (£)
	1769		0.40	
	1784		0.56	
Mineral Lord:	1769-1784	See under Grassington		
Worked by:	1769	Lupton Wrathall		

COWLING HILL Cowling SD965437

Production:	Lead	Ore(tons)	Lead (tons)	Value (£)
	1861	3.15	2.15	
	1866	20.25	13.40	
	1869	4.90	3.15	
Comment:	1863-1869	Smelted at Cononley		
	1861	3.40	2.10	
	1868	20.20	13.40	
	1869-1871	No detailed returns		
	1872	37.50	28.20	
	1873	No detailed returns		
Comment:	1873	Data from Hunt's Statistics		
Worked by:	1862-1863	Duke of Devonshire		
	1864-1868	Horner & Co.		
Agent:	1862-1863	James Ray Eddy		
	1870-1874	Thomas Ward		

CRACKPOT MOOR Grinton SD958962

Production:	Lead	Ore(tons)	Lead (tons)	Value (£)
	1824		4.66	
	1825		3.68	
	1827		0.37	
	1831		1.71	
	1837		2.89	
	1839		0.84	
Mineral Lord:	1824-1839	See AD Mines		
Worked by:	1824-1827	Woodward & Co.		
	1831-1839	Thomas Calvert		

CRACOE LIBERTY Cracoe SD978601

Production:	Lead	Ore(tons)	Lead (tons)	Value (£)
	1788		0.15	
Comment:	1788	Smelted at Grassington		
Worked by:	1788	James Brown		
	1860	7.10	5.20	
	1861	13.40	9.90	
	1862	5.80	4.30	
	1863	2.60	1.80	
	1864	3.20	2.00	
	1865	16.90	9.80	

	1866	1.70	0.90
	1867	8.60	6.10
	1868	5.90	4.30
	1869	2.80	2.00
	1870	2.00	1.20
	1871	No detailed returns	
Comment:	1860-1871	Data from Hunt's Statistics	
	1755-1860	See Also Carden	
	1865-1871	Including Elbolton	
Mineral Lord:	1755-1865	See under Grassington	
Worked by:	1862-1867	Metcalf & Co.	
Agent:	1862-1867	Thomas Wiseman	

CRAGGS HALL		Brotton	NZ702195
Production:	Iron	Ore(tons)	Value (£)
	1871	223984.00	55996.00
	1872	196508.00	
	1873	169507.00	50852.10
	1874	198000.00	59400.00
	1875	217539.90	
	1876	179639.00	
	1877	175211.90	
	1878	171992.00	
	1879	167675.80	
	1880	257491.90	
	1881	264001.50	
	1882-1891	No detailed returns	
Comment:	1892	Standing	
	1893	Abandoned - Lease expired	
Mineral Lord:	1871-1893	Chapman Trust; Maynard	
Worked by:	1871	Saltburn Iron Co.	
	1871-1880	Joseph W. Pease & Co.	
	1881-1893	Pease and Partners Ltd	
Agent:	1872	John Corrie	
	1873-1874	William Cockburn	
	1875-1882	William France	
	1883-1893	W. Moore	

CRANEHOW BOTTOM		Preston under Scar		SE064938
Production:	Lead	Ore(tons)	Lead (tons)	Value (£)
	1850		64.00	
	1851		180.00	
	1852		187.50	
	1853		87.25	
	1854		57.55	
	1855		116.90	
	1856		193.45	

	1857	501.60		
	1858	284.40		
	1859	162.00		
	1860	64.00		
	1861	58.40		
	1862	27.55		

Comment: 1845-1863 Data from Lord Bolton's Lead Book
1863-1872 See Keld Heads
Mineral Lord: 1845-1872 See under Keld Heads
Worked by: 1845-1862 Messrs Powlett & Co.
1863-1872 Keld Heads Mining Co.

CRAVEN CROSS Appletreewick SE100640

Production:	Lead	Ore(tons)	Lead (tons)	Value (£)
	1752-1795	No detailed returns		
	1869	63.00	48.00	
	1870	No detailed returns		
	1871	83.70	62.70	
	1872	26.20	19.60	
	1873	No detailed returns		

Comment: 1785 Boulton & Watt engine built
1795 Engine moved to Durham by John Horner
1795 Agreement to drive up Cockhill Level
1867 Craven Coop
1870-1871 Craven Moor
1873 Suspended
1876-1875 See Pateley Bridge, West
Mineral Lord: 1752-1875 See Appletreewick Liberty
Worked by: 1752-1790 William Wood & Co.
1803-1804 John Wood & Co.
1868 Craven Cross Co.
1869-1873 John Snell & Co.
Agent: 1867-1868 Matthew Newbould
1868 John Snell
1869-1873 William Newbould

CRAVEN CROSS No.2 Appletreewick SE102638

Production:	Lead	Ore(tons)	Lead (tons)	Value (£)
	1928	1024.00		9536.00
	1929	90.00		810.00
	1930	16.00		160.00

Comment: 1854-1865 Part of Craven Moor
1879-1883 Part of Craven Moor, East
1884-1887 Part of Craven Moor United

Production:	Fluorspar	Ore(tons)	Lead (tons)	Value (£)
	1926-1927	No detailed returns		
	1928	2588.00		1388.00
	1929	184.00		48.00

	1930-1932	No detailed returns
	1935-1944	No detailed returns
	1958	No detailed returns
Comment:	1926	Developing
	1929	In liquidation - closed February 2nd
	1930-1931	Standing
	1944	Abandoned - November
	1927-1958	See Appletreewick Liberty
Worked by:	1926-1929	Pateley Mines Ltd
	1930-1932	James Harold Clay & Arthur Kingham
	1932-1938	Caldbeck Company
	1939-1949	H. Green & J. Busfield: Tribute to Clay
	1958	Norman Lonsdale
Agent:	1926-1938	Arthur Kingham
	1927-1930	James Harold Clay
	1937-1938	E.T. Borlase

Employment:		Underground	Surface	Total
	1926	9	12	21
	1927	14	21	35
	1928	26	37	63
	1930	3	3	6
	1935	25	32	57
	1936	30	20	50
	1937	0	18	8
	1938	0	6	6
	1940	0	1	1
	1941	0	1	1
	1942	1	0	1
	1943	1	0	1

Comment:	1935-1938	Includes Gillfield & Cockhill
	1940-1944	Includes Gillfield

CRAVEN MOOR Appletreewick SE096634

Production:	Lead	Ore(tons)	Lead (tons)	Value (£)
	1769-1860	No detailed returns		
	1861	152.60	99.20	
	1862	140.80	89.40	
	1863	206.70	124.00	
	1864	187.10	128.60	
	1865	41.70	26.10	
	1866	90.60	67.90	
	1867	89.00	67.00	
	1868	32.30	21.00	
	1869	114.40	74.30	
	1870	101.20	84.10	
	1871	73.30	49.00	
	1915-1925	No detailed returns		

Comment:	1782	WYAS Yorke MSS DB151
	1864-1865	In liquidation
	1915-1925	Including: Foxholes, Gill and Jamie Mines
Mineral Lord:	1769-1925	See Appletreewick Liberty
Worked by:	1769-1804	William Bell & Co.
	1782	Henry Johnson & Co.
	1854	William Buck & Co.
	1854-1856	Craven Moor Mining Co. (Cost Book)
	1856-1865	Craven Moor Mining Co. Ltd
Agent:	1858-1864	William Barron
	1860-1864	Thomas Barran
	1867	Matthew Newbould
Secretary:	1857-1864	Edward Bolton

Employment:		Underground	Surface	Total
	1855			99
	1862	42		

CRAVEN MOOR UNITED Appletreewick SE102638

Production:	Lead	Ore(tons)	Lead (tons)	Value (£)
	1884	100.00	75.00	650.00
	1885	38.00	9.00	247.00
	1886	60.00	43.00	420.00
	1887	60.00		

Comment:	1884	East and West Craven Moor Companies merged
	1887	In liquidation
Mineral Lord:	1884-1889	See Appletreewick Liberty
Worked by:	1884-1889	Craven Moor United Lead Co. Ltd
Agent:	1884-1889	David Williams
	1884	Edward J. Drew
	1885-1887	Ernest Mansell

CRAVEN MOOR, EAST Appletreewick SE099638

Production:	Lead	Ore(tons)	Lead (tons)	Value (£)
	1879	110.50	83.00	1138.10
	1880	270.00	202.50	2565.00
	1881	330.00	231.00	3100.00
	1882	360.00	270.00	3060.00
	1883	207.00	155.20	1603.00

Mineral Lord:	1879-1883	See Appletreewick Liberty
Worked by:	1879-1883	East Craven Moor Lead Co. Ltd
Agent:	1879-1881	David Williams

Employment:		Underground	Surface	Total
	1879	30	16	46
	1880	38	14	52
	1881	47	18	65
	1882	40	12	52

CRAVEN MOOR, WEST Appletreewick SE092633

Production:	Lead	Ore(tons)	Lead(tons)	Silver(ozs)	Value(£)
	1855	67.10	39.00	273.00	
	1875	35.00	26.70	104.00	
	1876	30.00	22.50	100.00	
	1877	100.00	75.00	300.00	1250.00
	1878	136.00	95.20	380.00	1438.20
	1879	50.00	37.50	150.00	525.00
	1880	60.00	45.00	180.00	690.00
	1881	14.00	9.70	42.00	138.00
	1882	87.00	65.20		740.00
	1883	77.80	58.30		603.00

Comment: 1873-1884 See Blackhill
Mineral Lord: 1873-1884 See Appletreewick Liberty
Worked by: 1873-1884 West Craven Moor Lead Mining Co. Ltd
1873-1884 Granville Sharpe
1873-1883 David Williams

Employment:		Underground	Surface	Total
	1876			34
	1877	35	25	60
	1878	35	10	45
	1879	10	2	12
	1880	6	0	6
	1881	16	3	19
	1882	14	2	16

CRICKET Grassington SE014676

Production:	Lead	Ore(tons)	Lead (tons)	Value (£)
	1792		12.84	
	1793		15.70	
	1794		30.71	
	1795		5.65	
	1796		14.15	
	1797		11.75	
	1799		27.40	
	1800		0.30	
	1801		10.30	
	1802		0.80	
	1804		0.75	
	1805		0.25	
	1820	3.20	2.60	
	1821	7.85	6.20	
	1823	0.33	0.20	
	1824	8.85	4.50	
	1825	9.85	5.10	
	1826	4.82	2.55	

	1827	15.70	8.20	
	1828	102.55	71.65	
	1829	0.70	0.40	
	1830	4.58	2.15	
	1831	0.70	0.35	
	1832	78.93	45.60	
	1833	5.63	3.00	
	1834	10.00	3.95	
	1835	2.25	0.85	
	1836		27.00	
	1837	304.85	201.15	
	1838	215.38	153.60	
	1847	2.40	1.55	

Mineral Lord: 1792-1847 See under Grassington

CRONKLEY Lunedale NY838271

Production:	Lead	Ore(tons)	Lead (tons)	Value (£)
	1838	3.80		
	1839	0.24		
	1844	1.45		

Comment: 1838-1844 See Silverband
Employment: 1838-1844 See Lunehead

CROSS VEIN Grassington SE026672

Production:	Lead	Ore(tons)	Lead (tons)	Value (£)
	1736	27.84		
	1737	17.97		
	1738	16.82		
	1739	4.83		
	1742	1.00		
	1743	6.40		
	1744	7.23		
	1745	4.29		
	1747	2.90		
	1748	2.54		
	1757	0.33		
	1765	0.30		
	1810	1.50	0.95	
	1813	0.53	0.25	

Comment: 1758-1764 Data missing
Mineral Lord: 1736-1813 See under Grassington

CROWDER RAKE Grassington

Production:	Lead	Ore(tons)	Lead (tons)	Value (£)
	1812	0.85	0.50	
	1813	0.88	0.45	

Mineral Lord: 1812-1813 See under Grassington

DAMRIGG Arkengarthdale NY983034

Production:	Lead	Ore(tons)	Lead (tons)	Value (£)
	1782	53.30		
	1783	4.80		
	1784	4.70		
	1785	1.40		
	1786	36.80		
	1787	96.60		
	1788	144.60		
	1789	63.50		
	1790	321.00		
	1862	No detailed returns		

Comment:	1782-1783	November to November inclusive
	1783-1790	December to November inclusive
	1790-1791	December to May inclusive
Mineral Lord:	1782-1862	See Arkengarthdale
Worked by:	1782-1791	Charles Sleigh, William Hoar & Charles Foster
	1862	Arkendale Co.

Employment:		Underground	Surface	Total
	1782-1783	5		
	1783-1784	2		
	1784-1785	1		
	1785-1786	1		
	1786-1787	4		
	1787-1788	14		
	1788-1789	22		
	1789-1790	13		
	1790-1791	10		
	1862	7		

DANBY Arkengarthdale NY975035

Production:	Lead	Ore(tons)	Lead (tons)	Value (£)
	1782	53.30		
	1749	2.80		
	1750	3.50		
	1871	5.15		
	1872	2.05		
	1874	11.10		
	1875	5.15		
	1882	600.10		
	1883	442.50		
	1884	577.80		
	1885	97.25		
	1886	32.75		
	1887	26.90		

Comment:	1750	Year ending June

	1871	Year ending June		
	1873	Standing		
	1876-1881	Standing		
Mineral Lord:	1749-1891	See Arkengarthdale		
Worked by:	1749-1750	Charles Turner		
	1871-1891	Arkendale Mining Co.		

Employment:		Underground	Surface	Total
	1862	25		

DANBY HUSH		Arkengarthdale		NY075035
Production:	Lead	Ore(tons)	Lead (tons)	Value (£)
	1782	53.30		
	1749	2.80		
	1750	3.50		
Comment:	1750	January to June		
Mineral Lord:	1749-1750	See Arkengarthdale		

DARNBROOK		Malham Moor		SD917693
Production:	Lead	Ore(tons)	Lead (tons)	Value (£)
	1679-1804	No detailed returns		
Comment:	1659-1804	See Also Dew Bottom		
Mineral Lord:	1652-1804	Lord Lowther		
Worked by:	1697	John Lambert		
	1746-1747	Robert Pearson		

DARSEY RAKE		Arncliffe		SD936701
Production:	Lead	Ore(tons)	Lead (tons)	Value (£)
	1701		6.55	
	1773		1.60	
	1774		12.33	
	1775		5.27	
	1776		1.81	
	1777		0.69	
	1781		0.21	
	1813	16.80	10.30	
	1814	6.18	3.75	
	1815	1.50	0.55	
	1818	8.15	5.00	
	1819	0.65	0.40	
	1822	1.15	0.40	
	1846	2.40	0.80	
	1847	10.05	5.20	
Comment:	1701-1847	Smelted at Grassington		
	1779-1792	See Arncliffe Clowder		
	1822	From waste ore		
Mineral Lord:	1701-1847	See under Grassington		

Worked by:	1698-1701	John Blackburn & Co.		
	1748	James Simpson		
	1756	John Calvert		
	1757	John Stob & Mr Greenhow		
	1773-1781	Mr Holmes		
	1813-1819	Francis Ellerton		
	1822	Thomas Watson		
	1846-1847	William Jaques		

DEEP LEVEL		Grassington		SE027648
Production:	Lead	Ore(tons)	Lead (tons)	Value (£)
	1827	2.60	1.30	
	1796	Level begun		
Mineral Lord:	1796-1827	See under Grassington		

DERBYSHIRE FOUNDER			Grassington	SE028672
Production:	Lead	Ore(tons)	Lead (tons)	Value (£)
	1778		11.40	
	1780		48.00	
Mineral Lord:	1778-1788	See under Grassington		
Worked by:	1778-1782	Messrs Wilkinson		
	1782	Mr Bagshaw		
Agent:	1780-1783	George Hasleham		
	1782-1788	Jacob Bailey		

DEVIS HOLE		Grinton		SE053960
Production:	Lead	Ore(tons)	Lead (tons)	Value (£)
	1768	6.00	0.47	
	1848		34.65	
	1849		91.30	
	1850		47.79	
Comment:	1768	From 1762-1768		
	1848-1849	Data from DRO D/HH 6/4/30		
	1849-1850	Data from DRO D/HH 6/4/31		
	1851-1871	See under Grinton Liberty		
	1872	4.00	3.00	
	1873	1.20	0.80	
	1888-1889	No detailed returns		
	1890	37.00	25.00	330.00
	1891	40.00	23.00	450.00
	1892	73.00	51.00	529.00
	1893	43.00		290.00
Comment:	1872-1893	Data from Hunt's Statistics		
Mineral Lord:	1762-1897	See under Grinton		
Worked by:	1762-1768	James Raw & Co.		
	1848-1872	Grinton Moor Co.		
	1873	Grinton & Ellerton Mining Co.		

1874-1881 Ellerton Moor Mining Co.
1882-1886 J.C.D. Charlesworth
1887 Swaledale Mining Association Ltd
1888-1895 Grinton Mining & Smelting Co. Ltd

DEVONSHIRE Grassington SE012660

Production:	Lead	Ore(tons)	Lead (tons)	Value (£)
	1850	3.05	1.60	

Mineral Lord: 1850 See under Grassington

DEW BOTTOM Malham Moor SD917693

Production:	Lead	Ore(tons)	Lead (tons)	Value (£)

1679-1697 No detailed returns
1746-1747 No detailed returns
1802-1804 No detailed returns

Comment: 1679-1697 Smelted at Malham
1697-1747 See Darnbrook

Mineral Lord: 1652-1804 Lord Lowther

Worked by: 1683-1684 William Anderson & Co.
1746-1747 Thomas Marshall & Co.
1802-1804 George Gill

DIMMERDALE CROSS Kettlewell SD960715

Production:	Lead	Ore(tons)	Lead (tons)	Value (£)

1860 No detailed return

Mineral Lord: 1860 See Kettlewell

Worked by: 1860 George Wiseman & Jonathan Wiseman

DISPUTE Grassington SE022672

Production:	Lead	Ore(tons)	Lead (tons)	Value (£)
	1775		0.14	
	1777		0.25	
	1780		0.95	
	1781		0.10	
	1786		11.80	
	1787		5.25	
	1788		1.05	
	1789		5.63	
	1790		3.30	
	1791		2.01	
	1797		1.75	
	1801		0.10	
	1803		3.30	
	1804		8.55	
	1805		2.65	
	1806		1.65	
	1809	1.00	0.50	

	1811	2.00	1.05	
	1814	7.23	3.85	
	1818	5.00	3.00	
Mineral Lord:	1778-1788	See under Grassington		
Worked by:	1782	Mr Bagshaw		

DOD FELL		Buckden		SD843835
Production:	Lead	Ore(tons)	Lead (tons)	Value (£)
	1777		19.90	
	1851		0.50	
Comment:	1774	Also called Swarth Gill Head		
	1777	Smelted at Buckden		
	1784	Abandoned		
	1785	Looking for copper		
	1851	Smelted at Grassington		
Mineral Lord:	1774-1851	See under Grassington		
Worked by:	1774-1784	Thomas Kilby & Co.		
	1785	David Joy & Co.		
	1851	Edward Parker		

DOW COVE RAKE		Starbotton		SD962744
Production:	Lead	Ore(tons)	Lead (tons)	Value (£)
	1744		0.10	
	1827		6.25	
Comment:	1744	Smelted at Buckden		
	1827	Dove Cove Rake		
	1827	Smelted at Kettlewell		
Mineral Lord:	1744-1827	See under Grassington		
Worked by:	1744	James Simpson		
	1827	Joseph Wear		

DOWNHOLME		Downholme		SE115984
Production:	Lead	Ore(tons)	Lead (tons)	Value (£)
	1803-1805	No detailed returns		
	1856		3.50	
	1857		0.50	
	1864		5.80	
Comment:	1803-1805	See Also White Earth & High Rock		
	1856-1864	Data from Lord Bolton's Lead Book		
Mineral Lord:	1803-1927	See under Keld Heads		
	1927-2000	Ministry of Defence		
Worked by:	1866-1871	Dobson, Ray & Co.		

DREADNOUGHT		Conistone with Kilnsey		SE016702
Production:	Lead	Ore(tons)	Lead (tons)	Value (£)
	1768		0.27	
Comment:	1768	Smelted at Grassington		

Mineral Lord: 1768 See Conistone Liberty
Worked by: 1768 James Bell

DRY GILL No.1 Appletreewick SE081637

Production:	Lead	Ore(tons)	Lead (tons)	Value (£)
	1878	4.00	3.00	36.50

Comment: 1852-1882 See Nussey Knot & Yorkshire Mine
Mineral Lord: 1852-1882 See Appletreewick Liberty
Worked by: 1852-1856 Yorkshire Mining Co. (Cost Book)
1856-1882 Yorkshire Mining Co. Ltd

Employment:		Underground	Surface	Total
	1877-1880	4	-	4

DRY GILL No.2 Appletreewick SE080632

Production: Fluorspar Ore(tons) Value (£)
1949-1972 No detailed returns
Comment: 1963-1972 Including Blackhill, Burhill & Gill Heads
Mineral Lord: 1949-1972 See Applctrccwick Liberty
Worked by: 1949-1962 Fred. C. Walker
1963-1967 Clay Cross Company Ltd
1968-1972 Fred. C. Walker
Agent: 1963-1967 Fred. C. Walker

DUCK STREET Bewerley SE114638

Production: Fluorspar Ore(tons) Value (£)
1973-1975 No detailed returns
Worked by: 1973-1975 R.C. Conway Ltd

EAGLE Bewerley SE145653

Production:	Lead	Ore(tons)	Lead (tons)	Value (£)
	1840		6.88	
	1841		2.64	

Comment: 1840-1841 Smelted at Mr Yorke's (Heathfield) Mill
1825 Level begun 13th July
1844 Abandoned 12th March
Mineral Lord: 1825-1844 The White family
Worked by: 1825-1844 Eagle Mining Co.
1845-1866 H. & J. Hutchinson, John Barratt & Jos. Mason
1875-1879 Pateley Bridge Lead Mines & Smelting Co. Ltd

Employment:		Underground	Surface	Total
	1877-1880	4	-	4
	1839	6	-	6
	1844	8	-	8

EASINGTON Saltburn

Production:	Iron	Ore(tons)		Value (£)
	1877	90657.00		
Comment:	1877 See Port Mulgrave			

EAST & WEST 10 MEERS Thornthwaite with Padside SE109632

Production:	Lead	Ore(tons)	Lead (tons)	Value (£)
	1805		16.95	
	1806		20.20	
	1807		49.15	
	1808		24.30	
	1809	56.35	37.25	
	1810	48.65	31.40	
	1811	47.55	31.25	
	1812	25.10	16.15	
	1813	23.00	14.50	
	1814	12.15	8.00	
	1815	18.20	11.35	
	1816	1.35	0.80	
	1817	13.80	8.80	
	1818	5.58	3.30	
	1819	1.75	1.00	
	1820	21.35	13.70	
	1821	22.73	14.60	
	1822	8.70	5.30	
	1823	17.13	10.55	
	1824	11.20	6.25	
	1825	4.63	4.80	
Comment:	1805-1825 Smelted at Grassington			
	1825	13.48	9.62	
	1826		3.20	
	1827		3.56	
	1828		2.87	
	1829		5.67	
	1831		3.56	
	1832		4.54	
	1833		2.24	
	1835		10.04	
	1836		3.55	
	1837		0.51	
Comment:	1825-1837 Smelted at Greenhow			
Mineral Lord:	1805-1837 See under Grassington			
Worked by:	1805-1837 John Gill			

EAST 10 MEERS Thornthwaite with Padside SE111632

Production:	Lead	Ore(tons)	Lead (tons)	Value (£)
	1793		37.20	
	1794		8.05	
	1795		7.30	
	1796		20.60	
	1797		2.50	
	1798		24.70	
	1799		12.00	
	1800		11.75	
	1803		1.75	
	1804		10.25	
	1806		5.50	
	1807		4.05	
	1809	1.70	0.75	
	1810	9.90	6.65	
	1811	11.50	7.60	
	1812	0.70	0.45	
	1820	0.70	0.45	
	1822	3.55	2.30	
	1823	2.00	1.30	
	1824	2.40	1.45	
	1825	17.90	10.70	

Comment: 1793-1825 Smelted at Grassington
Mineral Lord: 1793-1825 See under Grassington
Worked by: 1793-1807 Isaac Wilkinson
1807 James Garth
1808-1825 Thomas Stoney

EAST WHIM SHAFT Arkengarthdale

Production:	Lead	Ore(tons)	Lead (tons)	Value (£)
	1782	31.70		
	1783	35.10		

Comment: 1782 November 1782 to November 1783 inclusive
1783 December 1783 to May 1784 inclusive
Mineral Lord: 1782-1784 See Arkengarthdale
Worked by: 1782-1784 Charles Sleigh, William Hoar & Charles Foster

Employment:	Underground	Surface	Total
1877-1880	4	-	4
1782-1783	8		
1783-1784	7		

EDGE SHAFT Arkengarthdale

Production:	Lead	Ore(tons)	Lead (tons)	Value (£)
	1784	1.50		
	1785	1.40		
	1786	1.00		

Comment:	1784 June to November inclusive			
	1785 June to November inclusive			
	1786 June to November inclusive			
Mineral Lord:	1784-1786 See Arkengarthdale			
Worked by:	1784-1786 Charles Sleigh, William Hoar & Charles Foster			
Employment:		Underground	Surface	Total
	1784	2		
	1785	1		
	1786	1		

ELBOLTON		Thorpe		SE006614
Production:	Lead	Ore(tons)	Lead (tons)	Value (£)
	1850	2.20	1.40	
	1858	1.80	1.25	
	1859	1.90	1.30	
	1862	1.05	0.65	
Worked by:	1850	Elbolton Co.		
	1858-1862	James Duckett & Co.		
	1859	4.90	3.45	
Worked by:	1859	Thomas Horner & J. Birch		
	1859	3.25	2.25	
Worked by:	1859	Christopher Duckett & Co.		
Comment:	1850-1862	Smelted at Starbotton Cupola		
	1853	2.25	1.55	
	1880		0.25	
Comment:	1853-1880	Smelted at Grassington		
Worked by:	1853	James Ibbotson		
	1860		2.50	
	1861		2.50	
	1862		1.35	
	1863		1.30	
	1865		2.65	
Worked by:	1860-1865	Christopher Duckett & Co.		
	1860		0.90	
	1861		0.50	
	1863		1.05	
	1865		2.25	
Worked by:	1860-1865	James Duckett & Co.		
	1862		0.70	
	1863		0.80	
	1864		2.10	
	1865		2.60	
Comment:	1860-1865	Smelted at Kettlewell		
Worked by:	1862	Robert Wilks & Co.		
	1863-1865	John Wilks & Co.		
Production:	Lead	Ore(tons)	Lead (tons)	Value (£)
	1862	1.10	0.70	

	1863-1871 No detailed returns			
	1872	9.50	7.10	
	1873	9.50	5.10	
	1876	2.20	1.50	29.20
	1878	4.00	3.00	40.00
	1879	2.00	1.50	20.60
	1880	5.00	3.70	47.50
	1881	6.00	4.20	60.00
	1882	15.00	11.20	128.00
	1883	26.00	19.50	200.00
	1884	26.00	18.00	150.00
	1885	26.00	17.00	169.00
	1886	30.00	20.00	195.00
	1890-1893 No detailed returns			
	1896	40.00	26.00	215.00
	1897	48.00	31.00	258.00
	1898	40.00	26.00	215.00
	1865-1871 See Cracoe			
Production:	Zinc	Ore(tons)	Lead (tons)	Value (£)
	1872	5.00		10.00
	1876	3.50		10.60

Comment: 1862-1898 Data from Hunt's Statistics
1850-1862 See Thorpe

Mineral Lord: 1860-1898 Mr Tempest

Worked by: 1865-1875 Wilks & Co.
1872-1900 Joseph Mason

Agent: 1865-1871 James Ray Eddy
1872-1875 Joseph Mason
1876-1881 George Farley

Employment:		Underground	Surface	Total
	1877-1879	2	-	2
	1881	3	-	3
	1882	2	-	2
	1898-1899		2	2

ELLERBECK Grassington SE022655

Production:	Lead	Ore(tons)	Lead (tons)	Value (£)
	1779		41.51	
	1781		1.08	
	1782		5.16	
	1791		0.93	
	1792		0.23	
	1793		0.55	
	1805		0.20	
	1807		1.00	
	1808		2.25	
	1809	4.80	1.60	

	1812	0.90	0.25
	1813	0.65	0.20
	1819	2.20	0.55
	1820	2.10	0.75
	1822	3.00	1.00
	1826	1.25	0.45
	1827	0.60	0.10
	1828	3.43	1.60
	1829	2.85	1.30
	1831	2.80	1.20
	1836	1.50	0.75
	1837	2.65	1.20
	1838	0.70	0.25
	1839	5.30	1.95
	1844	5.75	2.20
	1845	7.30	3.40
	1846	15.75	7.35
	1847	11.63	5.20
	1848	14.20	6.75
	1850	10.40	4.45
	1851	8.40	3.50
	1852	8.45	3.45
	1853	4.95	2.50
Mineral Lord:	1781-1853	See under Grassington	
Agent:	1781	Alexander Wearing	

ELLERTON MOOR Ellerton Abbey SE065958

Production:	Lead	Ore(tons)	Lead (tons)	Value (£)
	1754-1759	No detailed returns		
	1872	114.00	85.50	
	1873	84.30	63.00	
	1874	4.90	3.60	65.00
	1875	15.80	11.70	316.00
Comments:	1877-1883	Standing		
	1755	Henry Drax		
Mineral Lord:	1830-1837	Miss Drax		
	1860-1863	J.S.W.S.E. Drax		
Worked by:	1754-1759	William Sutton		
	1830-1837	Josias Morley & Co.		
	1854-1868	Marmaduke Wyvill		
	1869-1872	Grinton Moor Co.		
	1873	Grinton & Ellerton Mining Co.		
	1874-1881	Ellerton Moor Mining Co.		
	1882-1883	J.S.W.S.E. Drax		
Agent:	1871-1881	Emerson Alderson		
Secretary:	1877-1881	J.S.W.S.E. Drax		

Employment:		Underground	Surface	Total
	1862	18		

ELOQUENCE Thornthwaite with Padside SE108636

Production:	Lead	Ore(tons)	Lead (tons)	Value (£)
	1820	6.90	4.50	
	1822	1.20	0.70	
	1823	14.10	9.20	
	1824	6.45	3.90	

Comment: 1820-1824 Smelted at Grassington
Mineral Lord: 1820-1824 See under Grassington
Worked by: 1820-1824 Nathan Newbould

ENOCH'S WHIM Arkengarthdale NY990022

Production:	Lead	Ore(tons)	Lead (tons)	Value (£)
	1782	5.80		
	1783	53.50		
	1784	56.90		
	1785	43.40		
	1786	148.60		
	1787	87.60		
	1788	86.90		
	1789	53.30		
	1790	22.80		

Comments: 1782 November 1782 to November 1783 inclusive
1783-1790 December to November inclusive
1790 December 1790 to May 1791 inclusive
Mineral Lord: 1782-1791 See Arkengarthdale
1782-1791 Charles Sleigh, William Hoar & Charles Foster

Employment:		Underground	Surface	Total
	1782-1783	1		
	1783-1784	14		
	1784-1785	10		
	1785-1786	9		
	1786-1787	26		
	1787-1788	13		
	1788-1789	13		
	1789-1790	11		
	1790-1791	6		

ESK VALLEY Egton NZ822045

Production:	Iron	Ore(tons)	Value (£)
	1859-1861	No detailed return	
	1862	1000.00	150.00
	1863	3400.00	
	1872	No detailed return	
	1873	18847.00	5854.10
	1874	7500.00	2500.00
	1875	No detailed return	

Comments: 1859-1881 Avicula and Pecten Seams

	1875-1877	Including Glaisdale
	1875 & 1878-1883	Standing
Mineral Lord:	1862-1869	Trustees of Robert Cary Elwes
	1869-1883	Foster
Worked by:	1859-1869	Esk Valley Iron Co.
	1869-1877	South Cleveland Iron Co.
	1878-1883	John Foster & Son
Agent:	1863-1866	William Watkins
	1872-1883	Thomas Evans

ESKDALE Eskdaleside Cum Ugglesbarnby NZ838059

Production:	Iron	Ore(tons)	Value (£)
	1906-1915	No detailed returns	
Comments:	1906-1915	Avicular and Pecten Seams	
	1906	Opening	
	1908	Suspended May	
	1909-1915	Standing	
Mineral Lord:	1906-1915	Gladstone	
Worked by:	1906-1915	Grosmont Ironstone Co.	
	1907-1915	A. Gladstone & A. Dorman	
Agent:	1906-1919	J.F. Loyd	

Employment:		Underground	Surface	Total
	1906	14	24	38
	1907	73	8	81
	1908	125	9	134

ESKDALE Eskdaleside Cum Ugglesbarnby NZ861064

Production:	Iron	Ore(tons)	Value (£)
	1856	5438.00	
	1857-1866	No detailed returns	
	1867	23360.40	5840.10
	1868	2522.00	630.50
	1869	10957.00	2739.20
	1870	9956.00	1742.30
Comments:	1867-1870	Birds Birtley & California?	
Worked by:	1864-1868	Eskdale Iron Co.	
Agent:	1867-1868	M. Snowdon	

ESKDALESIDE Whitby NZ844061

Production:	Iron	Ore(tons)	Value (£)
	1871	29001.40	6750.10
	1872	30339.00	
	1873	19418.00	5825.00
	1874	20544.00	6163.10
	1875	8806.00	
Comments:	1876	No detailed return	
	1869-1883	Pecten Seam	

	1877-1883	Standing
Worked by:	1869-1883	Snowdon, Windle & Co.
Agent:	1869-1872	Joseph Robinson
	1873-1875	George Schofield
	1876	R. Robson
	1881-1883	T. Evans

ESTON Eston NZ563182

Production:	Iron	Ore(tons)	Value (£)
	1856	568156.00	
	1857	562473.00	
	1858	507265.00	76089.70
	1859	638620.00	95793.00
	1860	613391.00	92008.50
	1861	565285.00	84792.70
	1862	608420.00	91263.00
	1863	633206.00	
	1864	639404.00	
	1865	685980.00	171495.00
	1866	710156.00	177789.00
	1867	665975.00	166493.70
	1868	715248.00	178812.00
	1869	761594.00	190398.50
	1870	831787.50	207946.60
	1871	532821.50	133205.00
	1872	No detailed return	
	1873	705228.00	214568.40
	1874	569240.60	170772.00
	1875	571621.00	
	1876	581978.00	
	1877	592477.80	
	1878	557982.00	
	1879	540749.20	
	1880	1037654.00	
	1881	1094200.00	
	1882-1949	No detailed returns	

Comments:	1866-1869	Includes Upsal
	1880-1881	Including Chaloner
	1939	Abandoned
	1949	Abandoned September
Mineral Lord:	1850-1881	Sir Charles Lowther; Major Stapylton;
	1850-1881	Lady Hewley Trust; Greenwood
Worked by:	1850-1864	Bolckow & Vaughan
	1864-1929	Bolckow, Vaughan & Co. Ltd
	1929-1950	Dorman, Long & Co. Ltd
Agent:	1863-1865	William Spencer
	1866-1867	John Marley

	1868-1871	Thomas H. Richardson
	1872-1879	Thomas Lee
	1880-1910	John Thompson
	1911-1912	A.M. Hedley
	1913-1925	W.G. Grace
	1926-1932	T.E. Slater
	1933-1942	M. Hedley
	1943-1948	W.I.E. Hickman
	1950	W.J. Hickman

Employment:		Underground	Surface	Total
	1862	618		
	1883			1610
	1894	808	207	1015
	1900	868	219	1087
	1901	803	256	1059
	1902	808	207	1015
	1903	777	209	986
	1904	762	203	965
	1905	753	176	929
	1906	736	195	921
	1907	730	226	956
	1908	741	216	957
	1909	754	206	960
	1910	744	204	948
	1911	745	169	914
	1912	693	175	868
	1913	724	169	893
	1914	751	209	960
	1915	496	172	668
	1916	550	163	713
	1917	574	183	757
	1918	506	172	678
	1919	539	184	723
	1920	558	204	762
	1921	466	191	657
	1922	480	187	667
	1923	496	192	688
	1924	500	193	693
	1925	512	191	703
	1926	508	181	689
	1927	519	183	702
	1928	500	155	655
	1929	511	124	635
	1930	422	144	566
	1931	415	140	555
	1932	273	81	354
	1933	404	125	529

	1934	335	123	458
	1935	214	81	295
	1936	282	114	396
	1937	273	119	392
	1938	270	116	386
	1940	169	83	252
	1941	161	78	239
	1942	152	84	236
	1943	127	76	203
	1944	118	80	198
	1945	103	44	147
	1948	54	40	94
	1950	53	33	86
Comments:	1883	Includes Chaloner		
	1894-1927	Includes Upsal & Wilton		
	1894-1939	Includes Chaloner		

FAGGERGILL		Arkengarthdale		NY988069
Production:	Lead	Ore(tons)	Lead (tons)	Value (£)
	1782	2.30		
	1871	797.55		
	1872	516.65		
	1873	729.00		
	1874	994.10		
	1875	1262.10		
	1876	1196.65		
	1877	1239.15		
	1878	1427.25		
	1879	1297.85		
	1880	1121.30		
	1881	896.25		
	1882	932.10		
	1883	780.00		
	1884	369.70		
	1885	485.80		
	1886	569.15		
	1887	243.60		
	1888	322.45		
	1889	256.05		
	1890	166.25		
	1891	65.95		
	1907-1913	No detailed returns		
Comments:	1782	November 1782 to May 1783 inclusive		
	1891	To May 21st		
	1907-1913	See Nuthole & Stang		
	1910-1919	Standing		
Mineral Lord:	1782-1913	See Arkengarthdale		

Worked by:	1782-1783 Charles Sleigh, William Hoar & Charles Foster			
	1871-1891 Arkendale Mining Co.			
	1907-1913 Stang & Cleasby Lead Mines Ltd			
Agent:	1907-1913 Thomas Harker			
Employment:		Underground	Surface	Total
	1782-1873	1		
	1862	3		

FAGGERGILL & STANG Arkengarthdale NZ005068

Production:	Lead	Ore(tons)	Lead (tons)	Value (£)
	1880	101.30		
	1881	423.70		
	1882	413.00		
	1883	477.75		
	1884	621.20		
	1885	1185.50		
	1886	1575.10		
	1887	1436.45		
	1888	888.85		
	1889	492.20		
	1890	324.60		
	1891	369.95		
Comments:	1871-1916	See Stang		
	1891	To May 21st		
	1907-1913	See Nuthole		
Mineral Lord:	1871-1819	See Arkengarthdale		
Worked by:	1871-1891	Arkendale Mining Co.		

FANCARL END Appletreewick SE066630

Production:	Lead	Ore(tons)	Lead (tons)	Value (£)
	1782	No detailed return		
Comment:	1782	WYAS Yorke MSS DB151		
Worked by:	1782	James Coates (2 by 4 meers)		

FARNDALE Kirby Moorside SE680979

Production:	Iron	Ore(tons)	Value (£)
	1882	No detailed return	
Comments:	1872-1897	See Blakey	
	1880-1881	Standing	
	1883-1896	Standing	
Worked by:	1880-1896	Farndale Iron Co.	
Agent:	1880-1882	William Martin	

FEARNOUGHT Conistone with Kilnsey SE016703

Production:	Lead	Ore(tons)	Lead (tons)	Value (£)
	1831	2.50	1.98	
	1832	16.28	12.25	
	1833	21.40	16.31	
	1835	3.90	3.02	
	1836	32.60	25.92	
	1837	61.80	48.38	
	1838	20.30	15.54	
	1841	10.10	2.09	
Comments:	1831-1841	Smelted at Grassington		
	1859		1.45	
	1860		0.65	
	1861		2.70	
	1862		9.05	
	1863		0.58	
	1865		2.60	
	1866		2.25	
	1867	0.60	0.36	
	1870		3.25	
	1871		1.20	
Comment:	1859-1871	Smelted at Kettlewell		
Mineral Lord:	1831-1883	See Conistone Liberty		
Worked by:	1831-1838	Christopher Wiseman		
	1841	Francis Hammond		
	1861	John Hammond		
	1859-1871	Fearnought Mining Co.		
	1880-1883	E.P. Dawson		

FEARNOUGHT Grinton SD996955

Production:	Lead	Ore(tons)	Lead (tons)	Value (£)
	1767	2768.00	2174.70	
Comments:	1767	Includes production from 1761		
	1761-1767	Part of Whitaside		
Mineral Lord:	1761-1767	See under Grinton Liberty		
Worked by:	1761-1767	Richard Lonsdale & Co.		

FELDOM Marske NZ120040

Production:	Lead	Ore(tons)	Lead (tons)	Value (£)
	1675-1687	No detailed returns		
	1865	No detailed return		
Production:	Copper	Ore(tons)	Copper (tons)	Value (£)
	1710-1724	No detailed return		
Mineral Lord:	1675-1684	Thomas Wharton		
	1684-1685	Philip Wharton		
	1685-1687	Angelica (Pellisary) Wharton		
	1684	John Hutton (1)		

	1684-1731	John Hutton (2)
	1731-1768	John Hutton (3)
	1768-1782	John Hutton (4)
	1782-1841	John Hutton (5)
	1841-1865	John Timothy Darcy Hutton
Worked by:	1675-1681	Philip Swale & Robert Barker
	1681-1687	Philip Swale & Adam Barker
	1865	Thomas Smurthwaite & Company

FELL END Fremington NZ022032

Production:	Lead	Ore(tons)	Lead (tons)	Value (£)
	1869	0.35	0.30	
	1870	8.00	5.00	
	1871	9.10	6.70	
	1872	9.10	6.90	
	1873	2.10	1.50	
	1874	0.80	0.60	
	1876	1.10	0.80	
	1877	0.50	0.30	6.20
	1879	2.10	1.50	21.50
	1880	2.40	1.70	23.00
	1881	3.70	2.70	31.50
	1882	1.20	0.90	11.00
	1883	0.50	0.40	4.00

Comments:	1862	Fell End & Gutters
	1885	Standing
Worked by:	1862-1863	Owen Clough & Co.
	1866-1868	Arkendale Co.
	1869-1876	Fell End Co.
	1877-1881	Fell End Mining Co.
	1882-1885	James W. Close
Agent:	1861	Robert Daykin
	1866-1867	Thomas Raw
	1868-1870	Lancelot Wharton
	1868-1870	George Alderson
	1871-1881	Simon Cherry
	1871	Richard Peacock
	1872	James Alderson Clarkson
	1873-1881	Richard Peacock
	1882	James Alderson Clarkson
	1883-1884	James W. Close
Secretary:	1873-1881	James Alderson Clarkson

Employment:		Underground	Surface	Total
	1862	13		
	1877	8		8
	1878	7		7
	1879	10		10
	1880	6		6

FIDDLER PLET VEIN Grassington SE018676

Production:	Lead	Ore(tons)	Lead (tons)	Value (£)
	1736		0.82	
	1737		0.54	
	1738		5.30	
	1739		0.20	
	1771		0.06	
	1772		0.09	
	1782		0.16	
	1785		8.60	
	1786		3.84	
	1787		2.93	
	1788		11.50	
	1789		1.37	
	1790		29.90	
	1791		38.40	
	1792		53.40	
	1801		0.15	
	1827	11.86	7.60	
	1828	17.65	11.25	
	1829	23.08	15.00	
	1830	21.05	14.55	
	1831	6.45	4.50	
	1832	0.93	0.50	
	1836	0.80	0.30	
	1851	2.15	1.00	

Mineral Lord: 1736-1851 See under Grassington

FLATTING VEIN Grassington SE020674

Production:	Lead	Ore(tons)	Lead (tons)	Value (£)
	1829	3.48	1.50	
	1839	1.05	0.60	
	1849	2.00	0.90	

Mineral Lord: 1829-1849 See under Grassington

FOLEY GILL Pateley Bridge

Production:	Lead	Ore(tons)	Lead (tons)	Value (£)
	1877-1882 No detailed returns			

Worked by: 1877-1882 E. Newbould

FOLLY Arkengarthdale NY990028

Production:	Lead	Ore(tons)	Lead (tons)	Value (£)
	1749	2.80		
	1750	0.90		
	1782	14.60		
	1783	10.00		
	1784	9.40		

	1785	9.30		
	1786	6.20		
	1787	1.40		
	1789	0.30		

Comments:
1750 January to June
1782 November 1782 to November 1783 inclusive
1783-1788 December to November inclusive
1788-1789 Standing - December to May inclusive
1789 June to November inclusive

Mineral Lord: 1749-1789 See Arkengarthdale

Worked by: 1749-1750 Charles Turner
1782-1789 Charles Sleigh, William Hoar & Charles Foster

Employment:		Underground	Surface	Total
	1782-1783	8		
	1783-1784	3		
	1784-1785	2		
	1785-1786	5		
	1786-1787	2		
	1787-1788	2		
	1789	1		

FOLLY VEIN Grassington SE020676

Production:	Lead	Ore(tons)	Lead (tons)	Value (£)
	1758		3.97	
	1767		0.33	
	1768		0.15	
	1772		0.28	
	1773		0.10	
	1774		0.17	
	1799		0.20	
	1804		0.30	
	1805		0.30	
	1820	0.55	0.20	

Mineral Lord: 1767-1820 See under Grassington

FOREGILL Arkengarthdale NY997012

Production:	Lead	Ore(tons)	Lead (tons)	Value (£)

1862 No detailed return.

Mineral Lord: 1862 See Arkengarthdale

Worked by: 1862 Arkendale Co.

Employment:		Underground	Surface	Total
	1862	65		

FOREST MOOR Thornthwaite with Padside SE108632

Production:	Lead	Ore(tons	Lead (tons)	Value (£)
	1809	82.40	38.00	
	1810	58.55	38.05	
	1811	59.05	38.85	
	1812	25.80	16.60	
	1813	23.00	14.50	
	1814	12.15	8.00	
	1815	18.20	11.35	
	1816	1.35	0.80	
	1817	13.80	8.80	
	1818	5.58	3.30	
	1819	1.75	1.00	
	1820	28.95	18.65	
	1821	22.73	14.60	
	1822	12.25	7.60	
	1823	19.13	11.85	
	1824	13.60	7.70	
	1825	25.98	15.50	
	1826		15.25	
	1827		10.93	
	1828		11.88	
	1829		5.67	
	1830		35.13	
	1831		12.30	
	1832		11.63	
	1833		7.76	
	1834		5.26	
	1835		46.27	
	1836		12.90	
	1837		6.90	
	1838		3.08	
	1839		5.12	
	1840		0.80	
	1841		26.75	
	1842		15.45	
	1843		8.22	
	1844		4.28	
	1845		23.46	
	1846		4.31	
	1847		3.41	
	1848		0.56	
	1849		1.35	
	1850		0.47	
	1851		3.10	
	1852		0.99	

Comments: 1809-1825 Smelted at Grassington

1826-1852 Smelted at Greenhow
1809-1825 See East & West 10 Meers, East 10 Meers,
1809-1825 West 10 Meers and Eloquence
1826-1852 See East & West 10 Meers, West 10 Meers,
1826-1852 Pockstones and Galloway

Production:	Lead	Ore(tons	Lead (tons)	Value (£)
	1861	8.50	5.50	
	1862	44.60	28.40	
	1863	27.10	20.20	
	1864	19.20	12.80	
	1865	11.70	7.80	
	1866	6.40	4.10	

Comment: 1866 Data from Hunt's Statistics
Mineral Lord: 1809-1868 See under Grassington
Worked by: 1862-1866 Cockhill Mining Co.
Agent: 1862-1868 Matthew Newbould

Employment:	Underground	Surface	Total
1862	9		

FOUL HOLE Middlesmoor SE096767

Production:	Lead	Ore(tons)	Lead (tons)	Value (£)
	1914-1916 No detailed returns.			

Comment: 1916 Abandoned June
Worked by: 1914-1915 M. Nicholson & J. Nicholson
Agent: 1914-1915 J.T. Carling

Employment:	Underground	Surface	Total
1915	2		2

FOUNDER Grassington SE028672

Production:	Lead	Ore(tons)	Lead (tons)	Value (£)
	1805		0.15	
	1807		0.30	
	1809	1.25	0.65	

Mineral Lord: 1767-1820 See under Grassington
Agent: 1809 Henry Davis

FOURTEEN MEERS Grassington SE026672

Production:	Lead	Ore(tons)	Lead (tons)	Value (£)
	1737		32.50	
	1738		38.25	
	1739		10.50	
	1740		3.88	
	1766		138.95	
	1767		87.61	
	1768		6.10	
	1769		61.89	
	1770		12.84	

1771		35.44
1772		5.72
1773		5.71
1774		20.27
1775		9.42
1776		8.85
1777		6.99
1778		4.41
1779		7.50
1780		18.82
1781		11.51
1782		16.19
1783		0.20
1784		5.59
1785		7.16
1786		3.69
1787		0.80
1788		17.04
1789		63.32
1790		47.90
1791		96.94
1792		17.20
1793		39.15
1794		15.90
1795		17.85
1796		22.75
1797		10.95
1798		20.20
1799		3.15
1800		1.15
1801		1.85
1803		1.85
1804		0.85
1805		0.30
1806		0.40
1807		4.10
1808		7.65
1809	5.98	3.05
1810	3.10	1.90
1811	7.00	2.90
1812	15.95	9.20
1813	9.00	5.25
1814	9.78	5.80
1815	9.80	6.00
1816	1.88	0.95
1817	2.05	1.25
1818	1.60	0.90

	1819	4.73	1.75
	1820	3.75	1.35
	1821	6.20	2.40
	1823	1.70	0.80
	1824	1.55	0.70
	1825	4.95	1.65
	1826	50.25	31.10
	1827	16.56	11.30
	1828	7.93	4.10
	1829	7.60	3.35
	1830	0.60	0.25
	1832	1.85	0.80
	1836	0.80	0.50
	1838	0.60	0.30
	1840	1.40	0.65
	1841	0.80	0.50
	1847	3.15	1.40
	1848	8.05	3.50

Mineral Lord: 1737-1848 See under Grassington
Worked by: 1737-1754 William Kilvington & Co.
1755-1760 William Baynes & Co.
1823-1832 Duke of Devonshire
Agent: 1758-1764 William Airey (Steward)
1823-1832 John Barratt

FOXHOLES Appletreewick SE092633

Production: Lead Ore(tons) Lead (tons) Value (£)
1915-1920 No detailed returns.
Production: Barytes Ore(tons) Value (£)
1919-1920 No detailed returns.
Production: Fluorspar Ore(tons) Value (£)
1919-1920 No detailed returns.
Comment: 1915-1926 See Jamie
1921-1926 Standing
Mineral Lord: 1915-1928 See Appletreewick
Worked by: 1915-1928 Greenhaugh Mining Co. Ltd
Employment:

	Underground	Surface	Total
1915	2	2	4
1916	18	36	54
1917	14	10	24
1919	12	23	35
1920	11	8	19
1923	0	2	2
1924	0	2	2

FOXHOLES Grassington

Production:	Lead	Ore(tons)	Lead (tons)	Value (£)
	1735		4.28	
	1786		0.06	

Mineral Lord: 1786 See under Grassington

FRANKLAND FOULD Grassington SE018668

Production:	Lead	Ore(tons)	Lead (tons)	Value (£)
	1735		4.28	
	1736		7.10	
	1737		12.63	
	1738		0.57	
	1739		1.18	
	1740		0.42	
	1741		17.15	
	1742		9.75	
	1743		1.25	
	1744		4.96	
	1745		4.66	
	1746		12.44	
	1747		4.76	
	1748		4.55	
	1749		8.59	
	1750		2.44	
	1751		5.32	
	1753		1.53	
	1754		3.39	
	1765		1.70	
	1766		1.60	
	1767		8.69	
	1768		5.22	
	1769		11.73	
	1770		6.08	
	1771		5.22	
	1772		2.69	
	1773		3.18	
	1774		1.74	
	1775		0.46	
	1776		2.99	
	1777		1.04	
	1778		0.71	
	1782		6.89	
	1783		15.12	
	1784		11.29	
	1785		7.03	
	1787		1.34	
	1788		0.91	

1789		3.86
1790		3.99
1791		0.05
1792		3.41
1793		0.86
1794		1.95
1795		0.50
1796		0.60
1799		4.15
1800		3.10
1801		0.55
1802		1.70
1803		1.45
1804		1.10
1805		0.35
1806		5.00
1807		1.35
1808		2.95
1809	2.10	1.05
1810	2.30	1.00
1811	2.00	0.95
1812	4.00	1.70
1813	1.28	0.65
1814	1.25	0.45
1815	3.40	1.60
1817	0.93	0.45
1818	1.30	0.45
1820	1.80	0.60
1821	5.70	2.85
1822	2.95	1.50
1823	6.55	2.85
1825	19.45	7.95
1826	12.10	6.20
1827	23.30	13.65
1828	100.15	50.95
1829	46.45	22.40
1830	21.18	10.15
1831	19.05	9.75
1832	41.90	19.60
1833	8.88	3.45
1834	7.48	3.00
1835	13.43	6.05
1836	20.68	10.15
1837	22.35	8.90
1838	19.15	8.30
1839	24.65	12.05
1840	30.13	12.45

	1841	65.60	27.25
	1842	31.03	13.60
	1843	42.33	20.80
	1844	59.45	27.55
	1845	29.10	15.00
	1846	14.30	6.80
	1847	18.85	9.10
	1848	23.30	12.50
	1849	16.30	8.85
	1850	13.70	5.70
	1851	26.40	12.10
	1852	20.30	9.35
	1853	28.65	19.90

Comment: 1756-1764 Data missing
Mineral Lord: 1735-1853 See under Grassington

FREEDOM Grassington

Production:	Lead	Ore(tons)	Lead (tons)	Value (£)
	1806		11.55	
	1807		45.10	
	1808		22.25	
	1809	3.63	2.10	
	1810	12.70	7.50	
	1811	2.35	1.35	
	1812	17.30	9.80	
	1813	1.85	1.10	
	1814	5.90	3.70	
	1815	7.70	4.70	
	1816	11.50	7.15	
	1817	5.70	3.20	
	1818	6.30	3.90	
	1819	5.04	3.50	
	1820	3.10	1.55	
	1821	4.95	3.15	
	1842	2.85	1.15	
	1848	4.75	2.25	
	1849	3.25	1.40	

Mineral Lord: 1786 See under Grassington

FREEMAN BYCLIFFE Grassington SE023681

Production:	Lead	Ore(tons)	Lead (tons)	Value (£)
	1742		72.05	
	1743		67.40	
	1744		110.20	
	1745		24.50	
	1749		3.42	
	1750		1.72	

1751		1.04
1752		3.55
1754		19.47
1755		8.85
1764		19.47
1766		3.73
1767		0.95
1768		0.65
1769		0.81
1770		1.73
1771		1.32
1772		1.26
1773		2.76
1774		0.34
1776		1.45
1777		1.35
1778		5.70
1779		8.60
1780		7.18
1781		7.45
1782		9.78
1783		0.60
1784		1.65
1785		4.26
1787		6.17
1788		5.59
1789		4.58
1790		1.01
1791		2.76
1792		0.25
1794		0.25
1796		0.50
1800		0.80
1801		2.55
1802		3.00
1803		3.25
1804		3.85
1805		2.10
1806		2.25
1807		3.45
1810	4.05	1.90
1811	17.20	10.00
1812	33.08	17.30
1813	14.05	7.30
1814	19.73	10.85
1815	1.80	0.70
1817	15.73	9.15

Comments:	1742-1764	Also called Bycliffe West Ten Meers
	1756-1763	Data missing
Mineral Lord:	1742-1817	See under Grassington
Worked by:	1742-1745	Mr Freeman
	1749	John Birch & George Needham
	1750-1751	William Constantine
	1752	William Constantine & John Birch
	1753-1780	James Morley & John Summers & Co.
	1781-1790	John Summers
	1769	Widow Hudson
	1772-1774	John Hudson & James Hudson
	1791-1792	Ralph Summers
	1794	William Buck
	1796	John Hallam
	1800	Joseph Storey
	1801-1802	Anthony Storey & Joseph Storey
	1803-1806	Anthony Storey
	1807	Anthony & Joseph Storey
	1810	Anthony Storey
	1811-1813	John Shaw
	1814-1817	Various grantees

FREEMAN RAKE		Melbecks		NY953013
Production:	Lead	Ore(tons)	Lead (tons)	Value (£)
	1736	49.50		
	1750	7.90		
	1751	19.00		
	1752	12.10		
	1753	5.30		
Comments:	1736	December 1735 to May 1736		
	1750	June to December		
	1753	December 1752 to June 1753		
Mineral Lord:	1736-1753	See AD Mines		
Worked by:	1736-1753	Trustees of The Duke of Wharton		

FREMINGTON LIBERTY		Reeth		NZ022032
Production:	Lead	Ore(tons)	Lead (tons)	Value (£)
	1801-1804		253.98	
Comments:	1801-1804	Data from PRO LRRO 3/86		
	1801	February to 1804 July		
Mineral Lord:	1801-1804	The Crown		

FRIENDSHIP		Grassington		SE028670
Production:	Lead	Ore(tons)	Lead (tons)	Value (£)
	1821	6.95	3.20	
	1822	3.90	1.30	
	1823	35.68	21.20	

1824	112.08	66.30
1825	118.25	67.20
1826	111.35	68.45
1827	54.95	32.65
1828	9.48	4.55
1829	3.65	1.60
1830	1.73	0.85
1831	4.90	2.90
1832	4.80	2.30
1834	1.58	0.65
1835	1.00	0.55
1836	20.40	13.85
1837	92.63	58.15
1838	10.55	5.35
1839	31.15	13.05
1840	5.90	2.25
1841	19.10	7.30
1842	11.40	4.45
1843	13.00	5.40
1844	20.35	8.05
1845	9.05	4.05
1846	12.50	5.50
1847	15.10	6.65
1848	15.45	7.20
1849	17.50	6.95
1851	3.80	1.90
1852	4.10	1.95
1853	5.35	2.30

Comments: 1821-1853 Includes Six and Three Meers Grants
Mineral Lord: 1786 See under Grassington
Worked by: 1820-1841 Joseph Constantine

FRYERFOLD RAKE Melbecks NY942014

Production:	Lead	Ore(tons)	Lead (tons)	Value (£)
	1705	35.15		
	1736	39.50		
	1750	261.20		
	1751	569.40		
	1752	599.90		
	1753	271.60		
	1755	684.80		
	1756	686.70		

Comments: 1705 November to December
1736 December 1735 to May 1736
1750 June to December
1753 December 1752 to June 1753
1755 June to December

	1756	December 1755 to June 1756		
Mineral Lord:	1705-1756	See AD Mines		
Worked by:	1705	Thomas Wharton (5th Lord)		
	1736-1756	Trustees of The Duke of Wharton		

FRYER INTAKE		Melbecks		SD974976
Production:	Lead	Ore(tons)	Lead (tons)	Value (£)
	1738	32.00		
	1853	No detailed return.		
	1879-1879	No detailed returns.		
Mineral Lord:	1736-1742	See AD Mines		
	1742-1990	See Beldi Hill		
Worked by:	1736-1742	Abraham Fryer & Co.		
	1853	Ralph Milner & Co.		
	1875-1879	James Robinson Tomlin & Co.		

FRYUP		Danby		NZ746064
Production:	Iron	Ore(tons)		Value (£)
	1863-1874	No detailed returns.		
Mineral Lord:	1863-1874	H.K. Spark		
Worked by:	1874	Joseph Haswell		

GALLOWAY VEIN		Thornthwaite with Padside		SE108636
Production:	Lead	Ore(tons)	Lead (tons)	Value (£)
	1830		14.96	
	1831		1.73	
	1835		32.55	
	1836		1.82	
Comments:	1830-1836	Smelted at Greenhow		
Mineral Lord:	1830-1836	See under Grassington		
Agent:	1830-1836	Nathan Newbould		

GALLOWAY, WEST		Bewerley		SE109634
Production:	Lead	Ore(tons)	Lead (tons)	Value (£)
	1814	No detailed return.		
Mineral Lord:	1814	See under Bewerley		
Worked by:	1814	Anthony Hopper-Brown, Lease expired 1814		

GARR'S PASTURE		Grassington		
Production:	Lead	Ore(tons)	Lead (tons)	Value (£)
	1810	1.65	0.55	
	1811	1.80	0.55	
Comment:	1810-1811	See under Grassington		

GAYLE		Hawes		
Production:	Lead	Ore(tons)	Lead (tons)	Value (£)
	1872	12.10	9.50	

GENTLEWOMAN Kettlewell SD968735

Production:	Lead	Ore(tons)	Lead (tons)	Value (£)
	1859 No detailed return.			

Comment: 1859 See Stoney Rake
Mineral Lord: 1859 Trust Lords of Kettlewell
Worked by: 1859 John Tattersall & Co.

GIGGLESWICK LIBERTY Giggleswick SD800655

Production:	Lead	Ore(tons)	Lead (tons)	Value (£)
	1721		1.85	

Comment: 1721 Smelted at Grassington
Worked by: 1721 Mr Jackson & Ptrs

GILL BOTTOM VEIN Grassington

Production:	Lead	Ore(tons)	Lead (tons)	Value (£)
	1845	4.00	1.25	

Comment: 1845 See under Grassington

GILLFIELD Bewerley SE117648

Production:	Lead	Ore(tons)	Lead (tons)	Value (£)
	1782-1855 No detailed returns.			

Comment: 1782-1855 See Coldstones, North
Worked by: 1974-2000 University of Leeds - Training Mine

GILLFIELD & COCKHILL Bewerley SE114648

Production:	Fluorspar	Ore(tons)		Value (£)
	1933-1938 No detailed returns.			
Production:	Lead	Ore(tons)	Lead (tons)	Value (£)
	1935-1938 No detailed returns.			

Comment: 1933-1938 See Cockhill and Sunside-Cockhill
1944 Abandoned
Mineral Lord: 1933-1990 See Bewerley
Worked by: 1933-1938 Caldbeck Company
Agent: 1933-1938 Arthur Kingham

Employment:		Underground	Surface	Total
	1933	8	14	22
	1934	9	16	25

Comment: 1935-1944 Included with Craven Cross No.2

GILL HEAD Starbotton SD960770

Production:	Lead	Ore(tons)	Lead (tons)	Value (£)
	1816	24.55	15.65	
	1817	0.93	0.60	
	1820	9.48	5.65	
	1821	7.75	4.90	
	1823	1.20	0.70	
	1851	3.55	0.85	

	1852	4.40	2.15	
Comment:	1820-1823	Smelted at Grassington		
	1827		9.45	
	1828		8.50	
	1832		1.60	
Comment:	1827-1832	Smelted at Kettlewell		
Mineral Lord:	1820-1852	See under Grassington		
Worked by:	1816-1832	Bernard Lodge & Co.		
	1851-1852	Thomas Hudson		
Agent:	1816-1821	Thomas Wiseman		

GILL HEADS		Appletreewick		SE066621
Production:	Lead	Ore(tons)	Lead (tons)	Value (£)
	1782	No detailed return.		
	1838	No detailed return.		
	1878	0.50	0.30	100.00
	1880	7.30	4.60	70.50
	1882	7.00	5.20	59.00
	1883	1.70	1.20	14.00
	1886	15.00	12.00	112.00
	1887	10.00		
	1888	No detailed return.		
	1924	15.00		
Comments:	1782	WYAS Yorke MSS DB151		
	1877-1879	See Winns Level		
	1880-1881	Middlehill Level		
	1882-1888	Gill Head Level		
Production:	Fluorspar	Ore(tons)		Value (£)
	1921	459.86		521.43
	1922	4565.02		6420.89
	1966	No detailed return.		
	1973-1975	2135.00		
Comments:	1838	Fluorspar Producer		
	1921-1922	Includes Blackhill and Jamie hillocks		
	1926	Plus 200 tons of limestone		
	1928	Standing		
	1973-1975	Fluorspar production estimated		
Mineral Lord:	1782-1981	See Appletreewick Liberty		
Worked by:	1782	William Wood (30 meers)		
	1875-1876	Appletreewick Gill Mining Co.		
	1877-1881	Appletreewick Gill Heads Mining Co.		
	1882-1897	Appletreewick Mining Co.		
	1898-1900	Gill Heads Mining Co.		
	1917-1928	Greenhaugh Mining Co. Ltd		
	1930-1949	James Harold Clay		
	1945-1949	Fred C. Walker on Tribute to J.H. Clay		
	1966	Clay Cross Mining Co.		

	1973	Ian Gilmartin		
	1974-1975	J.T. Russum		
	1980-1985	Wharfedale Mining Co.		
Agent:	1875-1881	William Newbould		
	1898-1900	J.S. Winn		
	1917-1918	H.J.L. Bruff		
	1919-1925	W.W. Varvill		
Secretary:	1879-1881	Samuel Pullan		
Employment:		Underground	Surface	Total
	1882	6		6
	1920	5	17	22
	1921	6	9	15
	1922	13	20	33
	1923	17	25	42
	1924	10	23	33
	1925	13	26	39
Comments:	1924-1925	Includes Appletreewick		
	1926-1927	Included with Appletreewick		

GILL SHAFT Appletreewick SE091635

Production:	Lead	Ore(tons)	Lead (tons)	Value (£)
	1919	No detailed return.		
Comments:	1854-1865	Part of Craven Moor		
	1921-1928	Standing		
	1915-1928	See Jamie		
Mineral Lord:	1854-1928	See Appletreewick Liberty		
Worked by:	1915-1928	Greenhaugh Mining Co. Ltd		

GILL SHAFT Arkengarthdale

Production:	Lead	Ore(tons)	Lead (tons)	Value (£)
	1786	77.70		
	1787	24.60		
	1789	1.20		
Comments:	1786-1788	December to November inclusive		
	1788-1789	Standing: December to November inclusive		
	1790-1791	December to May inclusive		
Mineral Lord:	1786-1790	See Arkengarthdale		
Worked by:	1786-1790	Charles Sleigh, William Hoar & Charles Foster		
Employment:		Underground	Surface	Total
	1786-1787	2		
	1787-1788	7		
	1789-1790	1		

GILL'S PIPE Appletreewick SE090637

Production:	Lead	Ore(tons)	Lead (tons)	Value (£)
	1852	No detailed return.		
Mineral Lord:	1852	See Appletreewick Liberty		
Worked by:	1852	J. Gill & Sons		

GLAISDALE Glaisdale NZ779055

Production:	Iron	Ore(tons)	Value (£)
	1868	200.00	50.00
	1869	No detailed return.	
	1870	35926.00	8981.50
	1871	30000.00	7500.00
	1872	No detailed return.	
	1873	10920.00	3276.00
	1874	8000.00	2700.00
	1875	No detailed return.	

Comments: 1865-1875 Avicular and Pecten Seams
1875-1877 See Esk Valley
1877-1874 Standing
1875 Abandoned
1878-1883 Standing

Mineral Lord: 1868-1881 Newton

Worked by: 1865-1871 Firth & Hodgson & Co.
1871-1876 South Cleveland Iron Co.
1878-1883 South Cleveland Ironworks Co. Ltd

Agent: 1872 Herb. Crossley
1873-1874 Thomas Evans

GLEBE Middleton Tyas NZ232054

Production:	Copper	Ore(tons)	Copper (tons)	Value (£)
	1750-1780	No detailed returns.		

Mineral Lord: 1750-1763 John Mawer
1763-1780 D.W. Watson

Worked by: 1750-1770 George Tissington
1775-1780 Robert Shuttleworth & Ralph Lodge

Agent: 1775-1780 John Gordon

GLORY Grassington SE028672

Production:	Lead	Ore(tons)	Lead (tons)	Value (£)
	1791		0.61	
	1795		4.05	
	1796		13.50	
	1797		2.35	
	1800		0.30	
	1801		0.25	
	1802		3.05	
	1803		70.05	
	1804		96.30	
	1805		361.60	
	1806		303.15	
	1807		262.80	
	1808		174.55	
	1809	15.98	10.35	

1810	125.45	71.05
1811	81.68	48.10
1812	69.43	42.35
1813	29.93	17.95
1814	28.25	15.25
1815	34.00	20.80
1816	24.55	15.20
1817	61.90	39.05
1819	76.40	47.30
1820	10.45	6.00
1821	22.53	13.45
1822	13.56	5.65
1824	193.15	116.95
1825	127.33	73.45
1826	36.85	22.20
1827	99.25	60.90
1828	69.98	45.00
1829	71.08	44.05
1830	19.68	13.10
1831	40.65	26.20
1832	4.95	2.65
1833	3.75	1.60
1835	0.95	0.55
1837	15.50	8.35
1838	15.70	6.95
1839	2.20	0.95
1840	20.90	14.05
1841	68.80	44.35
1842	19.65	11.95
1843	3.93	2.05
1844	3.40	1.60
1845	5.18	2.80
1846	8.55	4.35
1847	11.20	6.20
1848	5.60	2.45
1849	7.50	3.30
1850	7.50	3.70
1851	4.45	2.35
1852	2.70	1.25
1853	2.85	1.45

Mineral Lord: 1791-1853 See under Grassington
Worked by: 1791-1844 William Bagshaw & Co.
Agent: 1788 Jacob Bailey
1804 Benjamin Wyatt
1804 Christopher Lawson
1835 Daniel Bowden

GLOVERGILL Muker SD879964

Production:	Lead	Ore(tons)	Lead (tons)	Value (£)
	1705-1750	No detailed returns.		
	1751	12.80	8.48	
	1752	9.60	7.20	
	1755	13.60	11.11	
	1816		2.69	
	1844		0.75	

Comments:	1735-1755	See AD Mines
	1751-1755	Lead estimated from AD returns
	1868-1871	See Lover Gill
Mineral Lord:	1705-1844	See AD Mines
Worked by:	1705	Thomas Wharton (5th Lord)
	1735-1755	The Mine Adventurers of England
Agent:	1731	William Smith
	1740	James Harries

GLUSBURN MOOR Glusburn SD984459

Production:	Lead	Ore(tons)	Lead (tons)	Value (£)
	1825	4.00	2.14	
	1827	4.25	2.97	
	1829	10.75	6.70	

Comments:	1739-1746	Working
	1739-1746	Smelted at Lumb Clough, Sutton?
	1825-1838	Smelted at Grassington
	1844-1882	Included with Cononley

Production:	Barytes	Ore(tons)	Value (£)
	1919-1920	No detailed returns.	
	1921	1537.00	
	1922	2034.00	
	1931	90.00	
	1932	1400.00	
	1933	234.00	

Comments:	1923-1925	Standing
	1933	Closed June
Mineral Lord:	1589-1600	Henry de Malham
	1666	William Garforth
	1820-1853	Thomas Garforth
	1854-1882	Exors of Thomas Garforth
	1927-1937	John Donald Horsfall
Worked by:	1589-1600	Lady Margaret Clifford
	1666	John Carre
	1825-1827	Walter Hall & Co.
	1829	Waters & Co.
	1844-1882	Duke of Devonshire
	1919-1925	Grassington Lead Mines Ltd
	1927-1930	British Barytes Ltd

	1930-1933	Industrial Minerals Corporation Ltd
	1934-1937	James Harold Clay
Agent:	1749	Richard Braithwaite (Steward)
	1919-1925	Edward Murgatroyd (Lessee)
	1927-1939	James Harold Clay (Lessee)
	1927-1933	Arthur Kingham

Employment:		Underground	Surface	Total
	1919		20	20
	1920		30	30
	1921	2	23	25
	1922	6	15	21
	1931	6	13	19
	1932	8	10	18
	1933	2	3	5

GOLDEN GROVES Redmire SE838945

Production:	Lead	Ore(tons)	Lead (tons)	Value (£)
	1851		21.65	
	1852		134.00	
	1853		19.60	
	1854		3.85	
	1856		17.05	
	1857		18.10	
	1858		4.50	
	1859		2.10	
	1860		5.15	
	1862		45.55	
	1863		82.80	
	1864		53.95	
	1866		7.75	

Comments:	1851-1866	Data from Lord Bolton's Lead Book
	1859	Includes Apedale Greets (Part)
Mineral Lord:	1849-1866	See under Keld Heads
Worked by:	1849-1866	George Harker

GOLDSBOROUGH Lythe NZ839142

Production:	Iron	Ore(tons)	Value (£)
	1912-1915	No detailed returns.	

Comments:	1912-1914	Sinking
	1915	Abandoned
Worked by:	1912-1915	Skinningrove Iron Co. Ltd
Agent:	1913-1915	A.H. Askew

Employment:		Underground	Surface	Total
	1913	4	5	9
	1914	6	4	10
	1915	3	4	7

GOOD HOPE Grassington SE009665

Production:	Lead	Ore(tons)	Lead (tons)	Value (£)
	1779		1.05	
	1782		0.74	
	1783		0.08	
	1784		0.26	
	1803		1.85	
	1804		2.50	
	1805		1.20	
	1807		1.85	
	1810	34.03	15.40	
	1812	12.60	5.55	
	1816	0.50	0.20	
	1818	4.80	2.60	
	1819	3.85	1.95	
	1820	11.40	4.85	
	1821	15.00	7.20	
	1822	29.45	11.70	
	1823	19.50	7.80	
	1824	17.18	7.65	
	1825	18.35	7.40	
	1826	5.43	2.40	
	1827	5.90	2.40	
	1828	2.78	1.30	
	1830	5.30	2.05	
	1831	0.55	0.30	
	1833	1.40	0.55	
	1834	11.15	5.05	
	1835	34.95	15.65	
	1836	21.90	10.50	
	1837	24.88	11.70	
	1838	25.80	12.25	
	1839	16.85	8.30	
	1840	18.95	8.90	
	1841	1.98	1.00	
	1842	2.50	1.20	
	1843	33.03	15.90	
	1844	17.60	7.90	
	1845	19.53	10.90	
	1846	7.98	4.15	
	1847	15.63	7.65	
	1848	11.90	5.45	
	1849	14.60	6.65	
	1850	2.55	1.30	
	1852	6.88	3.40	
	1853	5.10	2.45	

Mineral Lord: 1750-1756 See under Grassington

GORTON FIELD Melbecks NY950017

Production:	Lead	Ore(tons)	Lead (tons)	Value (£)
	1750	10.10		
	1751	5.60		
	1755	7.20		
	1756	6.70		

Comment: 1752-1753 No Production
Mineral Lord: 1750-1756 See AD Mines
Worked by: 1750-1756 Trustees of The Duke of Wharton

GOUTHWAITE Stonebeck Down SE132684

Production:	Lead	Ore(tons)	Lead (tons)	Value (£)
	1911	No detailed return.		

Comment: 1911 Prospecting
Mineral Lord: 1911 Thomas Edward Yorke

GRASSINGTON Grassington SE030667

Production:	Lead	Ore(tons)	Lead (tons)	Value (£)
	1658		37.33	
	1692		85.71	
	1693		77.60	
	1695		89.45	
	1696		42.64	
	1697		59.33	
	1698		238.28	
	1699		23.43	
	1701		56.65	
	1702		74.26	
	1703		78.08	
	1704		73.66	
	1705		114.77	
	1706		146.81	
	1707		153.29	
	1708		204.44	
	1709		105.50	
	1715		46.39	
	1716		72.87	
	1717		52.62	
	1718		23.44	
	1719		38.54	
	1720		24.27	
	1721		22.90	
	1722		1.39	
	1725		18.63	
	1726		28.29	
	1727		21.30	
	1728		48.71	
	1729		121.39	

1730	193.99
1731	223.95
1732	218.42
1733	156.09
1734	158.75
1735	206.24
1736	252.71
1737	201.18
1738	200.68
1739	119.81
1740	217.97
1741	399.47
1742	424.00
1743	405.71
1744	440.87
1745	273.73
1746	294.63
1747	191.66
1748	280.02
1749	309.26
1750	361.63
1751	459.36
1752	377.13
1753	318.96
1754	186.67
1755	556.28
1756	681.00
1757	56.00
1759	337.00
1760	371.00
1764	525.32
1765	734.52
1766	615.28
1767	535.79
1768	613.99
1769	687.87
1770	541.41
1771	562.92
1772	380.45
1773	447.83
1774	535.72
1775	648.41
1776	637.16
1777	445.79
1778	552.23
1779	582.86
1780	561.01
1781	407.86

1782		426.28
1783		399.63
1784		412.85
1785		451.29
1786		359.60
1787		386.55
1788		413.92
1789		351.25
1790		365.04
1791		317.59
1792		323.84
1793		336.50
1794		236.61
1795		386.55
1796		402.29
1797		180.46
1798		214.71
1799		161.24
1800		245.93
1801		188.35
1802		257.73
1803		295.10
1804		301.60
1805		563.45
1806		485.20
1807		458.75
1808		476.15
1809	572.13	305.65
1810	698.95	362.80
1811	668.30	366.05
1812	661.65	363.55
1813	535.60	297.15
1814	493.83	269.85
1815	359.80	202.60
1816	202.78	115.20
1817	383.85	218.65
1818	285.05	161.45
1819	500.56	298.45
1820	502.60	282.45
1821	517.80	280.25
1822	599.78	306.20
1823	493.33	285.50
1824	907.63	500.90
1825	1114.50	594.25
1826	1337.78	776.35
1827	1360.58	848.35
1828	1618.24	1004.15
1829	1228.20	718.50

1830	1016.68	575.75
1831	903.73	532.95
1832	1068.48	616.85
1833	942.83	532.55
1834	912.43	513.05
1835	954.55	574.20
1836	982.95	591.45
1837	1030.35	632.95
1838	1026.30	613.35
1839	1330.08	801.70
1840	1482.83	941.85
1841	1556.60	967.80
1842	1285.93	787.95
1843	1623.93	938.30
1844	1530.23	877.95
1845	1329.30	759.10
1846	1375.23	803.15
1847	1441.90	847.65
1848	1179.90	729.90
1849	1028.95	645.15
1850	1626.53	1042.75
1851	1834.98	1211.10
1852	1192.23	772.00
1853	1741.15	1163.00
1854	1895.95	1332.30
1855	1522.20	1085.75
1881		48.10
1882		60.05

Comments:

1658-1882 Data from smelting ledgers and accounts
1658-1849 Metal is smelt mill weight (i.e. = 2460 lbs/ton)
1658-1659 March 25th to March 25th
1756-1760 Estimated from duty returns
1756 July to December
1758 Data missing
1759 January to June
1760 April to October
1761-1763 Data missing
1860 611.5oz silver produced from 44.13 tons lead
1860 611.5oz silver sold for £168.16

Production:

Lead	Ore(tons)	Lead (tons)	Silver (ozs)	Value (£)
1845	1358.00	816.00		
1846	1313.00	788.00		
1847	1546.00	922.00		
1848	1159.00	707.00		
1849	1231.30	810.50		
1850	1766.80	1325.00		

1851	1489.90	997.40		
1852	1530.50	1036.00		
1853	2127.50	1494.00		
1854	1800.00	1270.00		
1855	1575.70	1121.30		
1856	2133.00	1538.90		
1857	1449.50	1049.20		
1858	1498.40	1134.90		
1859	1188.40	882.00		
1860	1216.70	931.70	385.00	
1861	886.10	772.30		
1862	1068.80	731.50	200.00	
1863	864.80	642.90		
1864	720.30	490.80		
1865	535.20	349.00		
1866	584.20	387.30		
1867	582.10	417.10		
1868	451.10	357.30		
1869	324.60	295.60		
1870	235.10	200.50		
1871	177.50	160.50		
1872	129.20	81.80		
1873	286.80	182.10		
1874	286.50	182.70		
1875	279.00	215.70	860.00	
1876	271.10	197.10	788.00	
1877	290.00	210.00	840.00	3625.00
1878	262.10	187.90	752.00	3144.00
1879	214.50	160.70	856.00	2304.00
1880	270.00	200.00	1080.00	3240.00
1881	20.00	13.00	80.00	195.00

Comments: 1845-1881 Data from Hunt's Statistics (all tons = 2240 lbs)
1848-1857 Including Yarnbury & Coalgrovebeck
1862 Ore = 944.8 in 1863 return
1875 Including Grassington royalties
1882 Not working

Production:

Lead	Ore(tons)	Lead (tons)	Value (£)
1916	7.07		
1917	9.81		
1918	4.40		

Production:

Barytes	Ore(tons)	Value (£)
1918	1406.23	
1919	466.86	
1920	71.95	

1921-1926 No detailed returns.

	1955-1964	No detailed returns.
Comment:	1921-1925	Standing
	1965	See Beevers

Production:	Fluorspar	Ore(tons)	Value (£)
	1946	No detailed return.	
	1954-1964	No detailed returns.	
Comment:	1964	Closed January	

Mineral Lord:	1605	George 3rd Earl of Cumberland
	1605-1640	Francis 4th Earl of Cumberland
	1640-1643	Henry 5th Earl of Cumberland
	1643-1675	Anne Baroness Clifford
	1675-1694	Charles Lord Clifford
	1695-1704	Charles 2nd Earl of Burlington
	1704-1716	Julianna, Countess of Burlington (Guardian)
	1716-1753	Richard 3rd Earl of Burlington
	1753-1758	Dorothy, Countess of Burlington (Guardian)
	1758-1769	Lord Mansfield (Guardian)
	1770-1811	William 5th Duke of Devonshire
	1811-1858	William Spencer 6th Duke of Devonshire
	1858-1891	William 7th Duke of Devonshire
	1891-1908	Spencer Compton 8th Duke of Devonshire
	1908-1938	Victor Christian William 9th Duke
	1938-1950	Edward William Spencer 10th Duke
	1950-2000	Andrew Robert Buxton 11th Duke
Worked by:	1605-1853	See individual mines
	1854-1982	Duke of Devonshire
	1916-1917	Edward Murgatroyd
	1918-1926	Grassington Lead Mines Ltd
	1946	Fred C. Walker
	1954	Grieve Brothers
	1955	Ernest Gregory
	1956-1964	Dales Chemicals Ltd
Barmaster:	1630	John Heles
	1642-1699	John Pulman
	1699-1705	William Stockdale
	1705-1708	Stephen Peart
	1708-1735	William Peart
	1735-1743	Solomon Bean
	1744-1754	Stephen Peart
	1744-1763	William Peart
	1763-1764	Richard Falshaw (at Buckden)
	1764-1743	George Bradley
	1799-1800	George Fletcher
	1800-1824	Joseph Mason Snr
Mineral Agent:	1801-1817	William Sheffield

	1818	John Taylor		
	1822-1834	John Barratt		
	1834-1861	Stephen Eddy		
	1861-1882	James Ray Eddy		
Agent:	1853-1868	Henry Daykin		
	1876-1881	Thomas Trevethan		
	1955-1964	F.A. Smith		
Secretary:	1825-1863	Joseph Mason Jnr		
	1918-1926	N. Broadbent		
Employment:		Underground	Surface	Total
	1862	73		
	1877	61	32	93
	1878	60	28	88
	1879	41	18	59
	1880	20	14	34
	1881	4	5	9
	1916		6	6
	1917		3	3
	1918		18	18
	1919		6	6
	1920		5	5

GRASSINGTON, EAST Appletreewick SE094640

Production:	Lead	Ore(tons)	Lead (tons)	Value (£)
	1886	88.00	63.00	616.00
	1887-1893	No detailed returns		
Comment:	1895-1896	In liquidation		
Mineral Lord:	1886-1895	See Appletreewick Liberty		
Worked by:	1887-1895	East Grassington Mines Ltd		
Agent:	1887-1893	David Williams		
Secretary:	1887-1895	Ernest Mansell		
Employment:		Underground	Surface	Total
	1889			54

GRASSINGTON, NEW Conistone with Kilnsey SE000703

Production:	Lead	Ore(tons)	Lead (tons)	Value (£)
	1870-1871	No detailed returns.		
Comments:	1870-1871	Not trading		
	1870-1871	See Conistone Moor Head		
Mineral Lord:	1870-1871	See under Conistone Liberty		
Worked by:	1870-1871	New Grassington Mining Co. Ltd		

GRASSINGTON ROYALTIES Grassington

Production:	Lead	Ore(tons)	Lead (tons)	Silver (ozs)	Value (£)
	1863	134.80	73.60	190.00	
	1864	104.50	61.40	120.00	
	1865	94.10	53.10		

	1866	59.60	33.50
	1867	55.50	28.40
	1868	39.90	19.10
	1869	34.60	19.30
	1870	55.80	30.10
	1871	32.20	18.60
	1872	34.30	18.80
	1873	29.90	21.10
	1874	9.80	5.70
	1875 No detailed return.		
Comment:	1875 See under Grassington		

GRASSINGTON SLAGS, FLUE DUST ETC SE030667

Production:	Lead	Ore(tons)	Lead (tons)	Value (£)
	1739		2.63	
	1741		2.25	
	1746		0.55	
	1747		0.44	
	1749		1.65	
	1750		0.08	
	1752		1.15	
	1753		1.41	
	1754		0.56	
	1755		0.68	
	1765		3.40	
	1766		1.93	
	1767		0.65	
	1768		3.02	
	1769		0.78	
	1770		4.00	
	1771		2.03	
	1773		1.31	
	1774		0.56	
	1775		2.00	
	1777		0.11	
	1778		0.78	
	1779		2.19	
	1780		40.18	
	1781		3.77	
	1782		1.38	
	1783		6.64	
	1784		0.69	
	1785		3.57	
	1786		1.96	
	1787		0.04	
	1788		0.30	
	1789		2.47	

1790	1.69
1791	1.66
1792	1.26
1794	1.00
1795	0.50
1796	1.80
1797	6.24
1798	8.75
1799	4.19
1800	1.05
1801	3.60
1802	8.65
1803	11.45
1804	5.95
1805	5.55
1806	2.95
1807	5.00
1809	1.90
1810	3.40
1811	1.55
1812	4.30
1813	6.90
1814	5.55
1815	13.10
1816	7.20
1817	3.50
1818	7.25
1819	11.25
1820	17.70
1821	25.15
1822	20.55
1823	28.70
1824	11.05
1825	8.22
1826	2.48
1827	8.00
1828	5.25
1829	1.50
1830	5.00
1831	3.63
1832	10.55
1833	10.20
1834	19.20
1835	26.30
1836	5.60
1837	16.15
1838	5.10

	1839	4.05
	1840	31.15
	1841	1.20
	1842	6.45
	1844	2.90
	1845	7.35
	1846	3.40
	1847	13.30
	1848	4.95
	1849	27.00
	1850	2.65
	1851	1.10
	1852	14.25
	1853	33.80

Comments: 1756-1764 Data missing
1605-1793 Low Mill (SE006633)
1756-1792 Moor Mill (SE025663)
1792-1882 Cupola Mill (SE025663)
Mineral Lord: 1605-1882 See under Grassington

GRASS WOOD Grassington SD991654

Production:	Lead	Ore(tons)	Lead (tons)	Value (£)
	1826	1.40	0.85	
	1846	0.43	0.25	

Comment: 1827-1845 No production
Mineral Lord: 1826-1846 See under Grassington

GREAT SLEDDALE Muker SD830991

Production:	Copper	Ore(tons)	Copper (tons)	Value (£)
	1907-1922	No detailed returns.		

Comments: 1801-1802 See Sleddale
1907-1911 Prospecting
Mineral Lord: 1907-1922 See AD Lessors
Worked by: 1907 Messrs Wagstaff, Taylor & Ward
1907-1908 Alfred Kempson (Tecolota Mining Syndicate)
1908-1911 Yorkshire & Westmorland Copper Co. Ltd
1922 John Thomas Ward
Secretary: 1908-1911 Harry Ernest Warner

GREEN Lunedale NY811265

Production:	Lead	Ore(tons)	Lead (tons)	Value (£)
	1679	No detailed return.		
	1757	1.20		
	1758	1.15		
	1789	13.30		
	1790	30.95		
	1796	0.40		

	1797	8.40		
Comment:	1835	See Birtle		
Mineral Lord:	1679-1848	See Lunehead		
Worked by:	1679	Christopher Wall & Ptrs		
	1800	Earl of Strathmore		

GREEN BYCLIFFE		Grassington		SE018683
Production:	Lead	Ore(tons)	Lead (tons)	Value (£)
	1747		8.75	
	1748		8.19	
	1750		0.68	
	1754		0.06	
	1781		0.60	
	1788		1.57	
	1790		0.25	
	1804		14.45	
	1805		22.10	
	1806		8.70	
	1807		12.15	
	1809	1.20	0.55	
	1810	11.53	6.10	
	1811	3.60	2.10	
	1812	5.10	2.85	
	1813	1.65	0.70	
	1814	4.60	2.40	
	1815	6.43	3.50	
	1816	2.25	1.25	
	1817	2.15	1.20	
	1835	2.65	1.40	
	1836	6.38	3.15	
	1837	8.60	4.35	
	1841	25.75	15.25	
	1842	5.15	2.85	
	1843	12.08	6.15	
	1845	11.10	6.55	
	1845	6.90	4.30	
	1846	1.28	0.60	
	1847	7.90	4.85	
	1848	8.85	5.40	
Comments:	1752-1800	See Whirler Rake		
	1756-1759	Data missing		
	1761-1764	Data missing		
Mineral Lord:	1747-1848	See under Grassington		
Worked by:	1747-1750	John Ripley Jnr & David Place		
	1754	William Waddelove		
	1781	George Gastill		
	1788	George Gastill & William Storey		

	1790	William Storey		
	1804-1805	Richard Waddelove		
	1806-1809	George Shaw		
	1810-1812	Various grantees		
	1813	John Rogers		
	1814-1815	George Shaw		
	1816-1817	Various grantees		

GREEN GARDEN		Grassington		SE015676
Production:	Lead	Ore(tons)	Lead (tons)	Value (£)
	1830	2.08	1.05	
Comment:	1830-1830	See Fiddler Plet		
Mineral Lord:	1830-1830	See under Grassington		

GREENGRAIN		Lunedale		NY882229
Production:	Lead	Ore(tons)	Lead (tons)	Value (£)
	1833	0.80		
	1837	0.74		
	1838	4.14		
	1843	0.58		
Mineral Lord:	1679-1843	See Lunehead		
Worked by:	1827-1831	John Barker & Co.		

GREEN GROOVES		Grassington		SE013676
Production:	Lead	Ore(tons)	Lead (tons)	Value (£)
	1772		0.44	
	1773		0.11	
	1835	1.00	0.55	
	1836	0.35	0.20	
Mineral Lord:	1772-1836	See under Grassington		

GREENHAW		Grassington		SE008659
Production:	Lead	Ore(tons)	Lead (tons)	Value (£)
	1739		2.95	
	1740		1.65	
	1773		2.95	
	1774		1.65	
	1782		0.47	
	1784		1.70	
	1785		0.10	
	1787		0.35	
	1788		0.42	
	1789		0.25	
	1792		0.23	
	1796		1.65	
	1797		2.15	
	1799		10.70	

	1800		0.65
	1811	6.90	3.60
	1812	16.00	7.90
	1813	13.20	7.15
	1814	19.33	9.60
	1815	8.58	4.35
	1819	0.35	0.15
	1822	2.45	1.25
	1824	1.85	0.90
	1825	2.20	0.80
	1826	4.20	1.85
	1827	2.45	1.40
	1828	2.40	1.05
	1829	1.60	1.05
	1831	3.80	2.00
	1832	7.00	2.75
	1833	7.38	3.10
	1834	4.15	2.15
	1835	9.80	3.80
	1836	8.90	3.90
	1837	18.63	9.20
	1838	10.83	5.00
	1839	6.40	3.30
	1840	5.04	2.20
	1841	5.75	2.60
	1842	4.23	2.15
	1843	15.15	7.95
	1844	8.30	4.25
	1845	10.80	5.70
	1846	5.08	2.30
	1847	9.75	4.45
	1848	5.40	2.85
	1849	5.55	3.10
	1850	5.15	2.55
	1852	7.60	3.35

Comment: 1739-1852 At the west end of New Rake
Mineral Lord: 1739-1852 See under Grassington

GREEN HILL Grinton SD990956

Production: Lead Ore(tons) Lead (tons) Value (£)
1761-1764 No detailed returns.
Comment: 1761-1764 See Whitaside

GREEN PLATT Grassington SE021676

Production: Lead	Ore(tons)	Lead (tons)	Value (£)
1798		2.35	
1800		29.85	
1801		20.50	
1802		67.25	
1803		41.35	
1804		8.45	
1805		5.50	
1806		1.90	
1807		2.80	
1808		2.70	
1810	1.05	0.60	
1811	6.10	3.75	
1812	7.20	4.25	
1813	0.35	0.20	
1816	1.05	0.65	
1822	0.50	0.25	

Mineral Lord: 1798-1822 See under Grassington

GREEN RIDGE Grassington SE008678

Production: Lead	Ore(tons)	Lead (tons)	Value (£)
1821	1.15	0.75	

Mineral Lord: 1798-1822 See under Grassington

GREENWICH Grassington SE018675

Production: Lead	Ore(tons)	Lead (tons)	Value (£)
1800		0.85	
1801		0.70	
1802		0.70	
1804		0.25	
1808		0.40	
1828	0.73	0.50	

Mineral Lord: 1798-1822 See under Grassington

GREGORY Grassington SE028671

Production: Lead	Ore(tons)	Lead (tons)	Value (£)
1785		32.63	
1786		17.71	
1788		117.75	
1789		14.40	
1790		47.45	
1793		5.25	
1794		59.40	
1796		132.00	
1797		1.50	
1798		1.10	

	1799		0.85	
	1800		8.65	
	1801		11.65	
	1802		3.90	
	1803		1.30	
	1804		0.50	
	1805		1.05	
	1806		1.55	
	1807		0.45	
	1809	6.50	2.70	
	1810	8.90	4.45	
	1812	4.00	2.20	
	1814	2.05	1.15	
	1820	1.10	0.55	
	1821	0.60	0.20	
	1833	1.40	0.55	
	1847	3.30	1.55	

Mineral Lord: 1785-1847 See under Grassington
Worked by: 1775-1793 Jacob Bailey
1794-1798 Exors of Jacob Bailey

GRIMEAR Grassington

Production:	Lead	Ore(tons)	Lead (tons)	Value (£)
	1848	5.68	3.15	
	1849	1.05	0.65	
	1850	1.80	0.95	

Mineral Lord: 1848-1850 See under Grassington

GRIMES GROVE Grassington SE014678

Production:	Lead	Ore(tons)	Lead (tons)	Value (£)
	1744		0.86	
	1746		2.92	
	1747		0.30	
	1749		0.13	
	1750		1.53	
	1753		1.20	
	1754		1.31	
	1759		0.39	
	1766		0.31	
	1775		0.13	
	1778		0.11	
	1781		1.45	
	1789		0.11	
	1801		0.40	
	1804		0.05	
	1806		0.45	
	1810	1.05	0.60	

	1813	3.90	2.00
	1824	1.60	0.90
	1826	0.65	0.45
	1833	2.80	1.50
	1835	1.00	0.55
	1837	1.25	0.60
	1843	10.13	6.30
	1844	9.40	5.30
	1845	5.65	3.50
	1846	7.70	4.60
	1847	2.40	1.45
	1850	0.53	0.15
	1851	0.95	0.55
	1852	2.50	1.10
	1853	3.40	1.25

Comments: 1756-1758 Data missing
1760-1764 Data missing
Mineral Lord: 1744-1853 See under Grassington

GRIMWITH Appletreewick SE056666

Production:	Lead	Ore(tons)	Lead (tons)	Value (£)
	1830-1840	No detailed returns.		
	1872		3.92	
	1873		1.88	
	1872-1873	Data from mine accounts		
	1872	3.10	1.90	

Comments: 1872 Data from Hunt's Statistics
1830-1840 Driving Speculation Level
1879-1881 Standing, in liquidation
Mineral Lord: 1863-1881 See Appletreewick Liberty
Worked by: 1863-1881 Grimwith Lead Mining Co. Ltd
Agent: 1830-1836 Nathan Newbould
1863-1868 John Jones
1868-1875 William Hawley
1876 W.A. Nowell
Secretary: 1863-1878 Thomas Sykes

Employment:		Underground	Surface	Total
	1862	4		
	1877	4	1	5
	1878		4	4
	1879	4		4

GRINKLE Hinderwell NZ760177

Production:	Iron	Ore(tons)	Value (£)
	1872	No detailed return	
	1873	87968.00	26390.40
	1875	10007.00	

	1876	No detailed return.
	1878	111699.00
	1879	128062.00
	1880	No detailed return.
	1881	168472.00
	1882-95	No detailed returns.
	1896-97	76615.00
	1897-98	119003.00
	1898-99	102785.00
	1899-00	No detailed return.
	1900-01	133814.00
	1901-02	123787.00
	1902-03	224743.00
	1903-04	245997.00
	1904-05	244714.00
	1905-05	265699.00
	1906-07	297079.00
	1907-08	241453.00
	1908-09	284073.00
	1909-10	No detailed return.
	1910-11	280766.00
	1911-12	238294.00
	1912-13	265607.00
	1913-14	253461.00
	1914-15	144631.00
	1915-16	117958.00
	1916-17	144461.00
	1917-17	74889.00
	1918	133745.00
	1919	110183.00
	1920	134891.00
	1921	17491.00
	1927	46224.00
	1929-30	150478.00
Comments:	1876	See Port Mulgrave
	1880	See Port Mulgrave
	1896-1930	Data from John Owen
	1896-1917	From July to following June
	1899-1914	Ironstone taken to Loftus for treatment
	1922-1926	Standing
	1928-1929	Standing (August to June)
	1930-1933	Standing (May onwards)
	1934	Abandoned June
Worked by:	1875-1899	Sir Charles M. Palmer
	1875-1899	Palmers Shipbuilding & Iron Co. Ltd
	1899-1934	Grinkle Park Mining Co. Ltd
Agent:	1878-1881	A. Palmer

1878-1885	John Hodgson
1886-1911	John Bruce
1912-1917	J.A. Lister
1919-1923	R.N. Hall
1924	John Hardy
1927-1934	T.F. Snow

Employment:

	Underground	Surface	Total
1883			309
1894	88	45	133
1895	70	39	109
1896	68	42	110
1897	84	44	128
1898	69	44	113
1899	89	47	136
1900	147	48	195
1901	122	45	167
1902	209	58	267
1903	252	68	320
1904	238	73	311
1905	258	77	335
1906	297	71	368
1907	314	79	393
1908	314	76	389
1909	375	92	467
1910	406	109	515
1911	419	119	538
1912	383	94	477
1913	386	100	486
1914	365	114	479
1915	184	109	293
1916	201	130	331
1917	213	112	325
1918	163	132	295
1919	220	130	350
1920	224	151	375
1921	216	161	367
1922	14	8	22
1923	9	14	23
1924	4	3	7
1926	45	21	66
1927	151	57	208
1928	16	10	26
1929	155	51	206
1930	143	48	191
1931	12	1	13
1932	6	1	7
1933	12	1	13
1934	6	1	7

GRINTON HOW Grinton SE018960

Production:	Lead	Ore(tons)	Lead (tons)	Value (£)
	1758-1767 No detailed returns			
	1768		7.90	
	1769-1774 No detailed returns			
	1775		2.53	
	1776		2.53	
	1780		1.06	
	1783		3.46	
	1786		3.39	
	1788		1.36	

Comments: 1758-1762 Data from NYCRO ZKU IX 1/43
1768 Output for 1763 to 1768 inclusive
1772-1774 Standing - September 72 to March 74

Mineral Lord: 1758-1788 See under Grinton Liberty

Worked by: 1758-1762 Thomas Dunn & Co. - 3.5 Meers Sun Rake
1758-1762 George Kendal & Co. - 4 Meers Sun Rake
1758-1762 John Harker & Co. - 3.5 Meers Sun Rake
1758-1762 James Simpson & Co. - 3.5 Meers Sun Rake
1758-1762 John Alderson & Co. - 4 Meers Sun Rake
1758-1762 A. Cradock Snr & Co. - 3 Meers Sun Rake
1758-1762 A. Cradock Jnr & Co. - 3 Meers Sun Rake
1758-1762 Tobias Cradock & Co. - ? Meers Sun Rake
1758-1762 John Emerson & Co. - 6 Meers North Rake
1762-1768 Harker & Kendal
1769-1897 See under Grinton Liberty

GRINTON LIBERTY Grinton SE049964

Production:	Lead	Ore(tons)	Lead (tons)	Value (£)
	1697		44.00	360.00
	1698		128.00	995.97
	1699		176.00	1399.22
	1700		91.00	722.49
	1701		34.00	253.98
	1702		217.00	1520.60
	1703		1158.00	7488.73
	1704		1003.00	6998.29
	1705		1347.00	9064.48
	1706			9018.21
	1707			9499.80
	1708			7580.06
	1709			2622.01
	1710			1213.07
	1711			885.54
	1712			1192.50
	1713			788.45
	1714			595.26

1715		401.42
1716		796.71
1717		399.30
1718		1054.90
1719		2639.60
1720		3642.41
1721		4301.56
1722		3199.68
1723		1885.69
1729-1730 No detailed returns		
1730	59.00	625.28
1731	88.00	931.51
1732	28.00	292.03
1733	32.00	301.90
1734	66.00	679.45
1735	53.00	946.91
1736	63.00	628.39
1737	8.00	97.78
1738	30.00	269.05
1739	25.00	237.70
1740	29.00	280.88
1741	20.00	181.52
1742	316.00	2896.02
1743	162.00	1615.08
1744	230.00	2370.89
1745	177.00	1819.64
1746	29.34	310.80
1747	14.53	152.78
1748	10.90	116.98
1749	14.89	157.87
1750	3.18	36.80
1751	1.57	18.00
1752	1.61	24.10
1753	1.56	25.35
1754	3.98	66.68
1755	22.76	312.38
1756	13.00	167.77
1757	1.00	16.96
1758	35.00	385.14
1759	29.00	295.19
1760	18.00	193.78
1761	21.00	268.59
1762	36.00	522.57
1763	57.00	738.98
1764	235.00	3156.63
1765	155.00	2242.28
1766	154.00	2300.08

1767	285.00	4134.88
1768	372.00	5063.52
1769	215.00	2895.91
1770	220.00	2979.21
1771	41.00	559.50
1772	190.00	2392.71
1773	79.00	971.05
1775	108.97	
1776	103.42	
1777	168.81	
1778	99.30	
1779	107.04	
1780	129.34	
1781	87.81	
1782	104.79	
1783	81.46	
1784	40.06	
1785	35.42	
1786	44.45	
1787	35.75	
1788	15.96	
1789	40.14	
1790	78.27	
1792	35.44	
1793	70.42	
1794	40.40	
1796	79.11	
1797	70.78	
1799	354.95	
1800	316.48	
1801	140.48	
1802	225.81	
1803	252.91	
1804	150.30	
1805	10.14	
1806	49.13	
1807	91.03	
1808 No detailed return		
1809	1.23	
1810	231.50	
1811	695.01	
1812	1311.83	
1813	1089.54	
1814	542.12	
1815	453.53	
1816	577.06	
1817	118.75	

1818-1819 No detailed returns			
1820		110.25	
1821		337.25	
1822		238.91	
1823-1834 No detailed returns			
1835			1672.04
1836			817.54
1838			1883.50
1839			7534.30
1840			3025.72
1841		58.29	990.38
1842		101.74	1600.75
1844		282.62	4171.59
1845		205.24	3268.74
1846			1727.72
1847		151.04	2225.04
1848		318.81	2937.73
1849		227.51	3154.11
1850		125.22	5040.99
1851		248.65	3481.07
1852		162.00	2872.48
1853			4983.71
1854		374.69	1723.23
1856			4215.20
1857			3602.58
1858			5799.85
1859			5401.38
1860			2239.18
1861 No detailed return			
1862			2650.10
1863			2060.55
1864			1708.68
1865			1417.20
1866			2800.44
1867			2868.72
1868			3258.84
1869			2160.48
1870			2849.40
1871			2339.52
1872	16.90	12.70	1342.56
1873	1.20	0.80	535.20
1874			497.76
1875			175.20
1876			196.68
1877-1887 No detailed returns			
1888	3.00		
1889	No detailed return		

	1890	37.00	25.00
	1891	40.00	23.00
	1892	73.00	51.00
	1893	43.00	

Comments:	1697-1876	Includes all mines in Grinton Liberty
	1697-1773	Data from PRO LRRO 3/85
	1697	June to November
	1698-1699	March to September
	1698-1746	Based on pieces weighing 165.28 Lbs
	1699-1774	Michaelmas to Michaelmas
	1729-1730	No lead sold
	1757-1774	Based on pieces weighing 145.14 Lbs
	1771	New lease began December 12th
	1771-1833	Duty at 1/5th
	1775-1801	Data from PRO CRES 2/1390
	1792	Including 1791
	1796	Including 1795
	1799	Including 1798
	1801	To February 23rd
	1801	New lease began February 23rd
	1801-1833	Duty 1/8th (reduced from February 23rd)
	1810-1817	From sundry wastes and mines in Grinton
	1820-1822	Data from PRO LR5/9. XC0629
	1833-1876	Data from PRO CRES 34/214
	1833	New lease began December 3rd
	1833-1861	Duty at 1/7th
	1833-1876	Value = based on Crown's duty revenue
	1835	To October 10th from December 3rd 1833
	1836	To October 10th from December 10th 1835
	1839	To January 5th from October 10th 1836
	1840	To January 5th from January 5th 1839
	1841	To January 5th from January 5th 1840
	1841	To October 10th from January 5th
	1841-1852	Data from PRO CRES 2/1391
	1841-1848	October 10th to October 10th
	1849	To December 26th from October 11th 1848
	1850	March 26th to June 30th
	1851	To October 10th from October 11th 1850
	1852-1853	October 11th to October 10th
	1854	January 10th to October 10th
	1854	Estimated weight of the 4900 pieces produced
	1855	New lease began January 5th
	1855-1860	January 5th to January 5th
	1861	August 26th to January 5th 1862
	1862-1875	January 5th to January 5th 1876
	1861-1875	Duty 1/12th (Reduced from August 26th)
	1875	Grinton Moor abandoned December 25th 1875

	1876-1887	Standing
	1888-1889	See Whitaside
	1894-1897	Standing
Mineral Lord:	1138-1876	The Crown
	1876-1880	J.C.D. Charlesworth
	1880-1888	A.H. Charlesworth
Worked by:	1504	Thomas Metcalfe (Farmer)
	1504	Christopher Conyers
	1531	James Metcalfe (Farmer)
	1531	William Conyers
	1561	John Mollineux (Farmer)
	1561	Leonard Close
	1582-1613	Lord Scroop
	1628-1649	Humphrey Wharton
	1696-1727	George Tushingham
	1727-1736	Reginald Marriott
	1736	Hugh Marriott
	1736-1752	Edmund Moore
	1752-1765	Frances Moore
	1765-1771	William Knighton
	1771-1801	Caleb Readshaw
	1802-1827	Josias Readshaw-Morley & Co.
	1828-1854	Francis Morley & Co.
	1854-1872	Grinton Moor Co.
	1873	Grinton & Ellerton Mining Co.
	1874-1881	Ellerton Moor Mining Co.
	1882-1886	J.C.D. Charlesworth
	1887	Swaledale Mining Association Ltd
	1888-1895	Grinton Mining & Smelting Co. Ltd
Barmaster:	1697	Mr Bayne
Agent:	1696-1698	John Ozell
	1698-1727	Reginald Marriott
	1742-1743	Thomas Rosewarne
	1743-1745	William Paul
	1754-1764	Thomas Rosewarne
	1764-1786	Leonard Hartley
	1790-1807	Sampson George
	1861-1863	Thomas Raw
	1862	George A. Robinson
	1864-1868	Robert Wharton
	1869-1881	Emerson Alderson
	1887-1893	John Ascough Rodwell
	1894	F. Rodwell
	1895-1897	J. Barker
Secretary:	1860-1863	Simpson & Co.
	1877-1881	J.C.D. Charlesworth
	1891	J.R. Lamb

Employment:

	Underground	Surface	Total
1697	68		
1861			26
1865			16
1868			6

GRIZEDALE HEAD Grassington SE022673

Production:	Lead	Ore(tons)	Lead (tons)	Value (£)
	1751		0.43	

Mineral Lord: 1751 See under Grassington

GROSMONT Eskdaleside Cum Ugglebarnby NZ829056

Production:	Iron	Ore(tons)	Value (£)
	1858	79155.00	12700.00
	1859	19000.00	2700.00
	1860	20000.00	2666.00
	1861	14988.00	2248.20
	1862	8500.00	1275.00
	1865	68091.00	20427.30
	1866	73551.90	22065.00
	1867	70981.00	19519.70
	1868	67443.00	16860.70
	1869	85355.70	21338.70
	1870	88952.00	22138.10
	1871	99509.40	24877.30
	1872	No detailed return	
	1873	101815.00	30544.50
	1874	105723.60	31716.90
	1875	108369.00	
	1876	86224.20	
	1878	120463.00	
	1879	86100.50	
	1880	134671.00	
	1881	133112.60	
	1882-1890	No detailed returns	

Comments:	1863-1890	Avicular and Pecten Seams
	1858	Ore including other mines
	1859	Including sundries
	1861	Including sundries
	1862-1864	See Bagnall & Co. Mines
	1865-1867	Grosmont Ironworks
	1866	Including Hays
	1874-1878	Including Birtley
	1878-1879	Including Hollins
	1890-1891	Standing
	1892	Abandoned
Mineral Lord:	1863-1890	Mrs Clark & others

Worked by:	1863-1880 Charles Bagnall & Thomas Bagnall			
	1881-1889 Bagnall & Co.			
Agent:	1863-1871 Josh. Greenhough			
	1872-1876 William Armstrong			
	1877 H. Talbot			
	1878-1883 William Armstrong			
	1884 H.B. Dunn			
	1885-1891 J.F. Lloyd			
Employment:		Underground	Surface	Total
	1883			263

GROSMONT, EAST North Riding

Production:	Iron	Ore(tons)	Value (£)
	1863	11554.00	
	1864	11540.00	

Comment: 1863-1864 Probably Grosmont

GROOVE GILL Grassington/Hebden SE040678

Production:	Lead	Ore(tons)	Lead (tons)	Value (£)
	1736		1.38	
	1739		2.13	
	1740		0.64	
	1741		0.55	
	1745		0.23	
	1819	33.55	20.35	
	1820	12.15	7.55	
	1821	3.40	1.80	
	1822	1.13	0.60	
	1827	5.78	3.25	
	1829	0.55	0.35	
	1830	2.40	1.50	
	1831	2.60	1.75	
	1835	1.30	0.70	

Mineral Lord: 1736-1835 See under Grassington

GROOVE GILL Hebden SE051673

Production:	Lead	Ore(tons)	Lead (tons)	Value (£)
	1750		0.35	
	1798		0.40	
	1849	0.25	0.15	
Comment:	1750-1849 Smelted at Grassington			
	1795		0.65	
	1802		0.29	
	1809		0.50	
	1814		0.35	
	1816		0.65	
	1836		4.11	

		Ore(tons)	Lead (tons)	Value (£)
	1839		0.40	
	1853	0.55	0.35	
Comment:	1795-1853	Barmasters' Book		
Mineral Lord:	1795-1853	See under Hebden		
Worked by:	1750	Joseph Birch		
	1795-1798	James Coates		
	1802-1809	James Lelland		
	1814-1816	Thomas Dickinson		
	1836	Thomas Chester		
	1839	Anthony Thompson		
	1849	John Hawley		
	1853	Thomas Clarke		

GROVEBECK Grinton SE025965

Production:	Lead	Ore(tons)	Lead (tons)	Value (£)
	1767	1422.40	1303.83	27667.50
	1768-1772	No detailed returns		
	1774	271.58	146.84	
	1788		2.22	
Comments:	1767	To November 1767 from 1761		
	1774	From 1772		
Mineral Lord:	1761-1774	See under Grinton		
Worked by:	1761-1774	Thomas Dunn & Co.		
	1774-1775	Fowler Hickes & Co.		

Employment:		Underground	Surface	Total
	1768			100
	1775			30
	1861			7
	1865			4
	1868			2

GROVEBECK, HIGH Grinton SE030964

Production:	Lead	Ore(tons)	Lead (tons)	Value (£)
	1763-1768	No detailed returns		
	1775		14.40	
	1776		11.28	
	1777		11.70	
	1779		3.23	
	1780		10.24	
	1781		8.22	
	1782		10.84	
	1783		10.85	
	1785		1.42	
	1786		2.79	
	1787		1.87	
	1788		2.22	

Worked by:	1775-1788 New partnership			
	1777		33.67	
	1778		3.97	
	1779		2.68	
	1780		1.13	
	1781		1.60	
	1782		1.16	
	1783		71.56	
	1785		0.68	
	1786		4.21	
	1795		35.35	
Comments:	1763	From 21st October		
	1768	Standing		
Mineral Lord:	1763-1788	See under Grinton Liberty		
Worked by:	1763-1768	James Simpson & Co.		
	1777-1782	Old partnership		

GROVEBECK, LOW		Grinton		SE030964
Production:	Lead	Ore(tons)	Lead (tons)	Value (£)
	1767		20.90	
	1779		2.81	
	1780		0.60	
	1782		3.78	
	1783		0.02	
	1785		0.66	
	1786		0.67	
	1787		0.60	
Comment:	1767	From 1762		
Mineral Lord:	1762-1787	See under Grinton Liberty		
Worked by:	1762-1767	James Simpson & Co.		

GROVE BOTTOM		Starbotton		SD961744
Production:	Lead	Ore(tons)	Lead (tons)	Value (£)
	1744		0.25	
Comment:	1744 Smelted at Buckden			
Mineral Lord:	1744 See under Grassington			
Worked by:	1744 James Nelson			

GROVE BROWS		Starbotton		SD961744
Production:	Lead	Ore(tons)	Lead (tons)	Value (£)
	1782 No detailed returns			
Mineral Lord:	1782 See under Grassington			
Worked by:	1782 Jno Parsable			

GROVE STY Grassington SE015667

Production:	Lead	Ore(tons)	Lead (tons)	Value (£)
	1806		0.50	
	1828	1.03	0.40	
Mineral Lord:	1806-1835 See under Grassington			

HAG Kettlewell SD953727

Production:	Lead	Ore(tons)	Lead (tons)	Value (£)
	1863		1.55	
	1864		1.00	
Comments:	1863-1864 Smelted at Kettlewell			
	1860-1862 See Middlesmoor			
	1871-1872 See Wharfedale			
	1874-1879 See Moor End			
Mineral Lord:	1863-1864 See under Kettlewell Liberty			
Worked by:	1863-1864 Thomas Weatherald			
	1864 George Wiseman & Jonathan Wiseman			

HAG END Starbotton SD951727

Production:	Lead	Ore(tons)	Lead (tons)	Value (£)
	1739		0.55	
Comments:	1739 Smelted at Buckden			
	1823	7.35	3.35	
	1824	3.55	2.00	
	1825	7.30	3.85	
Comments:	1823-1825 Smelted at Grassington			
	1826		7.05	
	1827		9.50	
	1828		1.50	
	1829		0.30	
	1838		0.60	
	1840		0.35	
	1841		1.25	
	1842		1.90	
	1843		1.75	
Mineral Lord:	1739 Mr Lister & John Wallas			
Worked by:	1823 William Holmes			
	1824 Henry Wiseman			
	1825-1826 John Wiseman & Co.			
	1827-1838 Henry Wiseman			
	1840 Joseph Wiseman			
	1841-1842 James Wiseman			
	1843 John Wiseman			
	1837		0.60	
	1838		1.15	
Worked by:	1837-1838 Christopher Wiseman			
	1828		0.80	

	1829		1.35	
	1838		0.75	
	1845		0.80	
	1851		4.70	
Comment:	1826-1851	Smelted at Kettlewell		
	1739-1741	See Middlemeer		
	1821-1828	See Moor End		
	1856-1857	See Providence, New		
	1857-1880	See Wharfedale		
Mineral Lord:	1739-1851	See under Grassington		
Worked by:	1828	Christopher Harrison		
	1829	William Brown & Matthew Bennett		
	1838-1845	Joseph Harrison		
	1851	William Craig		

HALLGATE PASTURE New Forest NZ078046

Production:	Lead	Ore(tons)	Lead (tons)	Value (£)
	1788	6.40		
	1789	27.80		
	1790	16.20		

Comment:	1788-1790	December to November inclusive
	1790-1791	December to May inclusive
Mineral Lord:	1788-1791	See Arkengarthdale
Worked by:	1788-1791	Charles Sleigh, William Hoar & Charles Foster

Employment:		Underground	Surface	Total
	1788-1789	1		
	1789-1790	3		
	1790-1791	3		

HARDCASTLE Bewerley SE122656

Production:	Lead	Ore(tons)	Lead (tons)	Value (£)
	1867-1892	No detailed return		
Comment:	1867	See Holebottom		
	1867-1884	See Prosperous & Providence		
Worked by:	1872-1876	Sunside & Merryfield Lead Mining Co. Ltd		

HARD LEVEL Reeth NY971007

Production:	Barytes	Ore(tons)	Value (£)
	1944-1948	No detailed return	
Comment:	1948	Abandoned March	
Mineral Lord:	1944-1948	See AD Mines	
Worked by:	1944-1948	Sunter Brothers	

HARD SHAFT Arkengarthdale NZ011034

Production:	Lead	Ore(tons)	Lead (tons)	Value (£)
	1787	2.30		
Comment:	1787	June to November inclusive		

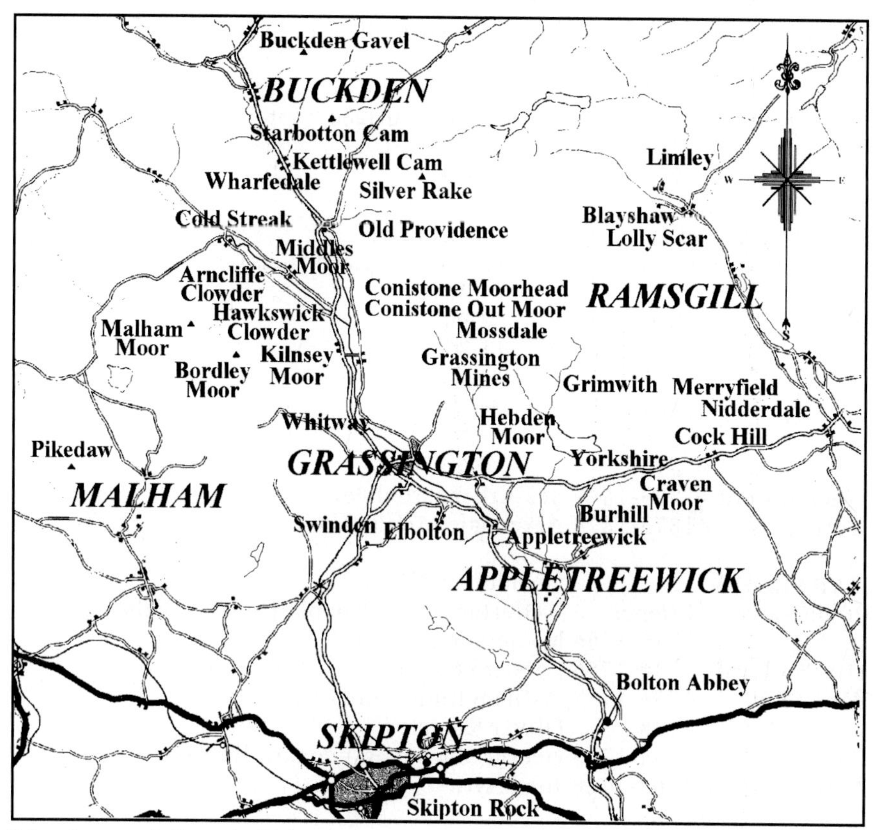

Map 2. Mines in Wharfedale and Nidderdale.

Mineral Lord:	1787	See Arkengarthdale		
Worked by:	1787	Charles Sleigh, William Hoar & Charles Foster		
Employment:		Underground	Surface	Total
	1787	1		

HARKER Grinton SE017973

Production:	Lead	Ore(tons)	Lead (tons)	Value (£)
	1768		3.45	
	1769-1774 No detailed return			
	1775		5.70	
	1776		1.65	
	1782		0.14	
	1783		7.50	
	1790		8.99	
	1792		0.14	
	1794		3.80	

Mineral Lord:	1766-1794 See under Grinton			
Worked by:	1766-1774 John Lee			
	1774-1775 James Stodart & Co.			
Employment:		Underground	Surface	Total
	1768			10
	1775			20

HARKER LEVEL		Arkengarthdale		NZ022037
Production:	Lead	Ore(tons)	Lead (tons)	Value (£)
	1873	34.45		
	1874	62.90		
	1875	11.75		
	1876	6.00		
	1877	4.35		
	1878	4.40		
	1879	0.50		
Mineral Lord:	1873-1879 See Arkengarthdale			
Worked by:	1873-1879 Arkendale Mining Co.			

HARTLEY'S		Middleton Tyas		NZ234056
Production:	Copper	Ore(tons)	Copper (tons)	Value (£)
	1736-1766	No detailed return		
Mineral Lord:	1736-1766	Leonard Hartley		
Worked by:	1736-1737	William Rutherford		
	1738	Oliver Kearsley		
	1754-1766	George Hartley & Leonard Hartley		
Agent:	1762-1766	John Ayre		

HARTOFT		Rosedale	
Production:	Iron	Ore(tons)	Value (£)
	1890-1891	No detailed return	
Worked by:	1890-1891	Hartoft Mining Syndicate	
Agent:	1890-1891	C.E. Parkin	

HARTOFT END		Pickering			
Production:	Iron	Ore(tons)			Value (£)
Comment:	1900	Prospecting			
	1901	Abandoned - drifts backfilled			
Worked by:	1900-1901	J. Cook			
Employment:		Underground	Surface	Total	
	1900	2		2	

HARWOOD WELL		Grassington		SD998657
Production:	Lead	Ore(tons)	Lead (tons)	Value (£)
	1745		0.05	
Comment:	1745	At Lea Green		
Mineral Lord:	1745	See under Grassington		

HAWKSWICK CLOWDER Hawkswick SD934684

Production:	Lead	Ore(tons)	Lead (tons)	Value (£)
	1765		1.42	
Worked by:	1765 John Calvert			
	1766		1.11	
Worked by:	1766 William Rodgers			
	1765		0.31	
	1775		1.27	
	1797		0.19	

Comment: 1797 See Merrybotton
1765-1797 Smelted at Grassington
Mineral Lord: 1765-1797 See Hawkswick Liberty
Worked by: 1765 John Calvert
1765-1775 Mr Holmes
1797 Marmaduke Proctor

HAWKSWICK LIBERTY Hawkswick SD955706

Production:	Lead	Ore(tons)	Lead (tons)	Value (£)
	1692		10.80	
	1693		18.05	
	1694		1.55	
	1696		4.40	
	1715		0.41	
	1716		1.41	
	1717		6.44	
	1718		2.64	
	1719		1.13	
	1720		1.78	
	1721		1.28	
	1725		8.27	
	1726		6.64	
	1727		5.08	
	1728		8.60	
	1729		0.09	
Comment:	1692-1729 Smelted at Grassington			
	1733		0.83	
	1768		23.60	
	1770		8.00	
	1772		11.65	
	1773		11.16	
	1774		6.65	
	1776		7.65	
	1777		13.13	

Comment: 1733-1777 Smelted at Kilnsey
1768-1769 May to October
1773-1774 January to August
1774-1776 August to March

	1776-1777 March to November			
	1777-1779 November to May			
	1860	2.40	1.20	
Comment:	1860 Data from Hunt's Statistics			
Mineral Lord:	1692-1753 Mr Tennant and the Earl of Burlington			
	1764-1863 Mr Tennant and the Duke of Devonshire			

HAWKSWICK MOOR Hawkswick SD954713

Production:	Lead	Ore(tons)	Lead (tons)	Value (£)
	1766		0.43	
Worked by:	1766 Christopher Paley			
	1833	8.15	5.30	
	1836	4.05	1.65	
	1837	1.58	0.90	
	1838	2.10	1.10	
	1841	1.55	0.80	
	1844	1.35	0.85	
	1845	2.70	1.70	
Worked by:	1833-1845 Richard Hancock			
	1839	2.60	1.15	
	1847	3.20	2.05	
	1848	3.75	1.80	
Worked by:	1839-1848 James Aldersley			
	1842	5.35	2.50	
Worked by:	1842 James Brown & John Brown			
	1843	5.03	3.50	
Worked by:	1843 John Brown			
	1843	1.85	0.75	
	1844	1.85	0.70	
Worked by:	1843-1844 Robert Pickles			
	1843	1.13	0.70	
	1845	6.18	3.80	
	1846	3.95	2.20	
	1847	3.70	2.10	
	1849	3.30	1.90	
	1850	1.00	0.60	
	1852	0.80	0.50	
Worked by:	1843-1852 John Hancock			
	1844	1.50	1.00	
	1845	0.90	0.55	
Worked by:	1844-1845 George Abedaile			
	1846	1.65	0.95	
Worked by:	1846 William Pattinson			
	1846	2.40	0.75	
Worked by:	1846 Jacob Shaw			
	1848	3.20	1.00	
Worked by:	1848 Edward Aldersley			

	1849	6.55	3.20
	1850	1.95	1.05
Worked by:	1849-1850 William Jaques		
	1849	1.60	1.00
	1850	2.25	1.50
Worked by:	1849-1850 Robert Bracefield		
	1849	2.45	1.50
Worked by:	1849 John Hesleden		
	1849	0.55	0.35
	1850	1.85	1.10
	1851	0.73	0.50
Worked by:	1849-1851 Bartley Pickard		
	1851	0.85	0.55
	1852	1.95	1.15
	1853	1.00	0.55
Worked by:	1851-1853 John Pickard		
	1852	0.95	0.50
Worked by:	1852 Richard Brailsford		
	1853	1.75	1.00
Worked by:	1853 Francis Apedale		
Comment:	1745-1853 Smelted at Grassington		
	1850	1.10	0.55
Worked by:	1850 John Hesletine		
	1852	1.30	0.70
	1853	0.80	0.40
Worked by:	1852-1853 John Hancock		
Comment:	1850-1853 Smelted at Starbotton Cupola		
	1863		0.37
Worked by:	1863 Anthony Slack		
Comment:	1863 Smelted at Kettlewell		
Mineral Lord:	1745-1863 See Hawkswick Liberty		

HAYS Eskdaleside Cum Ugglebarnby NZ828053

Production:	Iron	Ore(tons)	Value (£)
	1836-1859 No detailed returns		
	1860	2974.00	720.00
	1863	50000.00	
	1864	14209.40	
	1865-1866 No detailed returns		
Comment:	1836-1866 Avicular and Pecten Seams		
	1866 See Grosmont		
Mineral Lord:	1836-1866 Mrs Clark		
Worked by:	1836-1860 Whitby Stone Co.		
	1863-1866 Charles Bagnall & Thomas Bagnall		
Agent:	1863-1866 ? Dunn		

HAYSHAW MOOR Hayshaw SE160625

Production:	Lead	Ore(tons)	Lead (tons)	Value (£)
	1805	No detailed return		
Mineral Lord:	1805	John Ingilby		
Agent:	1805	Alexander Dunn Snr		

HAZEL KELL Reeth NY970014

Production:	Lead	Ore(tons)	Lead (tons)	Value (£)
	1751	2.60		
	1753	6.20		
Comment:	1750-1751	December to December		
	1752-1753	December to June		
Mineral Lord:	1751-1753	See AD Mines		
Worked by:	1750-1753	Trustees of The Duke of Wharton		

HEBDEN LIBERTY Hebden SE027652

Production:	Lead	Ore(tons)	Lead (tons)	Value (£)
	1737	1.50		
Worked by:	1737	Daniel Birch & William Birch		
	1737		1.10	
Worked by:	1737	Mr Rushworth		
	1737		1.45	
	1738		2.83	
	1739		0.45	
	1748		4.33	
	1767		2.30	
	1772		0.15	
Worked by:	1737-1739	William Verity		
	1748	Mr Price & Ptrs		
	1767-1772	Robert Birch		
	1768		0.50	
	1769		0.50	
	1771		0.15	
Worked by:	1768-1769	James Birch		
	1771	Benjamin Birch		
	1771		0.35	
	1775		0.10	
Worked by:	1771	George Tennant		
	1775	William Styles		
	1775		0.40	
	1778		0.25	
	1783		0.15	
Worked by:	1775	William Rodwell		
	1778	James Rodwell		
	1783	Ruth Bibey		
	1783		0.10	
	1788		0.15	

	1790		0.85	
	1791		0.40	
	1792		0.40	
	1793		0.50	
	1794		0.74	
	1832	0.70	0.30	
	1839	5.30	1.90	
Worked by:	1783	John Metcalfe		
	1788	John Hawley		
	1790	Francis Tennant		
	1791-1793	George Peacock		
	1794	John Blackow		
	1832	John Hawley		
	1839	James Aldersley		
	1839	3.75	1.40	
	1842	4.65	2.05	
	1843	3.10	1.35	
	1844	0.53	0.25	
	1855	34.51	20.10	
	1856	201.35	139.60	
	1857	389.68	258.44	
	1858	112.00	77.23	
Comment:	1737-1858	Smelted at Grassington		
	1750-1849	See Groove Gill		
Worked by:	1839	James Rodwell		
	1842	Robert Sunter		
	1843-1844	George Birch		
	1855-1858	Hebden Moor Mining Co.		
Production:	Lead	Ore(tons)	Lead (tons)	Value (£)
	1802		0.20	
	1842		0.80	
	1852		2.00	
	1855	34.73	20.10	462.30
	1856	203.88	139.60	3119.75
	1857	389.68	267.10	5847.75
	1858	130.00	84.08	1741.87
	1859	245.40	164.05	3424.81
	1860	197.60	162.55	3269.13
	1861	300.00	201.55	3813.23
	1862	410.00	300.66	5711.74
	1863		175.25	3415.75
	1864		95.81	1934.85
	1865		120.80	2275.43
	1866		60.00	722.58
	1867	9.13	5.95	110.07
	1868	10.10	7.26	125.28
	1870		47.93	780.29

	1872		4.18	73.06
	1873		2.28	47.78
Comment:	1802-1873	Barmasters' Book		
	1802	Bolton Gill		
	1842	Loss Gill Bank		
	1852	Bolton Gill		
Worked by:	1802	Sylvester Petyt		
	1842	Robert Sunter		
	1852	George Birch		
	1855-1873	Hebden Moor Mining Co.		
Production:	Lead	Ore(tons)	Lead (tons)	Value (£)
	1856	201.80	139.60	
	1857	275.10	182.10	
	1858	222.80	154.00	
	1859	242.40	164.00	
	1860	260.00	165.00	
	1861	300.00	201.50	
	1862	425.60	298.70	
	1863	352.20	229.70	
	1864	186.40	122.90	
	1865	57.60	35.60	
	1866	115.80	75.20	
	1867	73.60	47.50	
	1868	88.60	57.60	
	1869	84.20	54.70	
	1870	46.80	31.60	
	1871	31.20	23.40	
	1872	32.40	21.00	
	1873	No detailed return		
Comment:	1856-1873	Data from Hunt's Statistics		
	1870		41.90	
	1870 Smelted at Kettlewell			
	1870 Slags from Grassington Smelt Mill			
Production:	Barytes	Ore(tons)		Value (£)
	1918	22.48		
	1919	14.03		
Comment:	1759	See Pension Rake		
Mineral Lord:	1737-2000	Trust Lords of Hebden		
	1964-1974	Craven Water Board (Hebden Gill)		
	1974-2000	Yorkshire Water Authority (Hebden Gill)		
Worked by:	1853-1854	Hebden Mining Company		
	1854-1889	Hebden Moor Mining Company (Cost Book)		
	1889	Hebden Moor Mining Company Ltd		
	1916-1918	Edward Murgatroyd (Lessee)		
	1918-1921	Grassington Lead Mines Ltd		
Barmaster:	1788-1801	Francis Tennant		
	1801-1819	Joseph Constantine		

	1816-1819	John Brown
	1819	Thomas Lupton & Robert Brown
	1827-1853	Daniel Bowden
	1827-1855	Richard Walker
	1855-1868	John Armitstead Herd
	1855-1864	John Hawley
	1865-1884	William Hawley
	1868-1877	Edward Armstrong
Agent:	1853-1854	William Sigston Winn
	1855-1867	Thomas Job
	1863	Robert Place
	1865-1867	William Barron
	1867	Joseph Heslop
	1868-1880	William Hill
	1884-1889	Edwin Dunkin
Secretary:	1853-1860	William Shaw Jnr
	1864-1871	Joseph Storr
	1877-1878	James W. Close
	1918-1921	N. Broadbent

Employment:		Underground	Surface	Total
	1862	41		
	1877	10	2	12
	1878	10	4	14
	1879	11	1	12
	1880-1881	10	2	12
	1882	14	2	16

HEBDEN SMELTING MILL(S) Hebden

Production:	Lead	Ore(tons)	Lead (tons)	Value (£)
	1722-1728	No detailed returns		
	1729		0.42	
	1730		31.72	
	1731		17.81	
	1732		8.15	
	1858	28.00	14.00	
	1859	147.40	98.55	
	1860	197.60	162.45	

Comment:	1722	See Cockbur
	1722-1732	Not Bolton Gill Mill at SE 02466411
	1729-1732	Source of lead unknown
	1858-1860	Smelted at Bolton Gill Mill (Built 1858)

HECKLAR RAKE Grassington SE007677

Production:	Lead	Ore(tons)	Lead (tons)	Value (£)
	1772		0.34	
	1773		1.82	
	1774		4.50	
	1775		1.88	

	1776		0.53
	1777		0.01
	1778		1.48
	1779		1.75
	1780		2.41
	1781		6.93
	1782		24.90
	1783		13.88
	1784		11.06
	1785		2.10
	1786		2.96
	1787		2.23
	1788		0.93
	1791		0.41
	1792		0.17
	1795		0.20
	1807		1.20
	1808		3.35
	1809	0.55	0.35
	1810	10.80	6.35
	1811	9.93	6.05
	1812	2.25	1.20
	1815	1.95	1.15
	1817	1.50	0.95
	1819	0.11	0.05
	1823	1.25	0.75
	1824	1.50	0.60

Comment: 1772-1824 See also under Knucklebone
Mineral Lord: 1772-1824 See under Grassington

HEPTONSTALL LIBERTY Heptonstall SD921287

Production:	Lead	Ore(tons)	Lead (tons)	Value (£)
	1685	No detailed return		

Mineral Lord: 1685 Lord Halifax
Worked by: 1685 Lord Halifax

HETTON LIBERTY Hetton

Production:	Lead	Ore(tons)	Lead (tons)	Value (£)
	1773		0.30	

Worked by: 1773 Stephen Newhouse

HIGH MARK Bordley SD934678

Production:	Lead	Ore(tons)	Lead (tons)	Value (£)
	1837	0.65	0.35	
	1852	9.20	3.80	
	1853	8.65	4.20	

Comment: 1837-1853 Smelted at Grassington
1733-1830 See Bordley Liberty

Mineral Lord: 1837-1853 Mr Proctor
Worked by: 1837 Henry Wallis
1852-1853 Robert Aldersley & James Aldersley
1853 William Jaques

HIGH ROCK Downholme NZ118004
Production: Lead Ore(tons) Lead (tons) Value (£)
1803-1805 No detailed returns
Comment: 1803-1805 See Also White Earth & Downholme
Mineral Lord: 1803-1990 See under Downholme
Worked by: 1803 William Robinson & Co.

HIGH VIEW Bewerley SE124639
Production: Fluorspar Ore(tons) Value (£)
1940-1950 No detailed returns
Mineral Lord: 1940-1950 See Bewerley
Worked by: 1940-1950 George Mackwell
Employment:

	Underground	Surface	Total
1940	4	3	7
1941	3	2	5
1942	4	2	6
1943	2	2	4
1944	2	3	5
1945	2	2	4
1948	3	1	4
1950	0	2	2

HILL TOP Bewerley SE112639
Production: Fluorspar Ore(tons) Value (£)
1938-1950 No detailed returns
1938-1950 See Bewerley
Worked by: 1938-1945 J. Busfield
1948-1950 George Mackwell
Employment:

	Underground	Surface	Total
1938	3	1	4
1940	5		5
1941	1		1
1942	2		2
1943	2		2
1944	2		2
1945	2		2
1947	2		2
1948	2		2
1949	3	3	6
1950	3	3	6

HINDERWELL		Hinderwell		NZ798174
Production:	Iron	Ore(tons)		Value (£)
	1862	5000.00		750.00
Comment:	1854-1862	Top Seam		
	1854-1862	See Rosedale on the Coast		

HOB HILL		Marske		NZ656207
Production:	Iron	Ore(tons)		Value (£)
	1865	93366.00		28009.80
	1866	184264.00		46066.00
	1867	242582.00		60645.50
	1868	298769.00		74692.20
	1869	319115.10		79778.70
	1870	380828.00		95207.00
	1871	427295.60		106824.40
	1872	273548.00		
	1873	160430.00		48129.00
	1874	81946.00		24583.80
	1902-1923	No detailed returns		
Comment:	1875-1899	Standing		
Mineral Lord:	1864-1923	Lord Zetland		
Worked by:	1864-1874	J. Pease & Jos.W. Pease		
	1875-1923	Pease and Partners Ltd		
Agent:	1866-1874	William Cockburn		

HOLEBOTTOM		Bewerley		SE126654
Production:	Lead	Ore(tons)	Lead (tons)	Value (£)
	1867-1868	No detailed returns		
Comment:	1867	Including Hardcastle		
Worked by:	1867-1868	Nidderdale Lead Mining Co. Ltd		
Agent:	1867-1868	William Marshall		
Secretary:	1867-1868	Thomas Sykes		

HOLGATE MOOR		New Forest		NZ056049
Production:	Lead	Ore(tons)	Lead (tons)	Value (£)
	1840-1841	No detailed returns		
Comment:	1840	Hurst Letter Book		
	1840	Driving a level at east end of moor		
Mineral Lord:	1840	See Arkengarthdale		
Worked by:	1840	Mr Smithson (sub-lessee of Arkendale Mining Co.)		

HOLLIN HILL		Stanghow		NZ646147
Production:	Iron	Ore(tons)		Value (£)
	1864-1880	No detailed returns		
Comment:	1864-1880	See Slapewath		
	1880	Part of Spawood		
Mineral Lord:	1864-1880	Executors of H.W. Thomas		
Worked by:	1864-1880	Thomas Charlton & Co.		
	1880	B. Samuelson & Co.		

HOLLINS Rosedale West Side NZ729945

Production:	Iron	Ore(tons)	Value (£)
	1856-1879	No detailed returns	
Comment:	1856-1879	Top Seam and Magnetic Ore	
Mineral Lord:	1856-1879	Mrs Spink; Garbutt family	
Worked by:	1856-1859	Eskdale Iron Co.	
	1859-1864	Rosedale Iron Co.	
	1864-1879	Rosedale and Ferryhill Iron Co.	

HOLLINS Eskdaleside Cum Ugglebarnby NZ830056

Production:	Iron	Ore(tons)	Value (£)
	1865	16055.00	4013.70
	1866	No detailed return	
	1878-1879	No detailed returns	
Comment:	1878-1879	See Grosmont	
Mineral Lord:	1839-1879	Mrs Clark	
Worked by:	1863-1879	Grosmont Iron Co.	

HORTON IN RIBBLESDALE LIBERTY H. in R. SD811721

Production:	Lead	Ore(tons)	Lead (tons)	Value (£)
	1710-1767	No detailed returns		
Mineral Lord:	1767	The Freeholders		
Worked by:	1710	Mr Justice & Co.		
	1767	John Lawson & Co.		

HOW BANK Carperby cum Thoresby SD982903

Production:	Lead	Ore(tons)	Lead (tons)	Value (£)
	1864-1865	No detailed returns		
	1866	2.50	1.80	
	1867	No detailed return		
Comment:	1864-1865	See Keld Heads		
	1871	Including Wet Groves		
Mineral Lord:	1862-1871	See under Keld Heads		
Worked by:	1862-1869	Craig & Co.		
	1870-1871	John Tattersall		
	1871	John Bowman		

HOWGILL Grassington SE023682

Production:	Lead	Ore(tons)	Lead (tons)	Value (£)
	1849	2.95	1.25	
	1850	6.05	2.40	
Mineral Lord:	1849-1850	See under Grassington		

HUNGRY HUSHES Arkengarthdale NY986028

Production:	Lead	Ore(tons)	Lead (tons)	Value (£)
	1783	0.10		
	1784	0.20		

Comment:	1783	May to November inclusive		
	1783-1784	Standing: December to November inclusive		
	1784	December 1784 to May 1785 inclusive		
Mineral Lord:	1783-1785	See Arkengarthdale		
Worked by:	1783-1785	Charles Sleigh, William Hoar & Charles Foster		
Employment:		Underground	Surface	Total
	1782-1783	9		
	1784-1785	9		

HUNTCLIFFE Brotton NZ697217

Production:	Iron	Ore(tons)	Value (£)
	1872	180473.30	
	1873	173221.20	51966.30
	1874	184424.90	55327.20
	1875	145847.00	
	1876	121613.50	
	1877	166326.40	
	1878	190716.00	
	1879	198895.40	
	1880	173157.30	
	1881	154098.30	
	1882-1905	No detailed return	

Comment:	1870-1871	See Cliff
	1906	Abandoned
Mineral Lord:	1872-1906	Barrow family
Worked by:	1872-1873	Bell Brothers
	1874-1906	Bell Brothers Ltd
Agent:	1873-1881	Addison L. Steavenson
	1876-1881	Thomas Bell
	1881-1885	W. Anderson
	1886-1905	D.W. Dixon

Employment:		Underground	Surface	Total
	1883			199
	1894	102	19	121
	1895	98	20	118
	1896	88	21	109
	1897	95	21	116
	1898	89	22	111
	1899	91	25	116
	1900	91	26	117
	1901	69	39	108
	1902	70	38	108
	1903	69	26	95
	1904	63	25	88
	1905	38	16	54

HUNTERSLEETS 10 MEERS Carlton Highdale SD982760

Production:	Lead	Ore(tons)	Lead (tons)	Value (£)
	1774	No detailed return		
Comment:	1774	Data from *Leeds Mercury* 21/06/1774		
	1786-1868	See also Coverdale Liberty		
Mineral Lord:	1774	Rev. Dr Marton		

HURST Marrick NZ045023

Production:	Lead	Ore(tons)	Lead (tons)	Value (£)
	1661	198.00		
	1662	211.80		
	1663	80.10		
	1661-1663	Smelted at Marrick High & Low Mills		
	1660-1663	November to November		
	1660-1663	Including Copperthwaite		
	1711	189.98		
	1712	444.22		
	1713	350.41		
	1714	320.28		
	1715	296.93		
	1716	274.16		
	1717	236.87		
	1718	236.06		
	1719	157.63		
	1720	118.28		
	1721	169.70		
	1722	109.52		
	1723	225.26		
	1724	242.72		
	1725	166.04		
	1726	216.52		
	1727	170.72		
Comment:	1711-1718	Data from lead sales		
	1719-1727	From duty lead sales multiplied by seven.		
	1711	October to December		
	1727	January to August		
	1660-1727	Called Redhurst		
	1724-1727	See Copperthwaite		

Production:	Lead	Ore(tons)	Lead(tons)	Silver(ozs)	Value(£)
	1850-1851	No detailed returns			
	1852	426.00	264.00		
	1853	274.00	169.80		
	1854	225.00	168.00		
	1855	129.60	96.70		
	1856	118.00	87.00		
	1857	190.40	130.00		

1858	149.50	102.00		
1859	158.00	33.10		
1860	58.50	39.00		
1861	60.00	41.00		
1862	331.00	221.00		
1863-1864	272.00	176.00		
1865	137.20	95.90		
1866	465.80	197.40		
1867	1171.00	749.50		
1868	704.90	528.60		
1869	652.70	501.50		
1870	752.80	564.60		
1871	387.40	290.40		
1872	357.60	268.20		
1873	476.50	357.30		
1874	536.80	397.00		
1875	351.10	263.50	789.00	
1876	342.70	247.00	741.00	
1877	407.60	307.50	875.00	2238.50
1878	241.80	180.00	513.00	2662.00
1879	200.50	150.40	450.00	2065.10
1880	55.40	42.70	120.00	621.00
1885	200.00			1300.00
1886	798.00	568.00		5985.00
1887	1003.00			
1888	925.00	693.00		6475.00
1889	390.00	274.00		2389.00
1890	150.00	105.00		1189.00

Comment:
1850-1890 Data from Hunt's Statistics
1850-1851 See Swaledale and Arkendale
1864-1872 Or East Swaledale
1890 In receivership
1891-1897 Standing

Production:

Lead	Ore(tons)	Lead (tons)	Value (£)
1858	200.00	30.15	
1859	160.00	30.00	
1860	240.00	14.90	
1861		37.85	
1862		117.00	
1863		148.80	
1864		106.50	
1865		181.55	
1866	170.00	190.28	
1867	585.00	210.72	
1868	749.00	30.04	
1869	618.80	5.12	

1870	748.00	
1871	418.00	5.07
1872	345.00	
1873	500.00	
1874	545.00	0.20
1875	343.00	
1876	358.45	
1877	413.20	
1878	261.50	
1879	207.45	

Comment: 1858-1879 Data from lead/ore sales: Hurst Mining Co.
1937-1941 See Pryes Level (prospecting)

Mineral Lord: 1100-1512 The Aske family
1165-1512 Mines split between Askes & Marrick Priory
1512-1539 Mines split between Bulmers & Marrick Priory
1512-1535 Ralph Bulmer & Richard Bowes
1539-1554 Mines split between Bulmers and the Crown
1535-1554 Ralph Bulmer
1554-1584 John Sayer
1584-1618 Lawrence Sayer
1618-1649 Sayer family
1618-1671 Bulmer family
1649-1668 John Swinburne & Thomas Swinburne
1668-1671 Charles Powlett
1671-1683 Charles Powlett & John Blackburne
1683-1699 Charles Powlett (Duke of Bolton)
1699-1729 Lord William Powlett
1729-1757 William Powlett
1757-1781 Annabel Smyth (neé Powlett)
1781-1816 William Powlett-Powlett
1816-1827 Josias Readshaw Morley
1827-1834 Trustees of Francis Morley
1834-1854 Francis Morley
1854-1861 Trustees of Francis Morley
1861-1892 Francis Morley
1893-1895 Executors of Francis Morley
1895 Francis Riddell
1937-1939 Wilfred J. Hird

Worked by: 1165-1540 Marrick Priory
1540-1544 John Uvedale (Under Crown)
1549-1583 Avery Uvedale
1583-1589 John Uvedale
1589-1592 Richard Breckenbury
1592-1631 Timothy Hutton
1631-1651 Robert Blackburne
1651-1669 Gyles Blackburne
1669-1683 John Blackburne

	1683-1688	Charles Powlett
	1689-1699	Duke of Bolton
	1699-1718	Lord William Powlett
	1718-1727	Samuel Mellor & Co.
	1795	M. Stapleton
	1827-1842	Robert Jaques & Co.
	1842-1844	Francis Morley
	1844-1854	J. Harland, J. Brown Simpson & Co.
	1854-1856	J. Harland, W. Lister & Co.
	1856-1861	Christopher Lonsdale Bradley & Co.
	1861-1881	Hurst Mining Co.
	1881-1882	Faithfull Cookson
	1882-1888	Yorkshire Lead Mines Co. Ltd
	1888-1890	Hurst Lead Mines Ltd
	1890	Hurst Mines Syndicate
	1937-1939	North Riding Lead Mining Company Ltd
Steward:	1719	Thomas Kinnesley
	1769	John March
	1773	Thomas Walker
	1827-1854	John Harland
	1854-1861	Christopher Lonsdale Bradley
Agent:	1561	Henry Boardman
	1660-1663	John Fawcet
	1699-1711	Reuben Orton
	1711-1727	Robert Coatesworth
	1762	John Sherlock
	1762	George Arrowsmith
	1787-1852	George Chalder
	1841-1867	Robert Daykin
	1852	George Gladwin
	1864-1879	Ralph Metcalfe
	1874-1880	John Hillary
	1880-1897	W.A. Waggett
	1881-1889	John Retallick
	1890	Thomas Wilkins (Receiver/Manager)
	1889-1893	James Wood
Secretary:	1875-1879	James March
	1880	Henry Thomas Robinson
	1882-1888	James Kendrick Lamb
	1888-1890	Greenop & Sons

Employment:		Underground	Surface	Total
	1862	34		
	1877	66	26	92
	1878	53	25	78
	1879	55	18	73
	1880	21	5	26

HUSH SIDE Arkengarthdale

Production:	Lead	Ore(tons)	Lead (tons)	Value (£)
	1782	11.70		
	1783	0.60		
	1784	1.50		
	1785	7.50		
	1786	16.80		
	1787	24.00		
	1788	8.80		
	1789	1.40		

Comment:	1782-1783	November to November inclusive
	1783-1784	December to November inclusive
	1784-1785	Standing - December to May
	1785	June to November inclusive
	1785-1786	Standing - December to May
	1786-1787	June to May inclusive
	1787-1787	Standing - June to November inclusive
	1787-1789	December to May inclusive
	1789-1790	June to May inclusive
	1790	June to November inclusive
Mineral Lord:	1782-1790	See Arkengarthdale
Worked by:	1782-1790	Charles Sleigh, William Hoar & Charles Foster

Employment:		Underground	Surface	Total
	1782-1783	4		
	1783-1784	1		
	1785	1		
	1786	1		
	1786-1787	1		
	1787-1788	3		
	1788-1789	2		
	1790	1		

HUTCHINSON'S & BURNABY'S Bewerley SE132652

Production:	Lead	Ore(tons)	Lead (tons)	Value (£)
	1861	53.90	35.00	
	1863	51.00	23.00	
	1864	50.00	35.00	
	1865	No detailed return		

Comment:	1863	Including Mr Yorke's Royalty
Mineral Lord:	1861-1865	Hutchinson & Burnaby

HUTTON Hutton Lowcross NZ595133

Production:	Iron	Ore(tons)	Value (£)
	1854-1855	No detailed returns	
	1856	217253.00	
	1857	No detailed return	
	1858	257129.00	38582.80
	1859	217671.80	32650.50

	1860	90258.00		13537.50
	1861	80445.00		12066.70
	1862	69626.10		10443.90
	1863	124606.00		
	1864	171727.00		
	1865	39367.00		11810.00
	1866-1867	No detailed returns		
Comment:	1854-1867	Also at NZ603133		
	1863-1865	Or Cod Hill		
Mineral Lord:	1854-1867	Crown; J.W. Pease; Staveley		
Worked by:	1854-1867	J.W. Pease & Co.		
Agent:	1863-1865	William Cockburn		

INGLEBY Ingleby Greenhow NZ607023

Production:	Iron	Ore(tons)	Value (£)
	1858-1865	No detailed returns	
Comment:	1858-1865	Ellerbeck Bed	
	1863-1865	Suspended	
Mineral Lord:	1858-1865	Lord de L'Isle & Dudley	
Worked by:	1858-1865	Ingleby Mining Co.	

INGLETON LIBERTY Ingleton SD725745

Production:	Lead	Ore(tons)	Lead (tons)	Value (£)
	1703	No detailed return		
Comment:	1703	Smelted at Marrick Cupola		
Mineral Lord:	1703	Henry Bouch		
Worked by:	1703	John Blackburn & Co.		

ISOBELLA MEAH HILL Lunedale

Production:	Lead	Ore(tons)	Lead (tons)	Value (£)
	1745	39.20		
Mineral Lord:	1745-1771	See Lunehead		
Worked by:	1771	London Lead Company		

INVALID Grassington

Production:	Lead	Ore(tons)	Lead (tons)	Value (£)
	1799		15.00	
	1800		1.30	
	1801		0.45	
	1802		1.40	
	1803		1.65	
	1804		0.80	
	1811	8.18	4.70	
	1812	3.73	1.90	
	1815	0.80	0.50	
	1816	1.45	0.80	
	1818	1.60	0.95	
Mineral Lord:	1799-1818	See under Grassington		

JACOB BRADLEY Grassington SE019668

Production:	Lead	Ore(tons)	Lead (tons)	Value (£)
	1820	16.00	8.55	
	1821	4.75	2.40	
	1822	3.65	1.85	
Mineral Lord:	1820-1822	See under Grassington		

JAMIE Appletreewick SE097633

Production:	Lead	Ore(tons)	Lead (tons)	Value (£)
	1916-1919	No detailed returns		
Comment:	1854-1865	Part of Craven Moor		
	1920-1921	See Gill Heads		
	1921-1928	Standing		
	1928-1929	In liquidation		
Mineral Lord:	1854-1928	See Appletreewick Liberty		
Worked by:	1915-1928	Greenhaugh Mining Co. Ltd		
Agent:	1916-1919	Harald J.L. Bruff		
	1919-1926	W.W. Varvill		
Secretary:	1915	W. Stansfield		
	1916-1923	G.W. Middleton		
	1923	Arthur Kingham		

JOHN YOUNG GATE Grassington SE022667

Production:	Lead	Ore(tons)	Lead (tons)	Value (£)
	1747		2.17	
	1749		0.34	
	1750		0.25	
Mineral Lord:	1747-1750	See under Grassington		

JUSTICE VEIN Arkengarthdale NY988028

Production:	Lead	Ore(tons)	Lead (tons)	Value (£)
	1782	156.60		
	1783	171.80		
	1784	307.40		
	1785	65.30		
	1786	34.40		
	1787	124.90		
	1788	254.10		
	1789	77.30		
	1790	44.80		
Comment:	1782-1783	November to November inclusive		
	1783-1790	December to November inclusive		
	1790-1791	December to May inclusive		
	1782-1791	Inc: Justice, No.2 & No.3 Whim Shafts		
Mineral Lord:	1782-1791	See Arkengarthdale		
Worked by:	1782-1791	Charles Sleigh, William Hoar & Charles Foster		

Employment:		Underground	Surface	Total
	1782-1783	34		
	1783-1784	26		
	1784-1785	35		
	1785-1786	14		
	1786-1787	11		
	1787-1788	20		
	1788-1789	38		
	1789-1790	18		
	1790-1791	11		

KELBER GATE Grassington SE007680

Production:	Lead	Ore(tons)	Lead (tons)	Value (£)
	1787		0.59	
	1788		0.09	

Mineral Lord: 1787-1788 See under Grassington

KELD HEADS Preston under Scar SE080908

Production:	Lead	Ore(tons)	Lead (tons)	Value (£)
	1730-1764 No detailed returns			
	1850		150.30	
	1851		576.00	
	1852		597.10	
	1853		365.60	
	1854		636.30	
	1855		1035.90	
	1856		1444.20	
	1857		1019.40	
	1858		1145.85	
	1859		1425.40	
	1860		1521.90	
	1861		1212.00	
	1862		1175.40	
	1863		1013.75	
	1864		697.80	
	1865		644.45	
	1866		405.60	
	1867		353.10	
	1868		352.70	
	1869		421.00	
	1870		257.00	
	1871		554.00	
	1872		652.00	
	1873		448.00	
	1874		293.00	
	1875		97.40	
	1876		79.70	

	1877	111.90
	1878	175.70
	1879	159.50

Comment: 1850-1879 Data from Lord Bolton's Lead Book

Production:	Lead	Ore(tons)	Lead(tons)	Silver(ozs)	Value(£)
	1864	1300.80	932.20		
	1865	1200.00	840.00		
	1866	500.00	334.00		
	1867	498.80	300.00		
	1868	432.00	340.00		
	1869	532.00	340.00		
	1870	528.70	396.00		
	1871	525.00	394.00		
	1872	558.00	418.50		
	1873	424.40	318.30		
	1874	367.50	293.00		
	1875	89.30	60.00	180.00	1350.00
	1876	256.30	184.10	575.00	
	1877	232.60	201.50	600.00	3024.00
	1878	186.80	131.50	394.00	1975.20
	1879	400.00	300.00	900.00	4200.00
	1880	316.00	250.00	790.00	3476.00
	1881	241.30	184.00	360.00	2413.00
	1882	145.00	108.70		1305.00
	1883	216.00	197.50		2047.00
	1884	128.00			950.00
	1885	98.00			800.00
	1886	104.00	75.00		847.00
	1887	160.00			
	1888	77.00			539.00

Comment: 1864-1888 Data from Hunt's Statistics
1864-1865 Including 7 other mines
1866-1867 Including Cranehow Bottom
1888-1897 Standing

Mineral Lord: 1569 Henry Lord Scrope
1668-1683 Charles Powlett
1683-1699 Charles Powlett 1st Duke of Bolton
1699-1722 Charles Powlett 2nd Duke of Bolton
1722-1754 Charles Powlett 3rd Duke of Bolton
1754-1759 Harry Powlett 4th Duke of Bolton
1759-1765 Charles Powlett 5th Duke of Bolton
1765-1794 Harry Powlett 6th Duke of Bolton
1795-2000 The Orde-Powlett family - Lords Bolton
1795-1797 Thomas Orde-Powlett
1797-1807 Thomas - 1st Baron Bolton
1807-1850 William - 2nd Baron Bolton

	1850-1895	William Henry - 3rd Baron Bolton
	1895-1922	William Thomas - 4th Baron Bolton
	1922-1944	William George Algar - 5th Baron Bolton
	1944-1963	Nigel Amyas - 6th Baron Bolton
	1963-2000	Richard William Algar - 7th Baron Bolton
Worked by:	1827	Messrs Hall & Co.
	1845-1859	Weston, Tattersall & Co.
	1859-1879	Weston, Bowman & Co.
	1845-1879	Keld Heads Mining Co.
	1880-1887	Thomas Dymond
	1888-1897	Lord Bolton
Agent:	1854-1874	Jonathon Coatsworth
	1866-1868	Anthony Johnson
	1875-1876	Thomas Davidson
	1879-1885	C. Rodwell
	1877-1893	John Ascough Rodwell
	1879-1881	John Ascough Rodwell & Charles Rowe
	1894-1897	F. Rodwell
Secretary:	1860-1865	John Bowman & Co.
	1877-1879	Thomas Kirby & Co.

Employment:		Underground	Surface	Total
	1862	91		
	1877	55	21	76
	1878	74	20	94
	1879	77	22	99
	1880	63	20	83

KELD HEADS SMELT MILL Preston under Scar SE078910

Production:	Lead	Ore(tons)	Lead (tons)	Value (£)
	1852		27.40	
	1853		29.35	
	1854		46.75	
	1855		76.80	
	1856		85.00	
	1857		120.00	
	1858		86.10	
	1859		276.50	
	1860		41.55	

Comment:	1852-1860	Lead fume from condenser and flue
Worked by:	1852-1860	Keld Heads Mining Co.

KELD ING Arkengarthdale

Production:	Lead	Ore(tons)	Lead (tons)	Value (£)
	1783	0.60		
	1784	1.70		

Comment:	1783	May to November inclusive
	1783-1784	Standing: December to November inclusive

	1784	December 1784 to May 1785 inclusive		
	1785-1790	Standing: June to May inclusive		
	1790	June to November inclusive		
Mineral Lord:	1783-1790	See Arkengarthdale		
Worked by:	1783-1790	Charles Sleigh, William Hoar & Charles Foster		
Employment:		Underground	Surface	Total
	1783	1		
	1784-1785	1		
	1790	1		

KELDSIDE Muker NY875015

Production:	Lead	Ore(tons)	Lead (tons)	Value (£)
	1735-1749	No detailed returns		
	1750	104.00	68.92	
	1751	48.00	33.81	
	1752	36.80	27.61	
	1753	40.00	26.86	
	1818		0.78	
	1823		7.00	
	1824		6.00	
	1825		1.55	

Comment:	1750	June to December
	1751	December 1750 to December 1751
	1752	December 1751 to December 1752
	1753	December 1752 to June 1753
	1750-1753	Lead estimated from AD produce
	1751	Includes Glovergill
	1753-1767	See Birkdale
	1818-1825	Data from NYCRO ZLB 2/134 & 136
	1823-1824	Data from Jennings Thesis
	1812-1824	Including Lownathwaite & Swinnergill
	1829-1865	See Lane End & Keldside
Mineral Lord:	1735-1870	See AD Mines
Worked by:	1735-1753	The Mine Adventurers of England
	1806	William Wacker & Company
	1812-1824	Hopper & Co.
	1825	Little Moor Foot & Keldside Mining Co.
	1863-1865	Keldside Mining Co. Ltd
	1866-1870	Kisdon Mining Co. Ltd
Agent:	1740	James Harries
	1806	Jno Horner
Secretary:	1865	Thomas Thompson

KETTLENESS No.1 Lythe NZ831160

Production:	Iron	Ore(tons)	Value (£)
	1838-1866	No detailed returns	
Worked by:	1838-1842	Wylam Iron Co.	
	1854-1866	J. Watson	

KETTLENESS No.2 Barnby NZ824151

Production:	Iron	Ore(tons)			Value (£)
	1910-1915	No detailed returns			
Comment:	1915	Abandoned			
Mineral Lord:	1910-1915	Marquis of Normanby			
Worked by:	1910-1915	Skinningrove Iron Co. Ltd			
Agent:	1910-1912	W. Walker			
	1913-1915	A.H. Askew			
Employment:		Underground	Surface	Total	
	1910	7	8	15	
	1911	28	12	40	
	1912	31	12	43	
	1913	27	16	43	
	1914	42	29	71	
	1915	4	4	8	

KETTLEWELL LIBERTY Kettlewell SD974728

Production:	Lead	Ore(tons)	Lead (tons)	Value (£)
	1872		0.20	
	1879		0.40	
	1880		7.90	
	1881		9.85	
	1882		3.45	
	1883		1.05	
	1885		0.95	
Worked by:	1862	John Wiseman from Cam wastes		
	1879-1885	Joseph Wiseman & Co.		
	1876		0.15	
	1878		0.20	
	1880		0.95	
	1881		0.45	
Worked by:	1876-1880	George Calvert		
	1881	James Calvert		
	1879		0.40	
	1880		1.50	
	1881		30.50	
	1883		8.50	
Worked by:	1879-1883	William Jacques		
	1880		1.75	
	1882		0.15	
Worked by:	1880-1882	John Place Snr		
	1881		2.40	
	1882		5.50	
Worked by:	1881	Stephen Alderson		
	1882	Place & Alderson		
Comment:	1872-1885	All Smelted at Kettlewell		
Mineral Lord:	1563-1628	The Crown		

	1628-1656	Corporation of London
	1656-2000	Trust Lords of Kettlewell
Worked by:	1605	Humphrey Wharton
	1663-1669	Francis Smithson
	1669-1687	Francis Smithson & Philip Swale
	1687-1688	Chaytor & Co.
Agent:	1670-1680	Robert Barker
	1680-1684	Adam Barkcr
Barmaster:	1859-1872	Joseph Craig
	1872-1887	William Coates

KETTLEWELL & CONISTONE Kettlewell & Conistone

Production:	Lead	Ore(tons)	Lead (tons)	Value (£)
	1849	154.00	100.00	
	1850	150.00	96.00	
	1851	200.00	140.00	
	1852	180.00	120.00	
	1853	160.00	110.00	
	1854	110.00	70.00	
	1855	95.00	50.00	
	1856	156.50	100.00	
	1857	150.00	105.00	
	1858	154.00	101.50	
	1859	160.00	110.00	
Comment:	1849-1859	Date from Hunt's Statistics		
	1849-1856	Kettlewell & Conistone Liberties		
	1857-1858	Kettlewell, Conistone & Buckden districts		

KETTLEWELL SMELT MILL SD974728

Production:	Lead	Ore(tons)	Lead (tons)	Value (£)
	1859		2.85	
	1860		1.50	
	1861		1.40	
	1862		0.85	
	1863		1.50	
Worked by:	1859-1863	Francis Scott		
	1861		0.65	
	1862		0.50	
	1863		1.30	
	1865		0.70	
	1883		0.60	
	1885		2.50	
Comment:	1859-1885	From ore raised outside the liberty		
Worked by:	1861	Duckworth & Fawcett		
	1862	Benjamin Davis & William Simpson		
	1863	John Sidgwick		
	1865	John Robinson & Co.		
	1883	Thomas Hebden		

	1885	Mr Fawcett		
	1860		3.95	
	1862		2.50	
	1864		2.65	
	1868		13.65	
	1869		10.30	
	1870		7.30	
	1871		7.25	
	1876		6.35	
	1878		4.70	
	1881		2.05	
	1887		0.55	
Comment:	1860-1887	Recovered from flue dust		
	1860		0.60	
	1861		0.45	
	1862		0.40	
	1863		0.70	
Comment:	1860-1863	Recovered from plumber's ashes		
	1860-1863	Richard Gibson, plumber		
	1861		0.50	
	1862		0.45	
	1863		0.30	
Comment:	1861-1863	Recovered from plumber's ashes		
	1861-1863	Richard Bell, plumber, Castle Bolton		
	1862	41.10	25.20	
Comment:	1862	Data from Hunt's Statistics		
Mineral Lord:	1859-1887	See under Kettlewell Liberty		

KILDALE		Kirkdale		NZ625089
Production:	Iron	Ore(tons)		Value (£)
	1866-1878	No detailed returns		
Worked by:	1866-1878	Thomas Watson & Co.		
Agent:	1867-1878	Thomas Watson		

KILNSEY LIBERTY		Conistone with Kilnsey		SD950665
Production:	Lead	Ore(tons)	Lead (tons)	Value (£)
	1692		7.48	
	1745		0.07	
Comment:	1692-1745	Smelted at Grassington		
	1746-1827	No detailed returns		
Comment:	1746-1827	Smelted at Kilnsey?		
	1831	2.03	0.80	
	1834	1.20	0.30	
	1835		2.90	
	1842	1.00	0.60	
	1852	2.40	1.15	
	1853	4.60	2.05	

Comment:	1831-1853	Smelted at Grassington	
	1831	Recovered from slags	
	1835	Recovered from slags	
Worked by:	1831-1834	William Bell	
	1835	James Hugill	
	1842	Edward Watson	
	1852-1853	Ralph Lee	
	1852	6.75	3.10
	1858	2.70	1.00
	1862	2.75	1.15
Worked by:	1852-1862	Robert Aldersley & Co.	
	1854	1.00	0.50
	1855	0.90	0.55
Worked by:	1854-1862	Robert Breakley & Co.	
	1854	3.60	1.25
	1855	17.25	6.65
	1856	5.25	2.35
	1857	6.00	2.45
	1858	1.65	0.75
	1862	2.60	1.55
Worked by:	1854-1858	George Lee & Co.	
	1862	Ralph Lee	
	1855	1.35	0.30
Worked by:	1855	John Hesletine	
	1857	0.60	0.35
Worked by:	1857	James Wiseman	
	1862	2.40	1.50
Worked by:	1862	J. Bell & Co.	
Comment:	1852-1862	Smelted at Starbotton Cupola	
	1872		0.92
Comment:	1872	Smelted at Kettlewell	
Mineral Lord:	1692-1872	The Tennant family	
Worked by:	1872	William Brown & Thomas Rogers	

KILTON		Kilton	NZ693170
Production:	Iron	Ore(tons)	Value (£)
	1875	23834.00	
	1896-1928	No detailed returns	
	1940-1963	No detailed returns	
Comment:	1877-1895	Standing	
	1928	Discontinued July	
	1930	Discontinued March	
	1930-1938	Standing	
	1963	Abandoned	
Worked by:	1872-1873	Kilton Iron Co.	
	1874-1893	Kilton Ironstone Co.	
	1894-1914	Walker, Maynard & Co.	

	1915	Hugh Bell & A.T. Dorman		
	1916-1922	Bell Brothers Ltd		
	1923-1954	Dorman, Long & Co. Ltd		
	1955-1963	Dorman, Long (Steel) Ltd		
Agent:	1872-1876	William Walker		
	1877-1893	E. Hamilton		
	1896-1903	Ralph Clough		
	1904-1908	W. Walker		
	1909-1930	A.G. Thomson		
	1931-1933	M. Hedley		
	1934-1938	J.R. Tomlinson		
	1940-1950	J.C. Dack		
	1915-1963	A. Turnbull		
Employment:		Underground	Surface	Total
	1896	13	57	70
	1897	17	64	81
	1898	74	56	130
	1899	93	62	154
	1900	118	63	181
	1901	146	50	196
	1902	141	61	202
	1903	146	58	204
	1904	216	57	273
	1905	194	51	245
	1906	240	60	300
	1907	243	70	313
	1908	170	75	245
	1909	272	109	381
	1910	314	110	424
	1911	290	92	382
	1912	282	94	376
	1913	261	89	350
	1914	222	80	302
	1915	155	68	223
	1916	179	78	257
	1917	216	86	302
	1918	219	86	305
	1919	229	102	331
	1920	219	103	322
	1921	223	104	327
	1922	97	54	151
	1923	197	84	281
	1924	46	32	78
	1925	8	17	25
	1926	8	16	24
	1927	168	84	252
	1928	160	90	250

1929	65	45	110
1930	64	36	100
1931	4	8	12
1932	1	5	6
1933	1	5	6
1934	0	3	3
1935	0	2	2
1936	0	2	2
1937	13	41	54
1938	3	14	17
1940	201	70	271
1941	238	84	322
1942	239	79	318
1943	216	80	296
1944	185	64	249
1945	144	41	185
1948	100	43	143
1950	113	56	169
1951	167	73	240
1954	177	77	254
1955	111	56	167
1956	105	49	154
1957	95	51	146
1958	95	51	146
1959	110	53	163
1960	108	54	162
1961	123	58	181
1962	123	58	181
1963	76	50	126

KIRBY KNOWLE Thirsk

Production: Iron Ore(tons) Value (£)
1920-1921 No detailed returns
Comment: 1921 Abandoned
Worked by: 1920-1921 Bell Brothers Ltd
Agent: 1920-1921 W. Varty

Employment:	Underground	Surface	Total
1920	10	4	14

KIRKHAM Castle Howard

Production: Iron Ore(tons) Value (£)
1857-1878 No detailed returns
Comment: 1857-1878 Top Seam
Mineral Lord: 1857-1878 E.C. Taylor at Kirkham
1857-1878 Earl of Carlisle at Castle Howard
Worked by: 1857-1872 Snowdon & Lovel
1872-1878 H.J. Walduck & Co.
Agent: 1876-1878 Jos. Parkin

KIRKLEATHAM Tocketts NZ609187

Production:	Iron	Ore(tons)	Value (£)
	1873	19521.40	5856.30
	1874	88435.20	26530.00
	1875	118632.60	
	1876	140605.00	
	1877	112290.10	
	1878	114250.90	
	1879	65003.90	
	1880	92615.30	
	1881	78610.50	
	1886	No detailed return	

Comment: 1886 Abandoned - worked out
Mineral Lord: 1872-1886 Newcomen
Worked by: 1872 Robson & Co.
1873-1880 Kirkleatham Ironstone Co.
1881-1885 Walker, Maynard & Co.
Agent: 1872-1885 William Walker
1879 James Rutherford
Secretary: 1877-1879 Robson, Maynard & Co.

Employment:		Underground	Surface	Total
	1883			83

KISDON Muker SD895995

Production:	Lead	Ore(tons)	Lead (tons)	Value (£)
	1705	No detailed return		
	1816		1.34	
	1821		0.41	
	1823		1.41	
	1824		0.59	
	1828		0.49	
	1867	No detailed return		
	1868	6.70	5.10	
	1869-1877	No detailed returns		

Comment: 1816-1828 Data from NYCRO ZLB 2/134 & 136
1828 From slags
Mineral Lord: 1816-1877 See AD Mines
Worked by: 1705 Thomas Wharton (5th Lord)
1821 Thomas Fawcett
1823 James Alderson & Co.
1828 John Harker
1866-1870 Kisdon Co. Ltd
Agent: 1867-1870 John Ralph Place
Secretary: 1867-1870 James R. Tomlin

KNEETON		Melsonby		NZ214071
Production:	Copper	Ore(tons)	Copper (tons)	Value (£)
	1892	18.00	4.00	113.00
	1894-1895	2.00	0.50	18.00
	1896	10.00	1.00	18.00
Comment:	1897-1903 Standing			
Worked by:	1891-1895 Moulton Copper Mining Co.			
	1896-1903 Kneeton Copper Mining Co.			
Agent:	1891-1903 Christopher Calvert			

KNUCKLEBONE		Grassington		SE007679
Production:	Lead	Ore(tons)	Lead (tons)	Value (£)
	1811	0.30	0.20	
	1814	0.50	0.25	
	1825	0.45	0.10	
Comment:	1811-1825 Part of Hecklar Rake			
Mineral Lord:	1811-1825 See under Grassington			

KNUCKLEBONE		Starbotton		SD954760
Production:	Lead	Ore(tons)	Lead (tons)	Value (£)
	1800		8.40	
	1801		22.55	
	1802		24.10	
	1803		0.95	
	1832		0.55	
Comment:	1738-1778 See Coatework			
	1800-1832 Smelted at Grassington			
Mineral Lord:	1800-1832 See under Grassington			
Worked by:	1800-1801 William Maxfield			
	1802 John Musgrove			
	1803 George Shaw			
	1832 James Alderson			

LAMBERT PASTURE		Grassington		
Production:	Lead	Ore(tons)	Lead (tons)	Value (£)
	1809	1.05	0.45	
	1810	5.88	2.20	
	1811	1.50	0.45	
	1812	1.10	0.55	
	1819	0.60	0.30	
	1820	0.65	0.25	
Mineral Lord:	1809-1820 See under Grassington			

LANCASHIRE TRIAL		Lancashire		
Production:	Lead	Ore(tons)	Lead (tons)	Value (£)
	1791		0.04	
Comment:	1791 Smelted at Grassington			

LANE END Muker NY855008

Production:	Lead	Ore(tons)	Lead (tons)	Value (£)
	1801-1822	No detailed returns		
	1823		4.71	
	1824		2.81	
	1826		0.44	

Comment:	1823-1826	Data from NYCRO ZLB 2/134 & 136
	1735-1870	See Keldside
	1829-1865	See Lane End & Keldside
Mineral Lord:	1801-1828	See Beldi Hill
Worked by:	1801-1814	Thomas Butson & Co.
	1826	John Alderson & Co.

LANE END & KELDSIDE Muker NY855008

Production:	Lead	Ore(tons)	Lead (tons)	Value (£)
	1829-1834	No detailed returns		
	1835		23.04	
	1836		96.89	
	1837		49.34	
	1838		32.88	
	1841		24.07	
	1842		60.53	
	1843		18.92	
	1844		24.52	
	1845		16.57	
	1846		27.38	
	1847		8.18	
	1851		14.00	
	1852		26.00	
	1853		17.00	
	1854		9.00	
	1855		9.00	
	1859		4.00	

Comment:	1835-1847	Data from NYCRO ZLB 2/134, 136, 138
	1851	Data from Jennings Thesis
	1843-1866	See Swaledale, West
	1849-1858	Including Little Moor Foot
Mineral Lord:	1829-1865	See AD Mines
	1829-1865	See Beldi Hill (for Old Enclosures)
Worked by:	1829-1839	Jackson & Co.
	1843-1847	Cookson & Co.
	1849-1858	Christopher Lonsdale Bradley & Co.
Agent:	1830	Robert Raisbeck

LANE HEAD		Rosedale West Side		SE723952
Production:	Iron	Ore(tons)		Value (£)
	1876	3462.00		
	1877	3116.00		
	1880	3109.80		
	1881-1882	No detailed returns		
Comment:	1876-1883	Top Seam		
	1878-1879	Works standing June 1879		
	1883	Standing		
Mineral Lord:	1876-1881	H. Brewster Darley		
Worked by:	1876-1881	Rosedale & Ferryhill Iron Co.		
	1881-1883	Robert Hansell		
Agent:	1876-1883	Robert Hansell		

LANGERTON		Thorpe		SD994611
Production:	Lead	Ore(tons)	Lead (tons)	Value (£)
	1871	0.81	0.51	
Comment:	1871	Smelted at Grassington		
Mineral Lord:	1871	See Thorpe Liberty		
Worked by:	1871	Jacob Shaw		

LANGSCAR & HERON TREE			Preston under Scar	SE077924
Production:	Lead	Ore(tons)	Lead (tons)	Value (£)
	1850		7.55	
	1851		5.05	
	1852		3.00	
	1853		9.25	
	1854		12.40	
	1855		5.65	
	1856		3.15	
	1857		0.20	
	1858		0.75	
	1859		1.40	
	1861		0.35	
	1862		1.30	
	1863		1.75	
	1864		0.50	
Comment:	1850-1864	Data from Lord Bolton's Lead Book		
Mineral Lord:	1850-1864	See under Keld Heads		
Worked by:	1850-1864	Various partnerships		
	1864	Keld Heads Mining Co.		

LAYTON, EAST		East Layton		NZ160110
Production:	Copper	Ore(tons)	Copper (tons)	Value (£)
	1806-1813	No detailed returns		
Comment:	1806-1813	Cost Book Company		
	1812	December - Advertised for sale		
	1813	March - Advertised for sale		
Mineral Lord:	1810	William Barber		
Worked by:	1806-1810	William Clay & Ptrs		
	1810-1813	Thomas Lumley & Ptrs		
Agent:	1810-1813	Captain William Vivian		

LEA GREEN		Grassington		SD998657
Production:	Lead	Ore(tons)	Lead (tons)	Value (£)
	1747		0.36	
	1750		0.57	
	1753		0.58	
	1754		0.13	
	1761		0.25	
	1852	2.10	1.35	
	1853	1.68	1.25	
Comment:	1761	Includes Harwood Well		
Mineral Lord:	1747-1853	See under Grassington		

LEASE RIGG		Egton		NZ828052
Production:	Iron	Ore(tons)		Value (£)
	1837-1850	No detailed returns		
Comment:	1837-1850	Pecten Seam		
Mineral Lord:	1837-1850	James Pearson		
Worked by:	1837-1850	Whitby Stone Co.		

LEGERINS		Grassington		SE022679
Production:	Lead	Ore(tons)	Lead (tons)	Value (£)
	1741		0.92	
	1751		8.66	
	1753		13.18	
	1754		21.30	
	1765		0.81	
	1766		0.49	
	1768		0.21	
	1769		0.28	
	1770		0.81	
	1771		1.08	
	1772		1.34	
	1774		0.11	
	1775		0.58	
	1777		10.03	
	1778		5.15	

	1779		0.18
	1780		6.05
	1781		0.49
	1782		0.28
	1783		3.60
	1784		1.21
	1785		0.99
	1787		0.12
	1788		0.20
	1799		0.25
	1803		1.25
	1804		3.00
	1805		5.15
	1806		3.35
	1807		0.85
	1808		3.80
	1809	1.85	0.95
	1810	0.40	0.20
	1811	2.55	1.40
	1812	15.28	8.45
	1813	1.73	1.00
	1814	9.23	5.15
	1815	4.40	2.65
	1816	2.63	1.40
	1817	1.95	1.25
	1820	3.53	1.80
	1838	5.73	3.00
	1846	2.68	1.30
	1847	7.65	
	1848	4.65	5.00
	1849	4.65	2.75
	1850	2.75	1.35
	1851	2.60	1.55
	1852	2.55	1.60
Mineral Lord:	1741-1852 See under Grassington		

LEVEN VALE Kildale NZ625089

Production: Iron Ore(tons) Value (£)

1872-1874 No detailed returns

Comment: 1864-1871 Called Warren Moor

1872-1874 Top Seam

Worked by: 1872-1874 Leven Vale Ironstone Co.

Agent: 1872-1874 G. Hirst

LEVISHAM Pickering SE823930

Production:	Iron	Ore(tons)	Value (£)
	1863-1874	No detailed returns	
Comment:	1863-1874	Top Seam - No workable ironstone found	
Mineral Lord:	1863-1874	James Walker	
Worked by:	1863-1866	James Walker	
	1863-1874	William Walker	
Agent:	1863-1874	Thomas Watson	

LEYBURN MOOR ENCLOSURES Leyburn SE095922

Production:	Lead	Ore(tons)	Lead (tons)	Value (£)
	1848	No detailed return		
Comment:	1848	Data from Lord Bolton's Lead Book		
Mineral Lord:	1848	See under Keld Heads		
Worked by:	1848	Thomas Edmundson and Edward Peacock		

LEYBURN AND PRESTON MOOR Leyburn SE082931

Production:	Lead	Ore(tons)	Lead (tons)	Value (£)
	1845	No detailed return		
Comment:	1845	Data from Lord Bolton's Lead Book		
Mineral Lord:	1845	See under Keld Heads		
Worked by:	1845	Rev. John Orde & Co.		

LIMLEY Stonebeck Up SE099757

Production:	Lead	Ore(tons)	Lead (tons)	Value (£)
	1889	No detailed return		
	1891-1893	No detailed returns		
	1894	140.50	95.00	773.00
	1895	37.00	25.00	204.00
	1896	28.75	19.00	155.00
	1897	40.00	27.00	216.00
	1898	35.00	24.00	189.00
	1899	24.00	17.00	250.00
	1900	11.00	8.00	104.00
Comment:	1903-1908	Standing		
Worked by:	1889-1907	Joseph Cradock		
	1908	Joseph Cradock & Co.		

Employment:		Underground	Surface	Total
	1898-1900	6	2	8
	1901	2	2	4

LINGDALE Moorsholm NZ676165

Production:	Iron	Ore(tons)	Value (£)
	1877	19964.80	
	1878	82334.00	
	1879	65190.70	
	1880	98531.30	

	1881	118134.70
Comment:	1882-1931	No detailed returns
	1945-1962	No detailed returns
	1931	Discontinued August
	1931-1937	Standing
	1962	Abandoned
Worked by:	1871-1874	J. Pease & Jos.W. Pease
	1875-1880	Jos. W. Pease & Co.
	1881-1950	Pease and Partners Ltd
	1951-1962	The Lingdale Ironstone Mines Ltd
Agent:	1873-1874	William Cockburn
	1875-1907	Christopher Heslop
	1908-1917	W.B. Coxon
	1919-1931	James Howe
	1932	J.F. Payne
	1933-1938	George C. Heslop
	1945-1951	C.H.A. Howe
	1954	G.W. Pearson
	1954-1959	J. Clement
	1960-1962	J.G. Sparkes

Employment:		Underground	Surface	Total
	1883			126
	1894	75	23	98
	1895	89	33	122
	1896	121	52	173
	1897	138	50	188
	1898	101	39	140
	1899	105	46	151
	1900	105	50	155
	1901	46	43	89
	1902	79	75	154
	1903	45	50	99
	1904	162	59	221
	1905	165	63	228
	1906	194	72	266
	1907	244	79	323
	1908	257	103	360
	1909	317	83	400
	1910	352	100	452
	1911	373	112	485
	1912	390	108	498
	1913	406	117	523
	1914	414	112	526
	1915	302	98	400
	1916	275	86	361
	1917	308	101	409

1918	295	101	396
1919	301	102	403
1920	382	100	482
1921	392	113	505
1922	66	33	99
1923	183	79	262
1924	259	94	353
1925	222	89	311
1926	407	107	514
1927	421	112	533
1928	435	111	546
1929	404	109	513
1930	425	115	540
1931	382	104	486
1932	3	8	11
1933	5	11	16
1934	7	13	20
1935	7	11	18
1936	7	13	20
1937	7	13	20
1938	10	10	20
1940	73	37	110
1941	172	78	250
1942	159	93	252
1943	175	103	278
1944	171	99	270
1945	137	77	214
1948	102	69	171
1950	104	69	173
1951	107	52	159
1954	128	80	208
1955	100	65	165
1956	95	68	163
1957	90	71	161
1958	90	71	161
1959	114	64	178
1960	111	65	176
1961	135	68	203
1962	128	64	192

Comment: 1908 Includes Ayton

LINTON PASTURE Linton in Craven SD997628

Production:	Lead	Ore(tons)	Lead (tons)	Value (£)
	1789		0.23	

Comment:	1736-1810	See Also Swinden
	1789	Smelted at Grassington
Mineral Lord:	1789	See under Grassington
Worked by:	1789	John Lupton

LITTLE PUNCHARD Arkengarthdale NY964042

Production:	Lead	Ore(tons)	Lead (tons)	Value (£)
	1907-1916	No detailed return		

Comment:	1910-1916	Standing
Worked by:	1907-1916	"CB", Lead Mines Ltd
Agent:	1907-1916	Thomas Harker

Employment:		Underground	Surface	Total
	1907-1909	See Agnes		

LIVERTON Loftus NZ710182

Production:	Iron	Ore(tons)	Value (£)
	1871	290000.00	72500.00
	1872	266236.00	
	1873	278108.00	83432.00
	1874	243035.00	72910.50
	1875	311014.00	
	1876	262844.00	
	1877	135557.00	
	1902-1922	No detailed returns	

Comment:	1866-1871	Sinking
	1877-1881	Standing
	1877-1878	In liquidation, sold in 1878
	1901-1903	Standing for redevelopment
	1921-1923	Standing
	1923	Abandoned
Mineral Lord:	1871-1923	Downe Estates
	1906-1923	Mr Petch
Worked by:	1875-1878	Liverton Ironstone Co. Ltd
	1880-1882	Liverton Co. Ltd
	1882-1883	H.F. & John G. Swan
	1883-1923	Cargo Fleet Iron Co. Ltd
Agent:	1872-1881	Fran. Fox
	1873-1880	George Lee
	1879	F.J.H. Lascelles
	1881	Charles A. Rowlandson
	1883-1903	William Walker
	1903-1907	George A. Burton
	1908-1917	Armstrong Varty
	1918-1923	F.M. Robinson
Secretary:	1866-1876	J. Farrow
	1880-1882	H. Brown

Employment:		Underground	Surface	Total
	1883			35
	1894	130	76	206
	1895	133	67	202
	1896	135	72	207

1897	135	77	212
1898	126	103	229
1899	148	79	227
1900	140	90	230
1901	108	78	286
1902	7	30	37
1903	4	164	168
1904	222	122	344
1905	352	175	527
1906	347	139	386
1907	299	130	429
1908	319	138	457
1909	280	130	410
1910	313	129	442
1911	311	138	449
1912	299	129	428
1913	232	119	351
1914	247	117	364
1915	199	107	306
1916	213	115	328
1917	219	105	324
1918	222	114	236
1919	238	129	367
1920	219	114	333
1921	193	100	293
1922	5	15	20
1923	8	15	23

LOFTUS Loftus NZ713193

Production:	Iron	Ore(tons)	Value (£)
	1865	17688.00	5306.40
	1866	114138.00	28534.50
	1867	181671.00	45417.70
	1868	243903.00	60975.70
	1869	263544.60	65886.00
	1870	311221.00	77805.20
	1871	387376.90	96844.20
	1872	432455.00	
	1873	392748.00	117839.40
	1874	423251.00	126975.00
	1875	484464.40	
	1876	562459.00	
	1877	605244.50	
	1878	315497.00	
	1879	280819.40	
	1880	584049.80	
	1881	654096.60	

	1902-1938	No detailed returns
	1940-1958	No detailed returns
Comment:	1885	Absorbed Whitecliffe
	1938	Discontinued August
	1959	Abandoned
Mineral Lord:	1848-1958	Zetland Estate
Worked by:	1848-1850	Bolckow, Vaughan & Co.
	1850-1864	Losh, Wilson & Bell
	1866-1874	Jos.W. Pease & J. Pease
	1875-1880	Jos.W. Pease & Co.
	1881-1950	Pease and Partners Ltd
	1951-1958	Skinningrove Iron Co. Ltd
Agent:	1866-1874	William Cockburn
	1875-1881	William France
	1882-1918	W. Moore
	1919-1931	F. Seymour
	1932	T. Wheatman
	1933-1935	George C. Heslop
	1936	T. Wheatman
	1937-1951	George C. Heslop
	1954-1958	C.H.A. Howe

Employment:		Underground	Surface	Total
	1883			586
	1894	317	69	386
	1895	565	90	655
	1896	676	105	781
	1897	748	104	852
	1898	740	86	826
	1899	737	103	840
	1900	651	105	756
	1901	540	74	614
	1902	696	69	765
	1903	681	97	778
	1904	656	98	754
	1905	677	98	775
	1906	696	141	837
	1907	692	141	833
	1908	718	154	872
	1909	815	157	972
	1910	795	162	957
	1911	775	177	952
	1912	714	163	877
	1913	732	158	890
	1914	727	155	882
	1915	513	109	622
	1916	507	114	621

1917	551	117	668
1918	527	138	665
1919	570	137	707
1920	614	128	742
1921	604	132	736
1922	512	92	604
1923	591	112	703
1924	663	110	773
1925	629	107	736
1926	601	103	704
1927	637	100	737
1928	644	102	746
1929	640	102	742
1930	607	99	706
1931	694	98	792
1932	707	100	807
1933	469	75	544
1935	581	87	668
1936	588	113	701
1937	579	128	707
1938	488	122	610
1940	449	116	566
1941	458	125	583
1942	461	121	582
1943	443	120	563
1944	412	118	530
1945	361	91	452
1948	274	90	364
1950	273	90	363
1951	257	88	345
1954	252	85	337
1955	252	85	337
1956	162	14	176
1957	162	14	176
1958	131	53	184

LOFTUS, NORTH Brotton NZ709194

Production:	Iron	Ore(tons)	Value (£)
	1872	No detailed returns	
	1873	94583.00	28374.90
	1874	125158.00	37547.40
	1875	114528.00	
	1876	127905.00	
	1877	50665.30	
	1886-1889	No detailed returns	
	1894-1907	No detailed returns	

Comment: 1876-1877 Carlin How

	1877-1885 Standing			
	1890-1893 Standing			
Mineral Lord:	1872-1881 Maynard			
Worked by:	1872-1874 Lofthouse Iron Co.			
	1875-1876 Lofthouse Iron Co. Ltd			
	1877-1879 Loftus Iron Co. Ltd			
	1880-1889 Skinningrove Iron Co. Ltd			
	1894-1907 Pease and Partners Ltd			
Agent:	1872-1877 Ed. Hann			
	1876-1879 J. Westray			
	1886-1889 John Cowie			
	1894-1907 W. Moore			

Employment:		Underground	Surface	Total
	1895	5	16	21
	1896	10	29	39
	1897	10	31	41
	1898	10	31	41
	1899	10	31	41
	1900	10	28	38
	1901	10	31	41
	1902	10	31	41
	1903	5	17	22
	1904	5	18	23
	1905	6	10	16
Comment:	1894	Included with Loftus		
	1906-1907	Included with Loftus		

LOLLY SCAR Stonebeck Down SE107725

Production:	Lead	Ore(tons)	Lead (tons)	Value (£)
	1889-1893	No detailed returns		
	1894	557.50	371.00	3066.00
	1895	244.00	162.00	1342.00
	1896	85.25	56.00	464.00
	1897	250.00	166.00	1361.00
	1898	764.00	508.00	4159.00
	1899	728.00	512.00	5351.00
	1900	649.00	456.00	6165.00
	1901	540.00	359.00	4536.00
	1902	569.00	378.00	3556.00
	1903	720.00	479.00	4500.00
	1904	216.00	140.00	1510.00
	1905	83.00	55.00	600.00
	1906	70.00	44.00	560.00
	1907	103.00	70.00	930.00
	1908	85.00	65.00	601.00
	1909	78.00	59.00	527.00
	1910	5.00	4.00	50.00

Production:	Barytes	Ore(tons)	Value (£)
	1908	10.00	44.00

Comment: 1910-1911 Abandoned

Worked by: 1889-1911 Joseph Cradock

Employment:		Underground	Surface	Total
	1898	19	7	26
	1899	18	8	26
	1900	20	9	29
	1901	35	7	42
	1902	36	8	44
	1903	34	6	40
	1904	36	3	39
	1905	27	4	31
	1906	24	3	27
	1907	19	4	23
	1908	14	3	17
	1909	10	3	13
	1910-1911	4	6	10

LONGACRES Skelton NZ669195

Production:	Iron	Ore(tons)	Value (£)
	1876	102325.00	
	1877	251709.00	
	1878	246290.00	
	1879	195847.00	
	1880	240315.00	
	1881	199925.20	
	1902-1914	No detailed returns	
	1920-1954	No detailed returns	

Comment:	1915-1919	Standing
	1920-1934	Includes North Skelton
	1954	Abandoned
Worked by:	1873-1928	Bolckow, Vaughan & Co. Ltd
	1929-1954	Dorman, Long & Co. Ltd
Agent:	1875-1883	George Robinson
	1884-1910	John Thomson
	1911	A.M. Hedley
	1912-1917	F.M. Robinson
	1918-1927	H. Palmer
	1927	J.C. Brown
	1928-1932	J.R. Tomlinson
	1933-1951	T.E. Slater
	1954	G.A. Roberts

Employment:		Underground	Surface	Total
	1883			315
	1894	177	38	215
	1895	189	32	221
	1896	185	34	229
	1897	193	30	223
	1898	189	30	219
	1899	232	25	257
	1900	233	35	268
	1901	257	30	287
	1902	278	37	315
	1903	267	39	306
	1904	259	39	298
	1905	308	44	352
	1906	303	30	333
	1907	320	34	354
	1908	306	41	347
	1909	304	40	344
	1910	289	39	328
	1911	320	40	360
	1912	265	40	305
	1913	243	37	280
	1914	248	37	285
	1915	149	28	177
	1916	9	7	16
	1917	8	7	15
	1918	25	7	32
	1919	34	16	50
	1920	428	108	536
	1921	367	109	475
	1922	12	20	32
	1923	105	163	268
	1924	33	35	68
	1925	230	72	302
	1926	269	81	350
	1927	282	70	352
	1928	278	67	345
	1929	369	69	438
	1930	352	62	414
	1931	359	56	415
	1932	363	61	424
	1933	384	69	453
	1934	564	88	652
	1935	181	7	188
	1936	175	8	183
	1937	213	9	222
	1938	82	9	91

1940	96	14	110
1941	98	15	113
1942	93	18	101
1943	68	19	87
1944	77	15	92
1945	93	13	106
1948	67	12	79
1950	66	10	76
1951	60	10	70
1954	63	10	73

LONG CHANCE		Starbotton		SD968754
Production:	Lead	Ore(tons)	Lead (tons)	Value (£)
	1744		2.10	
Comment:	1744	Smelted at Buckden		
Mineral Lord:	1744	See under Grassington		
Worked by:	1744	Mr Simondson		

LONSDALE		Kildale		NZ615105
Production:	Iron	Ore(tons)		Value (£)
	1867	47695.70		11923.90
Comment:	1867	Lonsdale Vale		
Mineral Lord:	1865-1874	Trustees of R.B. Livesey		
Worked by:	1867-1874	Lonsdale Vale Iron Co.		

LONSDALE 12 MEERS		Grinton		SD984958
Production:	Lead	Ore(tons)	Lead (tons)	Value (£)
	1767	441.60	346.70	
Comment:	1767	Includes output from 1761		
	1761-1767	Part of Whitaside		
Mineral Lord:	1761-1767	See under Grinton Liberty		
Worked by:	1761-1767	Richard Lonsdale & Co.		

LORD NELSON LEVEL		Grassington		SE019669
Production:	Lead	Ore(tons)	Lead (tons)	Value (£)
	1808		12.70	
	1809	33.30	22.35	
	1810	0.75	0.30	
	1813	3.05	1.75	
	1814	5.18	2.75	
	1817	0.20	0.15	
Comment:	1810	Waste ores		
Mineral Lord:	1808-1817	See under Grassington		

LOSS GILL Grassington SE027656

Production:	Lead	Ore(tons)	Lead (tons)	Value (£)
	1736		0.92	
	1737		1.02	
	1747		0.26	
	1748		0.58	
	1750		0.73	
	1753		0.58	
	1773		1.49	
	1774		0.10	
	1782		0.13	
	1789		1.33	
	1790		0.95	
	1792		0.30	
	1808		0.60	
	1813	0.70	0.35	
	1829	2.08	0.12	

Mineral Lord: 1736-1829 See under Grassington

LOTHERSDALE & SKIPTON Lothersdale SD942453

Production:	Barytes	Ore(tons)	Value (£)
	1856-1857	1000.00	

Comment: 1856-1857 Probably Raygill

LOVER GILL Muker SD879964

Production:	Lead	Ore(tons)	Lead (tons)	Value (£)
	1868-1871	No detailed returns		

Comment: 1751-1844 See Glovergill
Mineral Lord: 1751-1871 See AD Mines

LOW SMELT MILL Grassington SE006633

Production:	Lead	Ore(tons)	Lead (tons)	Value (£)
	1829	1.08	0.35	
	1842	0.75	0.35	

Comment: 1829-1842 Slag etc from Low Mill, abandoned 1793
Mineral Lord: 1829-1842 See under Grassington

LOWNATHWAITE Melbecks NY935006

Production:	Lead	Ore(tons)	Lead (tons)	Value (£)
	1693	No detailed return		
	1705	18.45		
	1736	39.20		
	1750	84.80		
	1751	119.20		
	1752	117.80		
	1753	40.90		
	1755	35.20		

	1756	21.90	
	1762-1769	No detailed returns	
	1817		58.00
	1818		20.00
	1819		61.00
	1820		56.00
	1821		152.00
	1822		91.00
	1823		67.00
	1824		120.00
	1825		155.00
	1826		130.00
	1827		156.00
	1828		231.00
	1829		208.18
	1830		82.36
	1831		27.61
	1832		11.02
	1833		10.77
	1834		18.75
	1835		30.38
	1836		32.35
	1873-1883	No detailed returns	
Comment:	1817-1828	Data from Jennings Thesis	
	1829-1836	Data from NYCRO ZLB 2/134 & 136	
	1705	November to December	
	1735-1736	December to May	
	1750	June to December	
	1750-1751	December to December	
	1751-1752	December to December	
	1752-1753	December to June	
	1755	June to December	
	1755-1756	December to June	
	1812-1824	Including Arngill, Keldside & Swinnergill	
	1824-1832	Including Arngill & Swinnergill	
	1836-1872	See Blakethwaite	
Mineral Lord:	1693-1836	See AD Mines	
Worked by:	1705	Thomas Wharton (5th Lord)	
	1736-1756	Trustees of the Duke of Wharton	
	1693	James Gorton & Co.	
	1762-1769	Richard Alderson & Co.	
	1784	George Jackson & Co.	
	1812-1832	Hopper & Co.	
	1833-1836	Sundry waste workers	
	1836-1847	Ottiwell Tomlin & Co.	
	1848-1859	Thomas Bradley & Co.	
	1860-1866	Blakethwaite Co.	

	1867-1872	Sir George Denys		
	1873-1883	AD Lead Mining Company Ltd		
Agent:	1801	Captain Metcalfe		

LOW RAKE		Arkengarthdale		NY980029
Production:	Lead	Ore(tons)	Lead (tons)	Value (£)
	1749	59.90		
	1750	43.60		
	1782	10.40		
	1783	4.90		
	1784	3.50		
	1785	2.20		
	1786	39.80		
	1787	14.00		
	1788	3.90		
	1789	12.90		
	1790	2.80		
Comment:	1749	January to December		
	1750	January to June		
	1782-1783	November to November inclusive		
	1783-1790	December to November inclusive		
	1790-1791	December to May inclusive		
Mineral Lord:	1749-1791	See Arkengarthdale		
Worked by:	1749-1759	Charles Turner		
	1782-1791	Charles Sleigh, William Hoar & Charles Foster		
Employment:		Underground	Surface	Total
	1782-1783	4		
	1783-1784	5		
	1784-1785	2		
	1785-1786	1		
	1786-1787	4		
	1787-1788	3		
	1788-1789	2		
	1789-1790	3		
	1790-1791	2		

LUMPSEY		Brotton	NZ685188
Production:	Iron	Ore(tons)	Value (£)
	1881	510.00	
	1882-1930	No detailed returns	
	1933-1954	No detailed returns	
Comment:	1880	Sinking	
	1926-1938	Includes Carlinhow	
	1931-1932	Standing	
	1954	Abandoned	
Worked by:	1880-1922	Bell Brothers Ltd	
	1923-1950	Dorman, Long & Co. Ltd	

Agent:	1880-1881	Addison L. Steavenson		
	1881	Thomas Bell		
	1881-1918	D.W. Dixon		
	1919-1932	John Chapman		
	1933-1945	J.R. Tomlinson		
	1948-1954	G.A. Miller		
Employment:		Underground	Surface	Total
	1883			139
	1894	224	52	276
	1895	274	75	349
	1896	281	56	337
	1897	307	62	369
	1898	316	76	392
	1899	291	77	368
	1900	288	103	391
	1901	305	103	408
	1902	286	103	389
	1903	285	93	378
	1904	280	94	374
	1905	309	88	397
	1906	346	93	439
	1907	362	94	456
	1908	361	109	470
	1909	364	103	467
	1910	371	105	476
	1911	368	97	465
	1912	369	97	466
	1913	380	99	479
	1914	347	98	445
	1915	289	90	379
	1916	321	95	416
	1917	387	124	511
	1918	364	129	493
	1919	343	125	468
	1920	346	125	471
	1921	346	137	483
	1922	27	52	79
	1923	22	40	62
	1925	295	92	387
	1926	283	94	377
	1927	312	99	411
	1928	305	102	407
	1929	364	106	470
	1930	364	92	456
	1931	351	90	441
	1932	8	14	22
	1933	285	62	367

1934	338	71	409
1935	369	72	441
1936	490	78	568
1937	540	85	665
1938	469	81	550
1940	495	89	584
1941	465	92	557
1942	468	88	556
1943	462	89	551
1944	410	83	493
1945	300	63	363
1948	216	61	277
1950	215	60	275
1951	183	46	229
1954	159	45	204

Comment: 1924 Included with Carlin How

LUNEHEAD Lunedale NY846205

Production:

Lead	Ore(tons)	Lead (tons)	Value (£)
1741	171.30		
1745	2.50		
1746	14.40		
1757	56.95		
1758	32.01		
1762	1.75		
1796	14.95		
1797	16.00		
1806	36.00		
1807	4.40		
1833	2.45		
1834	4.38		
1835	130.80		
1836	184.95		
1837	215.45		
1838	331.20		
1839	268.75		
1841	209.05		
1842	112.55		
1843	156.00		
1844	123.25		
1845	106.25		
1852	32.00	24.00	
1853	31.20	23.20	
1854-1855 No detailed returns			
1856	4.30	3.00	
1857-1867 No detailed returns			
1868	86.50	64.50	

1869	140.60	105.40	
1870	72.20	54.00	
1871	38.70	27.80	
1884	12.00		71.00
1885	77.00		481.00
1886	47.00	32.00	235.00
1887	30.00		
1888	95.00		665.00
1889	81.00	57.00	618.00
1890	18.00	13.00	126.00
1891	4.00	3.00	28.00
1904	12.00	7.00	72.00
1906	5.00	4.00	50.00
1907	2.00	1.00	16.00
1908-1909	4.00	2.00	20.00
1910	3.00	2.00	15.00
1911	5.00	3.00	30.00
1912	2.00	2.00	17.00
1913	15.00	9.00	120.00
1919 No detailed return			
1920	32.00		
1921	8.00		
1922	10.00		
1923	10.00		
1924	6.00		
1926	5.00		
1927	4.00		
1928	5.00		
1929	6.00		
1932	10.00		
1933	5.00		
1934	7.00		
1936	6.00		
1940-1942 No detailed returns			
1961-1981 No detailed returns			

Comment:

1741-1845	Data from DCRO D/ST/B2
1796	May to July
1797	August to October
1797	August to October
1857-1860	See Pateley District
1855-1867	London Lead Company's Yorkshire Mines
1906	Lead estimated
1913	Lead estimated
1920	Inc. Swaledale, Merrybent, W. Silverband
1926	Inc. Old Gang

Production:	Barytes	Ore(tons)	Value (£)
	1884	53.00	47.00
	1886	1662.00	425.00
	1887	1254.00	
	1888	789.00	325.00
	1889	829.00	414.00
	1890	368.00	184.00
	1891	343.00	171.00
	1892	380.00	190.00
	1893	362.00	70.00
	1894	290.00	31.00
	1895	749.00	936.00
	1896	684.00	228.00
	1897	1556.00	962.00
	1898	2390.00	1100.00
	1899	2358.00	1050.00
	1900	2332.00	1025.00
	1901	694.00	955.00
	1902	1619.00	890.00
	1903	1348.00	830.00
	1904	169.00	259.00
	1905	887.00	1255.00
	1906	1251.00	1739.00
	1907	2016.00	1822.00
	1908	2712.00	2001.00
	1909	2001.00	1901.00
	1910	1814.00	1743.00
	1911	1650.00	1815.00
	1912	1542.00	1819.00
	1913	1967.00	1691.00
	1914-1919	No detailed returns	
	1920	1534.00	
	1921	561.00	
	1922	934.00	
	1923	1373.00	
	1924	1351.00	
	1925	1202.00	
	1926	922.00	
	1927	771.00	
	1928	937.00	
	1929	1158.00	
	1930	899.00	
	1931	716.00	
	1932	894.00	
	1933	945.00	
	1934	955.00	
	1935	1412.00	

	1936	887.00		
	1937	214.00		
	1938	No detailed return		
	1940-1942	No detailed returns		
	1961-1981	No detailed returns		
Comment:	1881-1882	Standing		
	1888-1889	Including Virgin Moss		
	1938	Discontinued August		
	1939	Standing		
	1942	Abandoned		
Mineral Lord:	1656-1767	Bowes family		
	1767-2000	Bowes family - Earls of Strathmore		
	1656-1707	William Bowes		
	1707-1760	George Bowes		
	1760-1767	Mary Eleanor Bowes		
	1767-1776	John (Lyon) Bowes, 9th Earl		
	1776-1820	John Bowes, 10th Earl		
	1820-1846	Thomas Bowes, 11th Earl		
	1846-1865	Thomas George Bowes, 12th Earl		
	1865-1904	Claude Bowes, 13th Earl		
	1904-1944	Claude Bowes, 14th Earl		
	1944-1949	Patrick Bowes, 15th Earl		
	1949-1972	Timothy Bowes, 16th Earl		
	1972-1987	Fergus M.C. Bowes, 17th Earl		
	1987-2000	Michael F. Bowes, 18th Earl		
Worked by:	1806-1807	Messrs Hopper & Co.		
	1831	Mr Kemp & Co.		
	1834-1855	Lunehead Mining Co.		
	1855-1882	London Lead Co.		
	1884-1885	John Slack & Co.		
	1886-1887	W. Williams		
	1888-1903	Lunehead Lead & Barytes Mining Co.		
	1904-1928	J.G. Reynoldson		
	1929-1935	N. Reynoldson		
	1936-1938	Exors. of N. Reynoldson		
	1939-1981	Athole G. Allen (Stockton) Ltd		
Agent:	1844-1882	Robert W. Bainbridge		
	1884-1885	John Slack		
	1886-1901	W. Williams		
	1902-1903	J.P. Buck		
	1904-1928	J.G. Reynoldson		
	1929-1935	N. Reynoldson		
Employment:		Underground	Surface	Total
	1862	48		
	1898		8	8
	1899-1903	3	6	9
	1904	3	9	12

1905	8	15	23
1906	8	16	24
1907	10	15	25
1908	14	14	28
1909	14	10	24
1910	12	14	26
1911	10	18	28
1912	12	13	25
1913	13	14	27
1914	10	12	22
1915	10	13	23
1916	11	24	35
1917	13	17	30
1918	12	25	37
1919	18	20	38
1920	13	17	30
1921	10	10	20
1922	9	12	21
1923	11	17	28
1924	11	16	27
1925	12	14	26
1926	10	14	24
1927	10	13	23
1928	11	11	22
1929		11	11
1930	10	11	21
1931	6	9	15
1932	8	10	18
1933	7	10	17
1934	9	10	19
1935	11	11	22
1936	7	10	17
1937	3	10	13
1938		10	10
1940	2	2	4
1941	2	4	6
1942	2	1	3

MAIZEBECK Lunedale NY799269

Production:	Lead	Ore(tons)	Lead (tons)	Value (£)
	1842	5.35		
	1843	12.20		
	1845	1.80		

Comment: 1837 See Birtle
1844 See Birtle
Mineral Lord: 1831-1845 See Lunehead
Worked by: 1831 John Coatsworth & Co.
1844-1845 London Lead Company

MALHAM LIBERTY		Malham		SD876640
Production:	Lead	Ore(tons)	Lead (tons)	Value (£)
	1747		0.45	
	1749		0.24	
	1809	51.90	24.35	
	1811	33.95	18.00	
	1812	23.50	12.35	
	1814	33.25	18.00	
	1815	0.30	0.20	
	1819	48.25	26.00	
	1820	1.50	0.60	
	1828	24.85	13.30	
	1830	40.75	21.00	
	1831	30.10	17.20	
	1832	15.73	6.35	
	1833	6.40	2.65	
	1834	10.15	4.35	
	1835	7.13	3.00	
	1836	15.55	7.60	
	1837	16.68	7.60	
	1839	14.70	7.90	
	1840	4.13	1.85	
	1872-1877	No detailed returns		
Comment:	1747-1840	Smelted at Grassington		

Production:	Calamine	Ore(tons)	Value (£)
	1810	240.60	
	1811	268.75	
	1812	414.05	
Comment:	1788-1812	Calamine Producer	
Mineral Lord:	1747	Squire Lister	
	1811-1820	Lord Ribblesdale	
Worked by:	1788-1806	George Tennant & Co.	
	1806-1820	Lord Ribblesdale	
	1828-1831	Jacob Shaw & Co.	
	1832-1840	Edward Watson	

MANGHAM 3 MEERS		Grassington		
Production:	Lead	Ore(tons)	Lead (tons)	Value (£)
	1810	0.45	0.20	
	1811	0.30	0.15	
	1812	4.60	2.55	
	1814	5.30	2.95	
	1815	1.40	0.70	
	1821	3.35	1.70	
	1822	2.20	1.20	
	1823	2.45	1.20	

	1825	1.65	0.65	
	1831	0.73	0.45	
	1832	2.65	1.50	
Mineral Lord:	1810-1832	See under Grassington		

MARCH SHAFT		Arkengarthdale		
Production:	Lead	Ore(tons)	Lead (tons)	Value (£)
	1782	3.40		
Comment:	1782	November 1782 to April 1783 inclusive		
Mineral Lord:	1782-1783	See Arkengarthdale		
Worked by:	1782-1783	Charles Sleigh, William Hoar & Charles Foster		
Employment:		Underground	Surface	Total
	1782-1783	1		

MARGRAVE PARK		Skelton	NZ638158
Production:	Iron	Ore(tons)	Value (£)
	1867-1869	No detailed returns	
	1871	No detailed return	
	1873	110017.00	33005.10
	1874	195327.00	58598.00
	1875	102434.00	
Comment:	1867	See Normanby	
	1869	See Normanby	
	1871	See Spa	
	1875	Or Stanghow	
Worked by:	1863-1872	Bell Bros.	
	1873-1874	John Gjers, Mills & Co.	
Agent:	1863-1872	Addison L. Steavenson	
	1873-1874	John Gjers	

MARTIN SHAFT		Arkengarthdale		NY979029
Production:	Lead	Ore(tons)	Lead (tons)	Value (£)
	1783	0.30		
	1786	0.20		
Comment:	1783	May to November inclusive		
	1783-1786	Standing: December to November inclusive		
	1786	December 1786 to May 1788 inclusive		
Mineral Lord:	1783-1787	See Arkengarthdale		
Worked by:	1783-1787	Charles Sleigh, William Hoar & Charles Foster		
Employment:		Underground	Surface	Total
	1782-1783	1		
	1786-1787	1		

MARY UMER		Grassington		
Production:	Lead	Ore(tons)	Lead (tons)	Value (£)
	1813	0.43	0.15	
	1816	0.60	0.02	
Mineral Lord:	1810-1832	See under Grassington		

MASON RAKE Grinton SE007969

Production:	Lead	Ore(tons)	Lead (tons)	Value (£)
	1785		7.15	
	1786		1.74	
	1787		0.47	
	1788		0.80	

Comment: 1785-1788 Also called Birks
Mineral Lord: 1785-1788 See under Grinton

MASON'S SHAFT Grassington SE016659

Production:	Lead	Ore(tons)	Lead (tons)	Value (£)
	1823	15.55	8.60	

Mineral Lord: 1823 See under Grassington

MERRYBENT Melsonby NZ213074

Production:	Lead	Ore(tons)	Lead(tons)	Silver(ozs)	Value (£)
	1864	150.00	107.00		
	1865	345.60	241.50		
	1866	205.00	150.00	750.00	
	1867	178.00	134.90		
	1868	No detailed return			
	1869	135.00	103.00		
	1870-1871	No detailed returns			
	1872	104.00	78.00		
	1873	131.50	97.80		
	1874	9.00	6.70		112.50
	1910	14.00	10.00	49.00	107.00
	1911	12.00	9.00		84.00
	1919-1920	No detailed returns			

Production:	Copper	Ore(tons)	Copper (tons)	Value (£)
	1863	463.00	46.30	
	1864	76.00	7.20	513.00
	1865	80.00	6.00	
	1870	80.70	28.50	
	1871	No detailed return		
	1872	137.00	8.20	1680.50
	1873	72.30	4.30	
	1874	128.50	35.30	2608.50
	1913	4.00		20.00
	1914-1928	No detailed returns		

Comment: 1863-1874 (P) Copper estimated
1877 In liquidation
1878-1879 Standing
1909 Low Merrybent
1912 Standing
1926-1927 Standing

	1928	Prospecting, Abandoned
Mineral Lord:	1861-1862	J. Alderson & F. Sanderson
Worked by:	1862-1865	Merrybent Mining Co.
	1865-1867	Merrybent & Middleton Tyas Mining & Smelting Co.
	1868-1879	New Merrybent & Middleton Tyas Mining & Smelting Co.
	1909	Christopher Calvert
	1910-1912	Merrybent Mining Syndicate Ltd
	1913	R. Wilson & W. Blackett & Son
	1914	Merrybent Mining Co.
	1915-1928	Robert Wilson
Agent:	1861-1862	Christopher Lonsdale Bradley
	1862-1866	John Cain
	1867-1869	Samuel Richardson
	1870-1871	John Tattersall
	1872-1877	Anthony Robinson
	1874-1877	W.B. Quelch
	1909	Christopher Calvert
	1910	George Miller
	1913-1928	Robert Wilson
Secretary:	1863-1866	Samuel Richardson
	1874-1877	John Wade

Employment:		Underground	Surface	Total
	1909	1		1
	1910-1911	3	3	6
	1913	4	2	6
	1914	6	1	7
	1915	3	2	5
	1916	4		4
	1917	3	1	4
	1918	4		4
	1919	4		4
	1920	3		3
	1921	3	2	5
	1922	3	2	5
	1923	3	1	4
	1924	5		5
	1925	3		3
	1928		3	3

MERRYBOTTON Arncliffe SD930682

Production:	Lead	Ore(tons)	Lead (tons)	Value (£)
	1791		0.24	
	1797		0.19	
	1798		0.16	

Comment:	1791-1798	Smelted at Grassington
	1779-1792	See Arncliffe Clowder
Mineral Lord:	1791-1798	See under Grassington
Worked by:	1791-1798	Marmaduke Proctor

MERRYFIELD Melbecks NY952013

Production:	Lead	Ore(tons)	Lead (tons)	Value (£)
	1736		29.20	
	1750		47.20	
	1751		83.80	
	1752		65.10	
	1753		20.90	
	1755		28.00	
	1756		12.00	

Comment:
1735-1736 December to May
1750 June to December
1752-1753 December to June
1755 June to December
1755-1756 December to June

MERRYFIELD Stonebeck Down SE109664

Production:	Lead	Ore(tons)	Lead (tons)	Value (£)
	1537-1844	No detailed returns		
	1861	23.40	15.20	
	1862	50.00	31.70	
	1863	24.70	14.50	
	1864	69.50	41.10	
	1865	90.40	53.00	
	1867	14.60	10.90	
	1872-1873	No detailed returns		
	1875	25.00	19.50	
	1876	150.00	112.50	

Comment:
1861-1898 Data from Hunt's Statistics
1874-1889 Old Merryfield & Stoney Groves

Mineral Lord:
1537-1538 Byland Abbey
1547-1568 Sir John Yorke
1568-1926 See Appletreewick Liberty

Worked by:
1537-1549 John Uvedale
1549-1554 Avery Uvedale
1757-1768 Storey & Co.
1793 John Horner & Co.
1815-1826 Atkinson, Jacques & Co.
1827-1841 William Watson & Co.
1841-1843 Cockerall & Co.
1841-1843 Yorkshire District Banking Co.
1854-1856 William Buck & Co.
1857-1866 Merryfield Mining Co. Ltd
1866-1871 Nidderdale Lead Mining Co. Ltd
1873-1874 Old Merryfield Lead Mining Co. Ltd
1874-1877 Ransgill Mining Co. Ltd
1887-1889 Bewerley United Lead & Barytes Mining Co. Ltd

Agent:
1860-1861 Capt. Williams
1860-1865 Joseph Broad Champion

	1866-1870	William Marshall		
	1875-1881	David Williams		
	1882-1891	Charles Williams		
Secretary:	1857-1866	George Yewdall		
	1867-1871	Thomas Sykes		
	1873-1874	E.J. Armstrong		
	1874-1877	James Lowick		
	1887-1889	John Prest Walker		
Employment:		Underground	Surface	Total
	1862	11		11
	1863	18		18

MERRYFIELD & PROSPEROUS Stonebeck Down & Bewerley SE112660

Production:	Lead	Ore(tons)	Lead (tons)	Value (£)
Comment:	1965-1969	Prospecting		
Worked by:	1965-1969	Bewerley Mines Ltd		

MEXICO Grassington SE027680

Production:	Lead	Ore(tons)	Lead (tons)	Value (£)
	1752		1.35	
	1753		0.82	
	1770		0.12	
Comment:	1744-1751	See Bycliffe Two Meers		
Mineral Lord:	1770	See under Grassington		
Worked by:	1752-1766	Robert Waterhouse & Co.		
	1766-1770	John Summers & Co.		

MIDDLE HILL AND STOREYS Appletreewick SE066621

Production:	Lead	Ore(tons)	Lead (tons)	Value (£)
	1880	7.30	5.40	70.00
Comment:	1880	Middle Hill Level		
	1880-1881	Middle Hill Level & Storeys Shaft		
Worked by:	1880-1881	Appletreewick Gill Head Mining Co.		
Agent:	1880-1881	Samuel Pullan		
Employment:		Underground	Surface	Total
	1880	8		8
	1881	4		4

MIDDLEMEER Starbotton SD951727

Production:	Lead	Ore(tons)	Lead (tons)	Value (£)
	1738		6.40	
	1741		2.40	
Worked by:	1738-1741	Mr Lister & John Wallase		
	1741		0.20	
Comment:	1738-1741	Smelted at Buckden		
	1739	See Hag End		
Mineral Lord:	1738-1741	See under Grassington		
Worked by:	1741	George Pickersgill		

MIDDLESMOOR Kettlewell SD962711

Production:	Lead	Ore(tons)	Lead (tons)	Value (£)
	1860		5.45	
	1861		5.50	
	1862		2.00	
	1863		1.50	
	1864		1.05	
	1865		0.50	
	1866		3.40	
	1867		5.65	
	1868		2.40	
	1869		3.75	
	1870		3.05	
	1871		1.70	
	1875		2.00	
Comment:	1860-1875	Smelted at Kettlewell		
	1867	10.20	5.60	
Comment:	1867	Data from Hunt's Statistics		
	1860	See Old Providence		
Mineral Lord:	1860-1875	Trust Lords of Kettlewell		
Worked by:	1860-1868	Appleton Charlton & Co.		
	1868-1869	William Pratt		
	1870-1871	Middlesmoor Mining Co.		
	1870	George Calvert Snr		
	1871	Christopher Wiseman		

MIDDLETON TYAS Middleton Tyas NZ232044

Production:	Copper	Ore(tons)	Copper (tons)	Value (£)
Comment:	1736-1766	See Hartley's		
	1740-1780	See Partners'		
	1750-1780	See Glebe		
	1863-1865	Not worked, See Merrybent		
	1891-1895	See Moulton		
	1891-1895	See South Fields		
Worked by:	1865-1867	Merrybent & Middleton Tyas Mining & Smelting Co.		
	1868-1879	New Merrybent & Middleton Tyas Mining & Smelting Co.		
Agent:	1865-1866	John Cain		

MIDDLE WHIM Arkengarthdale

Production:	Lead	Ore(tons)	Lead (tons)	Value (£)
	1787	38.30		
Comment:	1787	December 1787 to May 1788 inclusive		
Mineral Lord:	1787-1788	See Arkengarthdale		
Worked by:	1787-1788	Charles Sleigh, William Hoar & Charles Foster		

Employment:		Underground	Surface	Total
	1787-1788	8		

MIRKSIDE Eskdaleside Cum Ugglebarnby NZ816034

Production:	Iron	Ore(tons)		Value (£)
	1856-1861	No detailed returns		
Comment:	1856-1861	Top Seam		
	1858	See Grosmont		
Mineral Lord:	1856-1861	Trustees of Robert Cary Elwes		
Worked by:	1856-1858	Mirkside Iron Co.		

MOORCOCK Grassington SE020676

Production:	Lead	Ore(tons)	Lead (tons)	Value (£)
	1812	0.15	0.10	
	1813	0.45	0.30	
Mineral Lord:	1812-1813	See under Grassington		

MOOR COCK HEATHER Starbotton SD960770

Production:	Lead	Ore(tons)	Lead (tons)	Value (£)
	1780	No detailed return		
Comment:	1780	Driving a level		
Mineral Lord:	1780	See under Grassington		
Worked by:	1780	Lodge Calvert		

MOOR END Kettlewell SD955727

Production:	Lead	Ore(tons)	Lead (tons)	Value (£)
	1874		0.60	
	1875		1.40	
	1876		3.45	
	1877		8.15	
	1878		5.15	
	1879		3.90	
Comment:	1874-1879	Smelted at Kettlewell		
Mineral Lord:	1860-1879	Trust Lords of Kettlewell		
Worked by:	1860-1864	Wharfdale [sic] Mining Co. Ltd		
Agent:	1860-1864	Robert Place		

Employment:		Underground	Surface	Total
	1862	5		

MOOR END Newton in Bowland SD676510

Production:	Lead	Ore(tons)	Lead (tons)	Value (£)
	1575-1849	No detailed returns		
Comment:	1575	Silver Producer		
	1575	NB Bulmer's date is approximate.		
Mineral Lord:	1575	The Crown		
	1849	Mr Townley		
Worked by:	1575	Bevis Bulmer		
	1849	Stephen Eddy		

MOOR END Starbotton SD951727

Production:	Lead	Ore(tons)	Lead (tons)	Value (£)
	1821		4.90	
Comment:	1821	Smelted at Kettlewell		
	1822	1.44	0.55	
Worked by:	1821-1822	Thomas Wiseman		
	1822	2.36	1.45	
	1828	1.38	0.75	
Comment:	1822-1828	Smelted at Grassington		
	1737-1851	See Hag End		
	1856-1857	See Providence, New		
	1857-1879	See Wharfedale Mine		
Mineral Lord:	1821-1828	See under Grassington		
Worked by:	1822	William Holmes		
	1828	Ralph Lee		

MOORGATE Grassington SE025663

Production:	Lead	Ore(tons)	Lead (tons)	Value (£)
	1821	1.70	0.55	
	1831	32.60	13.45	
	1836	0.70	0.30	
Mineral Lord:	1821-1836	See under Grassington		

MOORHEN Grassington SE020676

Production:	Lead	Ore(tons)	Lead (tons)	Value (£)
	1799		3.30	
	1800		12.35	
	1801		7.80	
	1802		6.75	
	1803		11.50	
	1804		3.95	
	1805		0.35	
	1808		1.00	
Mineral Lord:	1799-1808	See under Grassington		

MORESDALE Arkengarthdale NZ053040

Production:	Lead	Ore(tons)	Lead (tons)	Value (£)
	1789	48.70		
Comment:	1789	December 1789 to November 1790 inclusive		
Mineral Lord:	1789-1790	See Arkengarthdale		
Worked by:	1789-1790	Charles Sleigh, William Hoar & Charles Foster		
Employment:		Underground	Surface	Total
	1789-179	10		

MOSS Grassington SE033672

Production:	Lead	Ore(tons)	Lead (tons)	Value (£)
	1808		0.30	
	1828	19.85	12.75	
	1831	5.83	3.80	
	1832	2.88	1.60	
	1838	1.90	0.90	
	1840	12.20	5.70	
	1841	8.95	4.00	
	1842	8.78	3.80	
	1843	4.58	1.75	
	1844	11.15	4.00	
	1845	3.90	1.85	
	1846	6.85	2.90	
	1847	4.30	2.25	
	1849	6.75	2.70	

Mineral Lord: 1808-1849 See under Grassington

MOSS, NEW Grassington SE032672

Production:	Lead	Ore(tons)	Lead (tons)	Value (£)
	1801		1.00	
	1804		4.10	
	1805		7.95	
	1807		14.65	
	1810	6.80	2.80	
	1827	0.38	0.20	
	1828	1.35	0.55	
	1832	1.93	0.95	
	1847	2.50	1.05	
	1848	0.73	0.35	
	1850	6.10	2.70	

Mineral Lord: 1801-1850 See under Grassington

MOSS, OLD Grassington SE035670

Production:	Lead	Ore(tons)	Lead (tons)	Value (£)
	1848	3.30	1.60	

Mineral Lord: 1848 See under Grassington

MOSSDALE Conistone with Kilnsey SE023703

Production:	Lead	Ore(tons)	Lead (tons)	Value (£)
	1854	5.00	3.51	
Comment:	1854 Smelted at Grassington			
	1859	104.40	74.15	
Comment:	1859 Smelted at Starbotton Cupola			
	1862	184.50	128.40	
	1872	10.50	8.10	
	1873	No detailed return		
Comment:	1862-1873 Data from Hunt's Statistics			
	1870		49.95	

	1871		45.00	
Comment:	1870-1871	Smelted at Kettlewell		
Mineral Lord:	1852-1878	See Conistone Liberty		
Worked by:	1853-1871	North Mossdale Mining Co.		
	1872-1874	Mossdale Lead Mining Co. Ltd		
Agent:	1764-1790	Jacob Bailey		
	1853	Thomas Job		
	1862-1868	Robert Place		
	1869	John Ralph Place		
	1871	John Hammond		
	1872-1878	John Ralph Place		
Secretary:	1872-1878	William R. Gibson		
Employment:		Underground	Surface	Total
	1872	13	5	18

MOSSDALE, SUN Conistone with Kilnsey SE022701

Production:	Lead	Ore(tons)	Lead (tons)	Value (£)
	1768		0.16	
Comment:	1768	Smelted at Grassington		
Mineral Lord:	1768	See Conistone Liberty		
Worked by:	1768	Thomas Frederick		

MOSSDALE 13 MEERS Conistone with Kilnsey SE023703

Production:	Lead	Ore(tons)	Lead (tons)	Value (£)
	1757	No detailed return		
Mineral Lord:	1757	See Conistone Liberty		
Worked by:	1757	William Bagshaw & Co.		
Agent:	1757	George Hasleham		
Employment:		Underground	Surface	Total
	1757	10		

MOSSDALE 33 MEERS, NORTH
Conistone with Kilnsey SE024702

Production:	Lead	Ore(tons)	Lead (tons)	Value (£)
	1772		61.84	
	1773		76.10	
	1775		10.90	
	1778		0.98	
	1779		87.41	
	1781		3.20	
	1782		10.40	
	1783		5.30	
	1788		4.75	
Comment:	1775	Clear Lead (i.e. duty taken at 1/13)		
	1775	Smelted at Grassington		
	1772-1788	Smelted at Kilnsey or Kettlewell		
Mineral Lord:	1772-1788	See Conistone Liberty		
Worked by:	1763-1781	Thomas Smith & Co.		
	1781-1790	Francis Wardle Co.		

MOULDS Arkengarthdale NY997026

Production:	Lead	Ore(tons)	Lead (tons)	Value (£)
	1871	28.95		
	1872	77.35		
	1873	40.85		
	1874	10.85		
	1875	2.05		
	1876	3.80		
	1877	3.35		
	1878	4.70		
	1879	4.10		
	1880	58.40		
	1881	31.95		
	1882	29.05		
	1883	19.75		
	1884	38.00		
	1885	7.05		
	1886	15.10		
	1887	32.50		
	1888	55.65		
	1889	9.70		
	1890	9.55		
	1891	6.35		

Comment: 1871 Year ending June
1891 Year ending May 21st
Mineral Lord: 1862-1891 See Arkengarthdale
Worked by: 1862 Arkendale Co.
1871-1891 Arkendale Mining Co.

Employment:		Underground	Surface	Total
	1862	29		

MOULDS, HIGH Arkengarthdale NY997025

Production:	Lead	Ore(tons)	Lead (tons)	Value (£)
	1748	27.80		
	1749	76.10		
	1750	40.10		
	1889	43.70		
	1890	42.30		
	1891	60.75		

Comment: 1748 July to December
1750 January to June
1891 Year ending May 21st
Mineral Lord: 1748-1891 See Arkengarthdale
Worked by: 1748-1750 Charles Turner
1871-1891 Arkendale Mining Co.

MOULDS, NEW Arkengarthdale NY999023

Production:	Lead	Ore(tons)	Lead (tons)	Value (£)
	1881	31.40		
	1882	0.60		

Mineral Lord: 1881-1882 See Arkengarthdale
Worked by: 1881-1882 Arkendale Mining Co.

MOULDS, OLD Arkengarthdale NY992022

Production:	Lead	Ore(tons)	Lead (tons)	Value (£)
	1658	1.00		
	1748	8.10		
	1749	31.90		
	1750	5.00		
	1782	8.10		
	1787	16.30		
	1789	14.00		
	1790	24.50		
	1791	8.90		

Comment:	1748	June to December
	1749	October to December
	1750	January to June
	1782	November 1782 to November 1783 inclusive
	1783	Standing December 1783 to May 1787
	1787	June to November inclusive
	1787-1789	Standing December 1787 to May 1789
	1789	June 1789 to May 1791 inclusive
Mineral Lord:	1658-1791	See Arkengarthdale
Worked by:	1658	John Bathurst
	1748-1750	Charles Turner
	1782-1791	Charles Sleigh, William Hoar & Charles Foster

Employment:		Underground	Surface	Total
	1782-1783	2		
	1787	1		
	1789	2		
	1789-1790	3		
	1790-1791	1		

MOULTON Middleton Tyas NZ232044

Production:	Copper	Ore(tons)	Copper (tons)	Value (£)
	1895	No detailed return		

Comment: 1894-1895 Standing
Worked by: 1891-1895 Moulton Copper Mining Co.
Agent: 1891-1895 Christopher Calvert

MR YORKE'S LIBERTY Nidderdale

Production:	Lead	Ore(tons)	Lead (tons)	Value (£)
	1855	342.00	227.60	
	1856-1860	No detailed returns		
	1861	4.50	2.90	
	1863	No detailed return		
	1864	100.00	60.00	
Comment:	1856-1860	See Pateley District		
	1863	See Hutchinson & Burnaby's		
	1864-1865	Stonebeck Up and Stonebeck Down		

MR YORKE'S ROYALTY Wharfedale

Production:	Lead	Ore(tons)	Lead (tons)	Value (£)
	1861	57.00	58.10	
Comment:	1861	Flue dust lead		
	1861	Appletreewick Liberty		

MUKER Muker SD910979

Production:	Lead	Ore(tons)	Lead (tons)	Value (£)
	1530-1544	No detailed returns		
Mineral Lord:	1530-1536	Rievaulx Abbey		
Worked by:	1536-1544	The Crown		
	1544-1568	Thomas Wharton (1st Lord)		
	1568-1906	See AD Mines		

MUKER EDGE Muker SD883968

Production:	Lead	Ore(tons)	Lead (tons)	Value (£)
	1818		3.00	
	1828		25.57	
	1829		7.18	
	1830		9.11	
	1831		1.83	
	1834		16.99	
	1835		14.86	
	1836		22.69	
	1837		65.85	
	1838		9.55	
	1839		9.21	
	1840		9.09	
	1842		0.84	
	1843		38.10	
	1844		18.44	
	1845		4.26	
	1846		2.05	
	1847		3.73	
Comment:	1818	Data from Jennings Thesis		
	1828-1847	Data from NYCRO ZLB 2/134, 136 & 138		

	1849		21.00	
	1850		15.00	
	1851		43.00	
	1852		9.00	
	1853		3.00	
	1854		6.00	
	1855		9.00	
	1856		7.00	
	1857		11.00	
	1858		2.00	
	1861		3.00	

Comment: 1849-1861 Data from Jennings Thesis
1849-1861 Includes Muker Side and Spout Gill
1864-1873 See Muker Side
Mineral Lord: 1818-1861 See AD Mines
Worked by: 1828-1861 Milner & Co.

MUKER SIDE Muker SD883968

Production:	Lead	Ore(tons)	Lead (tons)	Value (£)
	1867	228.40	170.00	
	1868	233.90	175.00	
	1869-1870	No detailed returns		
	1871	50.80	38.10	
	1872-1873	No detailed returns		

Comment: 1828-1847 See Muker Edge
1864-1873 See South Swaledale
1864-1873 Including Lover (Glover) Gill & Providence
Mineral Lord: 1864-1873 See AD Mines
Worked by: 1865-1873 South Swaledale Lead Mining Co. Ltd

MUSGRAVE FLAT Grinton SE027967

Production:	Lead	Ore(tons)	Lead (tons)	Value (£)
	1888-1897	No detailed returns		

Comment: 1888-1897 Grove Beck Level
1894-1897 Standing
Worked by: 1888-1897 Grinton Mining & Smelting Co. Ltd
Agent: 1888-1893 John Ascough Rodwell
Secretary: 1894 F. Rodwell
1895-1897 J. Barker

NETHERDALE

Production:	Lead	Ore(tons)	Lead (tons)	Value (£)
	1861	31.50	20.40	

Comment: 1861 Unknown, probably Nidderdale

NEW RAKE Grassington SE013657

Production:	Lead	Ore(tons)	Lead (tons)	Value (£)
	1735		19.11	
	1736		20.10	
	1737		13.01	
	1738		6.33	
	1739		14.25	
	1740		18.78	
	1741		7.60	
	1742		26.85	
	1743		50.80	
	1744		17.70	
	1745		14.91	
	1746		10.89	
	1747		43.75	
	1748		74.87	
	1749		127.28	
	1750		92.86	
	1751		106.19	
	1752		93.95	
	1753		72.90	
	1754		10.84	
	1755		39.08	
	1758		2.05	
	1762		5.28	
	1765		3.46	
	1766		10.67	
	1767		4.13	
	1768		3.14	
	1769		3.71	
	1770		4.82	
	1771		0.94	
	1772		1.55	
	1773		3.14	
	1774		1.62	
	1775		1.54	
	1776		2.42	
	1777		1.04	
	1778		1.46	
	1779		2.19	
	1780		1.58	
	1781		2.62	
	1782		1.05	
	1783		3.39	
	1784		1.26	
	1787		3.05	
	1788		6.46	

1789		17.33
1790		0.72
1791		0.29
1792		0.21
1794		0.20
1796		5.35
1797		4.10
1798		2.75
1799		4.00
1800		7.70
1801		0.20
1802		1.00
1803		0.35
1804		0.25
1805		0.40
1806		0.15
1807		0.85
1809	5.15	2.15
1810	8.50	3.70
1811	28.65	11.45
1812	16.05	6.50
1813	12.25	4.80
1814	9.95	4.40
1815	8.38	3.00
1816	6.85	2.65
1818	4.60	1.90
1820	4.00	1.50
1821	12.43	4.75
1822	3.25	0.95
1823	1.65	0.65
1824	3.75	0.90
1825	15.80	5.45
1826	17.18	7.80
1827	12.50	4.90
1828	35.13	13.10
1829	16.63	6.65
1830	35.58	15.20
1832	29.20	10.93
1833	38.00	14.05
1834	22.78	8.70
1835	47.30	17.50
1836	47.28	17.50
1837	38.13	17.05
1838	26.83	10.90
1839	2.00	0.85
1840	79.85	54.00
1841	370.93	261.95

	1842	143.45	91.05	
	1843	57.70	25.70	
	1844	67.33	27.70	
	1845	51.35	23.40	
	1846	32.85	15.65	
	1847	23.65	10.65	
	1848	18.35	9.55	
	1849	25.70	11.95	
	1850	18.40	8.10	
	1851	8.33	4.00	
	1852	11.75	5.65	
	1853	27.03	12.30	

Comment: 1756-1757 Data missing
1759-1761 Data missing
1763-1764 Data missing
1860 611.5 oz Silver produced from 44.13 tons lead
1860 611.5 oz Silver sold for £168.16

Mineral Lord: 1735-1863 See under Grassington

Worked by: 1823-1845 Rev. William Bagshaw & Co.
1846-1853 Duke of Devonshire

Agent: 1823-1836 Benjamin Wyatt
1845 Daniel Bowdin

NEW TRIALS Arkengarthdale

Production:	Lead	Ore(tons)	Lead (tons)	Value (£)
	1786	2.10		

Comment: 1786-1787 December to May inclusive

Mineral Lord: 1786-1787 See Arkengarthdale

Worked by: 1786-1787 Charles Sleigh, William Hoar & Charles Foster

Employment:		Underground	Surface	Total
	1786-1787	1		

NIDDERDALE Bewerley SE134657

Production:	Lead	Ore(tons)	Lead (tons)	Value (£)
	1863	3.70	2.40	
	1864	19.30	11.00	
	1865	59.60	35.50	
	1866	52.20	31.30	
	1867	40.40	26.30	
	1868	26.20	15.70	
	1869	17.40	10.40	
	1870	48.50	29.60	
	1871	13.80	9.60	

Comment: 1863-1868 Including Stoney Groves & Perseverance
1867-1875 Including Prosperous, Providence & part of Merryfield
1845-1898 See Sunside

Mineral Lord: 1859-1881 See Bewerley

Worked by:	1859-1871	Nidderdale Lead Mining Co. Ltd		
	1872-1876	Sunside & Merryfield Lead Mining Co. Ltd		
Agent:	1862	Benjamin Calvert		
	1869-1881	William Marshall		
Secretary:	1859-1871	Thomas Sykes		
Employment:		Underground	Surface	Total
	1863	6		6
	1880	12	11	23

NORMANBY Normanby NZ553168

Production:	Iron	Ore(tons)	Value (£)
	1856	131575.00	
	1857	159898.00	
	1858	166785.00	25017.70
	1859	204260.00	29325.00
	1860	186152.40	27922.50
	1861	83471.00	12520.60
	1862	235758.00	35363.70
	1863	140348.40	
	1864	148417.00	
	1865	139417.80	41825.00
	1866	147213.00	36803.20
	1867	482725.00	132749.30
	1868	169769.00	42692.20
	1869	499915.00	124978.70
	1870	215615.00	53903.70
	1871	256023.00	64005.00
	1872	254272.30	
	1873	221485.60	66445.50
	1874	224821.00	67446.30
	1875	238107.00	
	1876	199254.50	
	1877	238152.60	
	1878	228430.40	
	1879	239098.00	
	1880	160405.30	
	1881	123830.10	
	1882-1898	No detailed returns	

Comment:	1867-1869	Skelton, Margrave Park & Cliff
	1899	Abandoned
Mineral Lord:	1854-1899	Ward Jackson
Worked by:	1854-1873	Bell Bros.
	1874-1881	Bell Brothers Ltd
	1883-1899	Cargo Fleet Iron Co.
Agent:	1862-1871	Addison L. Steavenson
	1872-1874	Armstrong Varty
	1875-1881	Addison L. Steavenson
	1876-1877	Thomas Bell

	1878-1881	Armstrong Varty		
	1882-1898	W. Walker		
Employment:		Underground	Surface	Total
	1862	136		
	1883			124
	1894	78	33	111
	1895	83	30	113
	1896	49	11	60
	1897	16	9	25
	1898	11	7	18

NORTH HUSH		Arkengarthdale		NY988028
Production:	Lead	Ore(tons)	Lead (tons)	Value (£)
	1748	53.00		
	1749	124.80		
	1750	38.70		
Comment:	1748	July to November inclusive		
	1750	January to September inclusive		
Mineral Lord:	1748-1750	See Arkengarthdale		
Worked by:	1748-1750	Charles Turner		

NORTH RAKE		Arkengarthdale		NZ016032
Production:	Lead	Ore(tons)	Lead (tons)	Value (£)
	1783	5.00		
Comment:	1783	December 1783 to May 1784 inclusive		
Mineral Lord:	1783-1784	See Arkengarthdale		
Worked by:	1783-1784	Charles Sleigh, William Hoar & Charles Foster		
Employment:		Underground	Surface	Total
	1783-1784	1		

NORTH RAKE		Grassington		SE012659
Production:	Lead	Ore(tons)	Lead (tons)	Value (£)
	1765		4.37	
	1766		10.75	
	1776		1.65	
	1777		0.26	
	1787		0.11	
	1795		0.40	
	1796		0.25	
	1812	3.85	1.95	
	1821	5.65	3.60	
	1822	16.35	10.55	
	1823	6.00	3.80	
	1824	10.60	4.25	
	1825	5.13	2.20	
	1826	6.45	4.20	
Mineral Lord:	1765-1826	See under Grassington		
Worked by:	1765	Mr Shackleton & Co.		

NUSSEY KNOTT Appletreewick SE081636

Production:	Lead	Ore(tons)	Lead (tons)	Value (£)
	1783	No detailed returns		
Production:	Barytes	Ore(tons)		Value (£)
	1918	400.00		
	1919	530.00		
	1920	150.00		
	1965	No detailed return		
Comment:	1852-1874	See Yorkshire Mine		
	1921-1926	Standing		
Mineral Lord:	1783-1965	See Appletreewick Liberty		
Worked by:	1783	William Wood		
	1916-1926	Greenhaugh Mining Co. Ltd		
	1930	James Harold Clay		
	1965	William Houston: Sub-lessee to Clay Cross Co.		
Employment:		Underground	Surface	Total
	1919	6	2	8
	1920	8	0	8

NUTHOLE Arkengarthdale NY984069

Production:	Lead	Ore(tons)	Lead (tons)	Value (£)
	1907	5.00	3.00	45.00
	1908	85.00	66.00	714.00
	1909	150.00	117.00	1050.00
	1910	170.00	129.00	1190.00
	1911	77.00	59.00	540.00
	1912	18.00	14.00	165.00
Comment:	1907-1909	See Stang & Faggergill		
	1907-1913	Includes Sloate Hole		
	1913-1914	Standing		
Worked by:	1907-1913	Stang and Cleasby Lead Mines Ltd		
Agent:	1907-1913	Thomas Harker		
Employment:		Underground	Surface	Total
	1907	20	5	25
	1908	27	7	34
	1909	30	6	36
	1910	23	9	32
	1911	8	3	11
	1912	12	2	14
	1913	6	2	8

OLD GANG | Melbecks | NY961017

Production:	Lead	Ore(tons)	Lead (tons)	Value (£)
	1816		281.24	
	1817		958.15	
	1818		771.37	
	1819		788.47	
	1820		876.52	
	1821		734.28	
	1222		346.50	
	1823		505.67	
	1824		479.17	
	1825		627.58	
	1826		1760.37	
	1827		700.93	
	1828		496.63	
Comment:	1816-1828 Data from NYCRO ZLB 2/134			
	1829		677.90	
	1830		493.40	
	1831		655.57	
	1832		998.97	
	1833		996.90	
Comment:	1828-1833 Data from NYCRO ZLB 2/135			
	1834		985.92	
	1835		1211.38	
	1836		1321.01	
	1837		1402.98	
	1838		1247.76	
	1839		1930.23	
	1840		2376.22	
	1841		1831.88	
	1842		1868.51	
	1843		2150.81	
	1844		1558.61	
	1845		1048.39	
	1846		994.85	
	1847		837.81	
	1848		894.24	
	1849		994.85	
	1850		1129.00	
	1851		1037.00	
	1852		878.00	
	1853		894.00	
	1854		1001.00	
	1855		1033.00	
	1856		2056.00	
	1857		2097.00	
	1858		1963.00	

	1859	1276.00
	1860	1222.00
	1861	1196.00
	1862	969.00
	1863	686.00
	1864	717.00
	1865	736.00
	1866	1163.00
	1867	2071.00
Comment:	1834-1867 Data from Jennings Thesis	

Production:	Lead	Ore(tons)	Lead(tons)	Silver(ozs)	Value(£)
	1868	2172.00	1596.00		
	1869	3328.00	2300.00		
	1870	2532.60	1772.40		
	1871	2321.60	1740.00		
	1872	2759.80	2069.80		
	1873	2625.80	1969.00		
	1874	2250.30	1687.20		
	1875	1378.40	1033.50		
	1876	1075.40	753.00		
	1877	1046.10	690.60	1380.00	13935.00
	1878	910.70	628.70	1258.00	10293.80
	1879	865.80	590.90	1732.00	7883.50
	1880	650.60	488.00	1200.00	6708.00
	1881	294.20	210.00	500.00	2500.30
	1882	723.90	506.70	1518.00	5791.00
	1883	420.00	294.00	840.00	3255.00
	1884	318.00	246.00		1985.00
	1885	482.00			3014.00
	1886	282.00	210.00		2016.00
	1887	117.00			
	1888	12.00			84.00
	1889	112.00	59.00		739.00
	1890	176.00	100.00		1244.00
	1891	188.00	104.00		1200.00
	1892	123.00	63.00		861.00
	1893	126.00	66.00		627.00
	1894	78.00	40.00		388.00
	1895	85.00	44.00		470.00
	1896	44.00	23.00		265.00
	1897	48.00	25.00		315.00
	1898	94.00	50.00		658.00
	1899	158.00	90.00		1422.00
	1900	104.00	59.00		1440.00
	1901	51.00	29.00		352.00
	1902	21.00	12.00		126.00

	1903	18.00	10.00	105.00
	1904	19.00	12.00	112.00
	1905	22.00	14.00	140.00
	1906	38.00	23.00	308.00
	1907	15.00	9.00	132.00
	1908	9.00	5.00	54.00
	1909	8.00	4.00	46.00
	1910	5.00	3.00	30.00
	1911	4.00	2.00	24.00
	1912	3.00	1.00	18.00
	1913	5.00	3.00	41.00
Comment:	1868-1913	Data from Hunt's Statistics		
	1889	111.05		
	1890	144.75		
	1891	157.80		
	1892	108.75		
	1893	105.65		
	1894	71.05		
	1895	85.45		
	1896	44.30		
	1897	48.50		
	1898	86.05		
	1899	157.90		
	1900	104.20		
	1901	49.75		
	1902	21.30		
	1903	17.70		
	1904	18.45		
	1905	21.85		
	1906	No detailed return		
	1907	17.65		
	1908	7.05		
	1909	6.50		
	1910	4.65		
	1911	1.55		
	1912	1.80		
	1913	5.35		
	1914	5.35		
	1925	4.39		
Comment:	1889-1925	Data from Barker MSS (Cherry's Reports)		
Production:	Barytes	Ore(tons)		Value (£)
	1892	12.00		57.00
	1893	No detailed return		
	1924	40.00		
	1947-1990	No detailed return		
Comment:	1887	Standing: Lease surrendered		
	1901-1902	Including Sir Francis		

	1903-1909	Including Sir Francis +4 other mines
	1906	October: In liquidation
	1915-1924	Standing
	1925-1926	Prospecting
	1927-1928	Standing
Mineral Lord:	1736-1990	See AD Mines
Worked by:	1722-1756	Trustees of The Duke of Wharton
	1764-1785	George Fermor (2nd Earl of Pomfret)
	1785-1787	George Fermor (3rd Earl of Pomfret)
	1787-1811	AD Proprietors
	1811-1827	George Alderson & Co.
	1828-1849	Robert Jaques & Co.
	1849-1887	Richard Machell Jaques & Co.
	1889-1906	Old Gang Lead Mining Co. Ltd
	1906-1914	A.D. Lessors
	1924	E.C. Vickers
	1925	Richard Coates
	1925-1926	Swaledale Lead Mines Ltd
	1926-1927	T.K. Saunders
	1928	J. Radcliffe
	1947-1964	Swaledale Mines Ltd
	1964-1990	Shevels, Shevels & Woodward
Agent:	1811-1814	John Davies
	1814-1818	Frederick Hall
	1819	Francis Gill
	1841-1844	William Kidd
	1861-1862	Thomas Coates
	1864-1867	Thomas Raw
	1868-1869	Francis Taylor
	1868-1871	Richard Peacock
	1872-1882	James A. Clarkson
	1873-1880	Samuel Richardson
	1873-1881	Simon Cherry
	1874-1881	Richard Peacock
	1877	William Lorne
	1883-1896	John Reynoldson
	1896-1901	Simon Cherry
	1901-1919	Edward Cherry
	1925-1926	E.C. Vickers
	1926-1927	T.K. Saunders
	1949-1950	T. Shevels
Secretary:	1841-1844	William Spensley
	1860-1863	Jacques, Simpson & Co.
	1870	Francis Taylor
	1871-1872	Simon Cherry
	1873-1881	James A. Clarkson
	1891-1913	Edward Cherry

Employment:		Underground	Surface	Total
	1862			229
	1877	173	60	233
	1878	156	63	219
	1879	130	58	188
	1880	126	52	178
	1898	36	12	48
	1899	35	10	45
	1900	32	10	42
	1901	30	6	36
	1902	14	3	17
	1903	15	5	20
	1904	12	4	16
	1905	20	4	24
	1906	8	2	10
	1907	7	3	10
	1908	6	2	8
	1909	5	1	6
	1910	4	1	5
	1911	2	1	3
	1913	2		2
	1914	2	2	4
	1925	2	1	3
	1926	4		4
	1949		6	6
	1950		6	6

OLD RAKE		Melbecks		NY959014
Production:	Lead	Ore(tons)	Lead (tons)	Value (£)
	1736	93.10		
	1750	154.50		
	1751	241.20		
	1752	268.10		
	1753	163.60		
	1755	118.70		
	1756	113.10		

Comment: 1736-1756 See AD Mines
1735-1736 December to May
1850-1860 June to December
1852-1753 December to June
1755 June to December
1755-1756 December to June

Mineral Lord: 1736-1756 See AD Mines

Worked by: 1736-1756 Trustees of The Duke of Wharton

OLD RIDDLE Grassington SE031671

Production:	Lead	Ore(tons)	Lead (tons)	Value (£)
	1839	60.88	33.55	
	1840	35.50	20.20	
	1841	25.95	14.60	
	1842	12.50	6.90	
	1843	8.55	5.00	
	1844	5.60	3.35	

Comment: 1839-1844 See Ridley Old Work
Mineral Lord: 1839-1844 See under Grassington

OLD WHIM Arkengarthdale

Production:	Lead	Ore(tons)	Lead (tons)	Value (£)
	1782	1.30		
	1784	0.30		
	1787	0.60		
	1787	2.10		
	1789	3.60		
	1789	224.80		
	1790	96.70		

Comment: 1782-1783 November to November inclusive
1783-1784 Standing: December to November
1784-1785 December to May inclusive
1785-1787 Standing: June to May
1787-1788 June to May inclusive
1788-1789 Standing: June to May
1789-1791 June to May inclusive
Mineral Lord: 1782-1791 See Arkengarthdale
Worked by: 1782-1791 Charles Sleigh, William Hoar & Charles Foster

Employment:		Underground	Surface	Total
	1782-1783	1		
	1784-1785	1		
	1787	1		
	1787-1788	1		
	1789	2		
	1789-1791	34		

ONE CROSS Starbotton SD963737

Production:	Lead	Ore(tons)	Lead (tons)	Value (£)
	1744		0.10	

Comment: 1744 Smelted at Buckden
1744 Location uncertain
Mineral Lord: 1744 See under Grassington
Worked by: 1744 Thomas Sidgewick

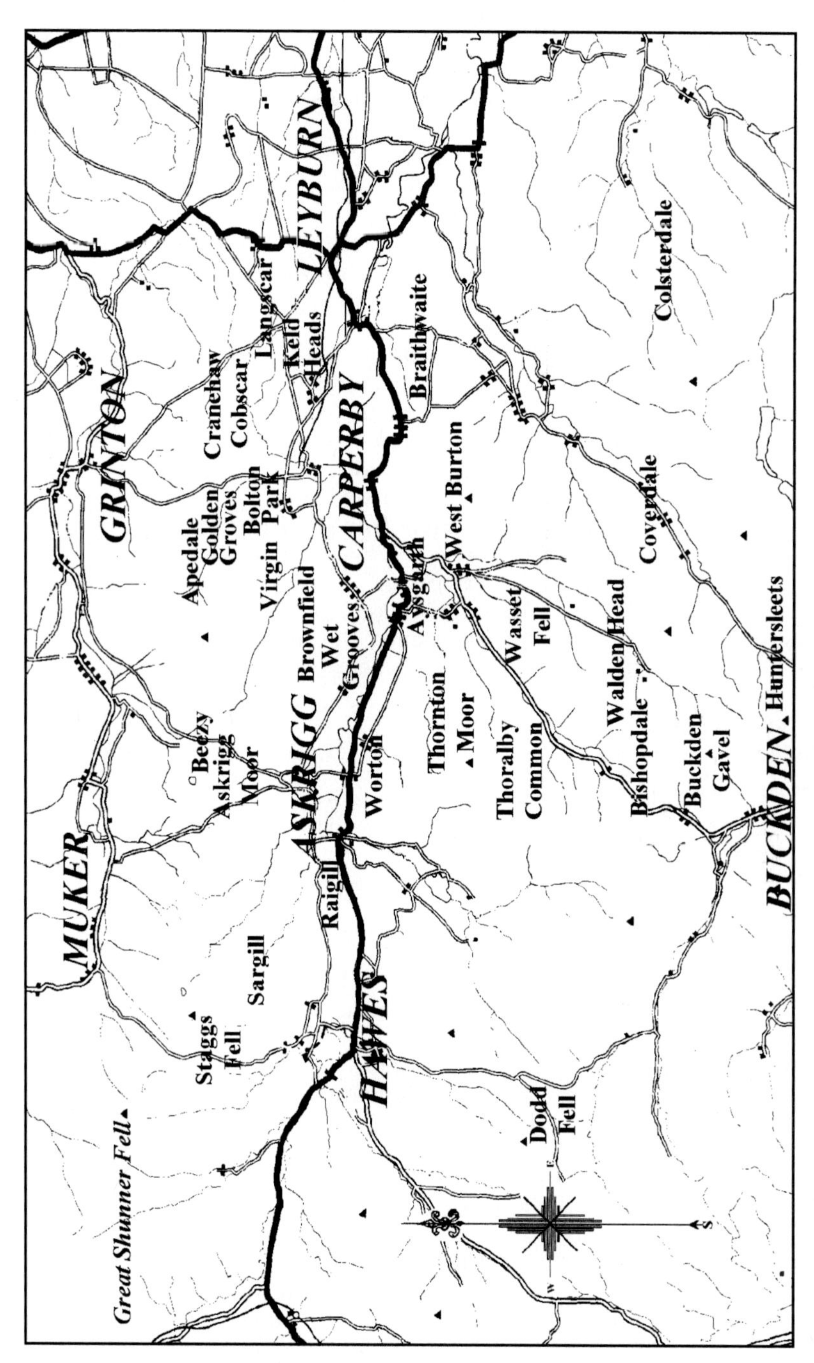

Map 3. Mines in Wensleydale.

ORMESBY Ormesby NZ543166

Production:	Iron	Ore(tons)		Value (£)
	1865-1872	No detailed returns		
	1873	64487.00		19496.10
	1874	58777.50		17633.10
	1875	74193.00		
	1876	73805.00		
	1877	82623.00		
	1878	91553.30		
	1879	139819.40		
	1880	144609.60		
	1881	168909.70		
	1882-1892	No detailed returns		
Comment:	1892	Abandoned exhausted		
Mineral Lord:	1865-1892	Ward Jackson; Miss Brown		
Worked by:	1865-1878	Swan, Coates & Co.		
	1879-1882	Cargo Fleet Iron Co.		
	1883-1892	Cargo Fleet Iron Co. Ltd		
Agent:	1872-1876	G. Davison		
	1877-1881	John G. Swan		
	1878-1892	William Walker		
Employment:		Underground	Surface	Total
	1883			78

OXNOP GILL Muker SD938944

Production:	Lead	Ore(tons)	Lead (tons)	Value (£)
	1824		1.20	
	1826		1.61	
	1836		1.37	
	1839		0.90	
	1909	1.00		
	1912	0.75		
	1916	0.50		
Comment:	1824-1839	Data from NYCRO ZLB 2/134 & 136		
	1909-1919	Data from Barker MSS (Cherry's reports)		
	1918	Prospecting		
Mineral Lord:	1824-1839	See AD Mines		
Worked by:	1824-1826	Edmund Metcalfe		
	1836	Richard Carter		
	1839	William Alton		
	1909-1916	George Calvert		
	1918	Fawcett & Pickup		

PARKHEAD Carlton SD965477

Production:	Lead	Ore(tons)	Lead (tons)	Value (£)
	1774		6.95	
	1775		4.65	
	1776-1865	No detailed returns		

Comment:	1774-1775	Smelted at Grassington		
	1849-1865	Prospecting		
Mineral Lord:	1774-1865	See under Grassington		
Worked by:	1774-1775	Mr Swire		
	1774-1775	Anthony Craddock		
	1774-1775	William Wiseman		
	1849	Matthew Lambert & Co.		
	1849	Duke of Devonshire		
	1865	Richard Newbould		

PARTNER'S MINES Middleton Tyas NZ234059

Production:	Copper	Ore(tons)	Copper (tons)	Value (£)
	1740-1742	No detailed returns		
	1743	0.60		
	1744	2.10		
	1746	2.30		
	1747	3.00		
	1748	1.20		
	1749	0.50		
	1750	3.80		
	1751	4.40		
	1752	No detailed return		
	1753	0.60		
	1754	2.85		
	1755	3.80		
	1757	1.25		
	1758	0.35		
	1759	0.52		
	1760	0.52		
	1761	No detailed return		
	1762	0.20		
	1763	0.75		
	1764	0.75		
	1765	0.60		
	1766	1.10		
	1767	1.40		

Comment:	1746-1755	Includes part of previous year
	1757	Includes 1756 and part of 1755
	1758-1760	Includes part of previous year
	1766	Includes part of 1765
	1767	Includes part of 1766
Mineral Lord:	1740-1749	Richard Shuttleworth
	1749-1773	James Shuttleworth
	1773-1816	Robert Shuttleworth
Worked by:	1740-1767	D'Arcy, Hutton, Yorke & Wilkinson
	1775-1780	Robert Shuttleworth & Ralph Lodge
Agent:	1742-1767	Ralph Hutchinson
	1775-1780	John Gordon

PATELEY BRIDGE, WEST Appletreewick SE100640

Production:	Lead	Ore(tons)	Lead(tons)	Silver(ozs)	Value(£)
	1878	42.00	27.70	55.00	443.10
	1879	185.00	138.70		2000.00
	1880	350.00	262.50		3360.00
	1881	115.00	75.00		950.00
	1882	38.50	28.80		327.00
	1883	34.80	26.10		270.00
	1884	73.00	54.00		450.00
	1885	4.00	3.00		26.00

Comment: 1752-1873 See Craven Cross
Mineral Lord: 1875-1892 See Appletreewick Liberty
Worked by: 1876-1885 West Pateley Bridge Lead Mines Ltd
Agent: 1875-1884 David Williams
1875-1876 James Blenkiron
1876 Charles Williams
Secretary: 1876-1877 William John Lavington
1877-1885 J. Jameson Truran

Employment:		Underground	Surface	Total
	1878	40	12	52
	1879	55	20	75
	1880	46	13	59
	1881	14	5	19
	1882	6	4	10

PATELEY DISTRICT Pateley Bridge

Production:	Lead	Ore(tons)	Lead (tons)	Value (£)
	1845	930.00	698.00	
	1846	886.00	665.00	
	1847	1000.00	660.00	
	1848	937.00	609.00	
	1849	905.00	591.00	
	1850	875.00	500.00	
	1851	981.30	652.70	
	1852	950.00	632.50	
	1853	796.00	531.00	
	1854	680.00	477.00	
	1855	No detailed return		
	1856	671.70	501.50	
	1857	760.00	535.70	
	1858	865.00	577.50	
	1859	913.00	609.00	
	1860	958.00	694.00	

Comment: 1855 See separate mines
1856 Includes five mines
1857-1860 Includes Lunehead: Sunside mines & others

PAWFREY		Grassington		SE016680
Production:	Lead	Ore(tons)	Lead (tons)	Value (£)
	1742		2.05	
	1749		1.68	
	1750		0.28	
	1756		4.22	
	1762		0.28	
	1766		9.58	
	1767		0.79	
	1768		3.74	
	1769		4.27	
	1770		1.42	
	1771		0.55	
	1772		2.71	
	1773		3.56	
	1774		5.00	
	1775		0.25	
	1776		1.98	
	1777		0.48	
	1778		2.58	
	1779		7.26	
	1780		4.61	
	1781		5.77	
	1782		1.43	
	1783		4.37	
	1785		1.24	
	1786		4.26	
	1787		3.64	
	1788		0.39	
	1799		1.56	
	1805		0.30	
	1811	2.25	1.15	
	1813	7.68	4.60	
	1814	2.00	1.30	
	1815	0.60	0.20	

Comment: 1757-1761 Data missing
1762-1764 Data missing
1811-1815 Called Palfrey
1833-1853 See under Porphery
Mineral Lord: 1736-1815 See under Grassington

PENSION RAKE		Hebden		SE029654
Production:	Lead	Ore(tons)	Lead (tons)	Value (£)
	1759	No detailed return		
Mineral Lord:	1759	See Hebden Liberty		
Worked by:	1759	John Pickersgill & Co.		
Agent:	1759	William Ridley		

PERSEVERANCE Bewerley SE135656

Production:	Lead	Ore(tons)	Lead (tons)	Value (£)
	1825-1844	No detailed returns		
Mineral Lord:	1825-1844	See Bewerley Liberty		
Worked by:	1825	Perseverance Mining Co.		
	1859-1871	Nidderdale Lead Mining Co. Ltd		
	1872-1875	Sunside & Merryfield Lead Mining Co. Ltd		
	1875-1879	Pateley Bridge Lead Mines & Smelting Co. Ltd		

PERSEVERENCE Blubberhouses SE138554

Production:	Lead	Ore(tons)	Lead (tons)	Value (£)
	1872-1877	No detailed returns		
Comment:	1866-1873	See Blubberhouses		

PERU Grassington SE036678

Production:	Lead	Ore(tons)	Lead (tons)	Value (£)
	1807		0.15	
	1810	14.30	8.70	
	1811	0.85	0.45	
	1812	1.35	0.75	
Mineral Lord:	1811-1812	See under Grassington		

PERU SOUTH Grassington SE036678

Production:	Lead	Ore(tons)	Lead (tons)	Value (£)
	1798		1.85	
	1799		3.00	
Mineral Lord:	1798-1799	See under Grassington		

PERUVIAN Grassington SE036678

Production:	Lead	Ore(tons)	Lead (tons)	Value (£)
	1791		0.49	
Mineral Lord:	1791	See under Grassington		

PIKEHAW BOTTOM Grassington SE018668

Production:	Lead	Ore(tons)	Lead (tons)	Value (£)
	1749		0.81	
	1755		2.61	
	1760		1.87	
	1765		2.90	
	1766		0.40	
	1767		0.40	
	1768		3.28	
	1769		12.71	
	1770		2.22	
	1771		0.41	
	1773		0.65	
	1777		0.15	

	1780		0.20	
	1781		0.10	
	1784		0.27	
	1785		2.87	
	1786		5.70	
	1787		20.82	
	1788		18.23	
	1789		9.70	
	1790		4.29	
	1751		2.76	
	1762		3.03	
	1763		1.20	
	1794		1.10	
Comment:	1749-1794 See under Grassington			

PIKEHAW RIDGE		Grassington		SE009668
Production:	Lead	Ore(tons)	Lead (tons)	Value (£)
	1755		2.48	
	1756		3.30	
	1762		0.25	
	1801		0.75	
	1804		0.45	
Comment:	1757-1761 Data missing			
	1763-1764 Data missing			
	1762 Includes Pikehaw Gate			
Mineral Lord:	1755-1804 See under Grassington			

PIPER PLETT		Grassington		SE023675
Production:	Lead	Ore(tons)	Lead (tons)	Value (£)
	1736		17.45	
	1739		16.77	
	1740		1.75	
	1742		0.53	
	1743		3.25	
	1744		2.79	
	1745		7.81	
	1746		2.87	
	1747		0.50	
	1749		0.13	
	1751		0.18	
	1752		3.64	
	1755		0.74	
	1761		0.60	
	1766		1.58	
	1768		0.15	
	1770		0.38	
	1773		0.27	

	1774		0.21	
	1775		0.35	
	1776		0.46	
	1777		0.11	
	1778		0.11	
	1789		0.35	
	1799		0.85	
	1802		0.55	
	1807		0.35	
	1810	6.60	3.70	
	1813	1.30	0.55	
	1830	0.70	0.30	
Comment:	1756-1760 Data missing			
	1762-1764 Data missing			
Mineral Lord:	1736-1830 See under Grassington			

PIPER PLETT FLATTING		Grassington		SE020674
Production:	Lead	Ore(tons)	Lead (tons)	Value (£)
	1838	2.08	0.75	
Mineral Lord:	1838 See under Grassington			

PIT MOSS		Grassington		SE035670
Production:	Lead	Ore(tons)	Lead (tons)	Value (£)
	1765		51.55	
	1766		10.75	
	1767		20.80	
	1769		12.05	
	1770		3.00	
	1771		0.39	
	1772		9.00	
	1774		2.05	
	1777		0.85	
	1778		9.10	
	1779		6.89	
	1780		2.58	
	1781		2.75	
	1782		22.63	
	1783		105.81	
	1784		36.50	
	1785		11.62	
	1786		19.50	
	1787		47.72	
	1788		19.73	
	1789		9.46	
	1790		4.90	
	1791		22.28	
	1792		9.79	

1793		7.20
1794		3.90
1795		29.25
1796		12.80
1797		11.05
1798		12.95
1799		7.95
1800		5.75
1801		2.65
1802		6.35
1803		10.00
1804		6.75
1805		4.40
1806		10.85
1808		8.30
1809	35.30	22.15
1810	29.75	16.35
1811	20.00	11.80
1812	19.95	11.10
1813	64.43	37.80
1814	88.80	54.35
1815	3.40	2.95
1816	18.30	10.70
1817	111.28	67.55
1818	117.70	70.65
1819	150.25	91.53
1820	100.90	55.55
1821	126.50	74.35
1822	24.23	9.55
1823	12.90	7.70
1824	7.70	3.85
1825	108.60	64.75
1826	129.68	82.60
1827	235.13	144.50
1828	268.60	167.85
1829	335.43	202.85
1830	237.95	135.35
1831	372.75	224.45
1832	302.60	182.25
1833	319.15	186.30
1834	218.08	130.40
1835	146.03	100.60
1836	72.50	46.80
1837	11.23	5.70
1838	0.90	0.50
1839	4.15	1.85
1847	8.10	3.45

	1848	3.35	1.25	
	1851	6.80	3.10	
	1852	10.80	4.95	
	1853	15.50	6.85	

Comment: 1774 Wilkinson's purchased rights to use shaft
1774 See Wilkinson Pits

Mineral Lord: 1765-1881 See under Grassington

Worked by: 1765-1777 Mr Shackleton & Co.
1782-1804 Johnson Atkinson Busfield & Co.
1820-1841 Robert Fell & Co.
1851-1881 Duke of Devonshire

Agent: 1782-1804 Christopher Lawson

PLET HEAD Grassington SE022676

Production:	Lead	Ore(tons)	Lead (tons)	Value (£)
	1741		8.50	
	1744		1.59	
	1745		1.65	
	1746		13.62	
	1747		26.46	
	1748		19.75	
	1749		6.50	
	1750		32.25	
	1751		7.64	
	1752		9.45	
	1753		0.92	
	1755		0.53	
	1758		0.71	
	1762		0.28	

Comment: 1756-1757 Data missing
1759-1761 Data missing

Mineral Lord: 1741-1762 See under Grassington

POCKSTONES Thornthwaite with Padside SE090597

Production:	Lead	Ore(tons)	Lead (tons)	Value (£)
	1764		44.40	
	1765		12.05	
	1766		6.20	
	1773		1.64	
	1774		1.40	
	1830		2.26	

Comment: 1764-1774 Smelted at Forest Mill (Hoodstorth)
1759-1761 Smelted at White's Mill

Mineral Lord: 1764-1830 Dukes of Devonshire

Worked by: 1773 John Summers
1774 Ralph Summers
1830 Thomas Pratt

POORGRESS Grassington

Production:	Lead	Ore(tons)	Lead (tons)	Value (£)
	1812	0.55	0.30	
	1813	2.35	0.95	

Mineral Lord: 1812-1813 See under Grassington

PORPHERY Grassington SE016680

Production:	Lead	Ore(tons)	Lead (tons)	Value (£)
	1833	14.08	6.45	
	1834	15.20	6.05	
	1835	13.15	6.20	
	1836	21.88	12.05	
	1837	17.18	8.10	
	1838	18.93	9.50	
	1839	17.58	7.85	
	1842	5.85	2.30	
	1843	9.35	3.90	
	1844	17.50	7.75	
	1845	17.03	9.15	
	1846	26.15	14.20	
	1847	33.28	17.30	
	1848	26.58	15.95	
	1849	22.05	11.40	
	1850	15.75	7.90	
	1851	25.80	14.30	
	1852	83.63	47.00	
	1853	43.70	22.25	

Comment: 1736-1815 See Pawfrey
Mineral Lord: 1833-1853 See under Grassington

PORT MULGRAVE Hinderwell NZ798177

Production:	Iron	Ore(tons)	Value (£)
	1858-1861	No detailed returns	
	1862	93900.00	14085.00
	1863	135530.00	
	1864	140000.00	
	1865	144000.00	43200.00
	1866	156600.00	39150.00
	1867	118608.00	32362.00
	1868	127372.00	31843.00
	1869	140000.00	35000.00
	1870	150541.00	37635.20
	1871	135000.00	33750.00
	1872	141525.00	
	1873	156801.00	46824.00
	1874	150000.00	50000.00
	1875	124773.00	

	1876	132147.00		
	1877	38504.00		
	1880	170576.00		
Comment:	1858-1861	See Belmont		
	1863-1876	Or Rosedale on Coast		
	1876	Including Grinkle		
	1877	Including Easington		
	1878-1893	Standing		
	1880	Including Grinkle		
	1915	Abandoned		
Mineral Lord:	1856-1869	Marquis of Normanby		
	1869-1885	Charles Mark Palmer		
Worked by:	1856-1868	Charles Mark Palmer & Co.		
	1869-1874	Palmers Shipbuilding & Iron Co.		
	1875-1893	Palmers Shipbuilding & Iron Co. Ltd		
Agent:	1863-1868	P.A. Berkley		
	1869-1871	A. Palmer		
	1872	William Logan		
	1873-1875	John Hodgson		
	1876-1881	A. Palmer		
	1878-1885	John Hodgson		
	1886-1893	J. Bruce		

POSTGATE		Glaisdale		NZ757045
Production:	Iron	Ore(tons)		Value (£)
	1870-1876	No detailed returns		
Worked by:	1870-1876	South Cleveland Iron Co.		

POTT SCARRS		Grassington		
Production:	Lead	Ore(tons)	Lead (tons)	Value (£)
	1752		2.64	
	1753		2.39	
	1768		0.30	
Comment:	1756-1764	Data missing		
Mineral Lord:	1752-1768	See under Grassington		

PRIVY GILL		Starbotton		SD967767
Production:	Lead	Ore(tons)	Lead (tons)	Value (£)
	1782	No detailed return		
	1823	1.55	0.55	
	1824	6.60	2.00	
Comment:	1823-1824	Smelted at Grassington		
Mineral Lord:	1782-1824	See under Grassington		
Worked by:	1782	Joseph Spense		
	1818-1822	Bernard Lodge & Co.		
	1823-1824	Thomas Hillery		

PROSPEROUS & PROVIDENCE Bewerley SE120660

Production:	Lead	Ore(tons)	Lead (tons)	Value (£)
	1839		110.35	
	1840		201.48	
	1841		265.32	
	1842		228.94	
	1843		125.46	
	1844		45.66	
	1845-1854	No detailed returns		
	1855	18.00	13.10	
	1856-1860	No detailed returns		
	1861	18.40	12.00	
	1862	40.10	25.50	
	1863	80.00	35.70	
	1864	78.30	55.90	
	1865	47.00	31.40	
	1866	85.50	55.60	
	1867	74.00	56.00	
	1868	50.70	33.00	
	1869	43.50	35.50	
	1870	43.30	28.10	
	1871	49.10	19.50	

Comment:	1844	January to June 21st
	1839-1844	Smelted at Prosperous Mill
	1853-1856	Cost Book Company
	1845-1860	See Pateley District
	1863-1871	See Nidderdale
	1861-1871	Including Stoney Groves
Mineral Lord:	1839-1889	See Bewerley Liberty
Worked by:	1781-1793	John Lupton & Co.
	1793-1814	John Wood & Co.
	1814-1822	John Horner & Co.
	1837-1841	William Watson & Co.
	1841-1843	Cockerill & Yorkshire District Bank Co.
	1843-1844	Thomas White
	1853-1856	Prosperous & Providence Mining Co.
	1863-1871	Nidderdale Lead Mining Co. Ltd
	1872-1874	Sunside & Merryfield Mining Co. Ltd
	1874-1877	Ransgill Mining Co. Ltd
	1887-1889	Bewerley United Lead & Barytes Mining Co. Ltd
Agent:	1862-1865	Matthew Newbould
	1866-1868	William Marshall
Secretary:	1887-1889	John Prest Walker

Employment:		Underground	Surface	Total
	1841	72		

PROSPERS Grassington

Production:	Lead	Ore(tons)	Lead (tons)	Value (£)
	1826	3.50	2.25	

Mineral Lord: 1826 See under Grassington

PROVIDENCE Muker SD883968

Production: Lead Ore(tons) Lead (tons) Value (£)

1828-1871 No detailed returns

Comment: 1828-1847 Muker Edge

1828-1847 Muker Side

Mineral Lord: 1828-1871 See AD Mines

Worked by: 1865-1871 South Swaledale Lead Mining Co. Ltd

PROVIDENCE Bewerley SE118660

Production:	Lead	Ore(tons)	Lead (tons)	Value (£)
	1855-1860 No detailed returns			
	1861	31.10	20.20	
	1863	10.00	4.80	

Comment: 1855-1860 See Prosperous & Providence

1863-1871 See Nidderdale

Mineral Lord: 1855-1875 See Bewerley Liberty

Agent: 1862-1866 John Ashworth

PROVIDENCE, NEW Kettlewell SD955727

Production: Lead Ore(tons) Lead (tons) Value (£)

1868-1874 No detailed returns

Mineral Lord: 1868-1874 Trust Lords of Kettlewell

Worked by: 1868-1874 Charlton & Co.

PROVIDENCE, NEW Starbotton SD951727

Production: Lead Ore(tons) Lead (tons) Value (£)

1857-1858 No detailed returns

Comment: 1821-1828 See under Moor End, Starbotton

1857-1858 See Wharfedale Mine

Mineral Lord: 1857-1858 See under Grassington

Worked by: 1857-1858 Wharfdale [sic] Mining Co. Ltd

PROVIDENCE, OLD Kettlewell SD993726

Production:	Lead	Ore(tons)	Lead (tons)	Value (£)
	1860		3.65	
	1862		5.85	
	1863		33.25	
	1864		70.25	
	1865		84.10	
	1866		127.10	
	1867		120.00	
	1868		186.45	

	1869		96.40	
	1870		52.45	
	1871		34.80	
	1872		22.20	
	1873		5.50	
	1874		3.00	
	1875		0.75	
Comment:	1859-1875	Smelted at Kettlewell		
Production:	Lead	Ore(tons)	Lead (tons)	Value (£)
	1860	79.50	46.00	
	1862	11.60	5.80	
	1863	47.50	35.20	
	1864	88.90	60.20	
	1865	171.80	105.00	
	1866	205.30	124.80	
	1867	325.20	173.00	
	1868	192.20	120.50	
	1869	117.80	73.10	
	1870	72.50	47.10	
	1871	68.60	45.30	
	1872	16.00	12.00	
	1873	15.00	11.20	
	1874	4.70	3.50	55.00
	1875	1.40	0.70	15.10
Comment:	1860-1883	Data from Hunt's Statistics		
	1860	Including Silver Rake & Middlesmoor		
Mineral Lord:	1859-1990	Trust Lords of Kettlewell		
Worked by:	1846-1883	Christopher Wiseman & Co.		
	1857-1860	Old Providence Lead & Coal Field Co. Ltd		
	1860-1875	Providence Mining Co.		
	1873-1883	William Sykes-Ward		
Agent:	1862	William Craig		
	1869-1879	John Ralph Place		
Secretary:	1857-1860	William Marshall		

Employment:		Underground	Surface	Total
	1862	19		
	1877-1878	2		2

PRYES LEVEL Hurst NZ066025

Production:	Lead	Ore(tons)	Lead (tons)	Value (£)
	1937-1941	No detailed returns		
Comment:	1937-1938	Developing		
	1939-1940	Standing		
	1941	Abandoned March		
Mineral Lord:	1937-1939	See under Hurst		
Worked by:	1937-1939	North Riding Lead Mining Co. Ltd		
Agent:	1937-1939	Walter S. Rider		

Employment:		Underground	Surface	Total
	1937	4	1	5
	1938	7	1	8

PUNCHARD Arkengarthdale NY957033

Production:	Lead	Ore(tons)	Lead (tons)	Value (£)
	1521-1747	No detailed returns		
	1748		31.00	
	1749		19.70	
	1750		1.20	
	1782		9.80	
	1783		6.20	
	1784		7.20	
	1785		1.50	
	1789		1.10	
	1871		6.45	
	1872		0.45	

Comment:	1748	July to December inclusive
	1750	January to June inclusive
	1782-1783	May to November inclusive
	1783-1784	November to November inclusive
	1784-1785	Standing: December to May
	1785-1786	June to May inclusive
	1786-1789	Standing - June to May inclusive
	1789	June to November inclusive
	1871	Year ending June
Mineral Lord:	1521-1872	See Arkengarthdale
Worked by:	1521-1531	Christopher Conyers
	1748-1750	Charles Turner
	1782-1790	Charles Sleigh, William Hoar & Charles Foster
	1871-1872	Arkendale Mining Co.

Employment:		Underground	Surface	Total
	1782-1783	1		
	1783-1784	1		
	1784-1785	1		
	1785-1786	1		
	1788-1789	1		

RAGG HILL Grassington

Production:	Lead	Ore(tons)	Lead (tons)	Value (£)
	1753		10.50	
	1754		3.84	
	1757		0.34	
	1762		1.88	
	1765		0.15	
	1768		0.91	
	1769		0.17	

	1772		0.63	
	1773		0.28	
	1774		0.23	
	1775		0.18	
	1777		0.08	
	1809	2.80	1.25	
Comment:	1756	Data missing		
	1758-1761	Data missing		
	1763-1764	Data missing		
Mineral Lord:	1753-1809	See under Grassington		

RAIGILL		Bainbridge		SD902898
Production:	Lead	Ore(tons)	Lead (tons)	Value (£)
	1862-1871	No detailed returns		
Comment:	1855-1872	See Wensleydale Mine		
Mineral Lord:	1862-1871	Trust Lords of Bainbridge		
Worked by:	1862-1871	Leeds Mining Co.		
Employment:		Underground	Surface	Total
	1862	11		

RAITHWAITE		Newsholm-Cum-Dunsley		NZ868117
Production:	Iron	Ore(tons)		Value (£)
	1854-1855	No detailed returns		
	1856	5916.00		
	1857-1858	No detailed returns		
	1858	2062.00		
Comment:	1854-1858	Top Seam		
	1858	For value see Grosmont		
Mineral Lord:	1854-1858	English; Wilkinson & others		
Worked by:	1854-1858	Eskdale Iron Co.		

RATLOCK		Grassington		
Production:	Lead	Ore(tons)	Lead (tons)	Value (£)
	1915-1918	No detailed returns		
Mineral Lord:	1915-1918	See under Grassington		
Worked by:	1915-1918	George Stobbs		

RAVEN NEST		Grassington		SE014682
Production:	Lead	Ore(tons)	Lead (tons)	Value (£)
	1809	4.58	2.55	
	1810	6.15	3.70	
	1811	17.55	10.40	
	1812	4.35	2.60	
	1813	6.73	3.15	
	1815	5.28	3.10	
	1817	5.00	3.00	
	1818	0.43	0.25	
	1819	0.35	0.20	

1835	0.78	0.45	
1836	2.95	1.65	
1838	3.05	1.75	
1839	1.10	0.70	

Mineral Lord: 1809-1839 See under Grassington

RAVENSTONES ALLOTMENT Bewerley SE105645

Production: Lead Ore(tons) Lead (tons) Value (£)
1786-1800 No detailed returns

Mineral Lord: 1786-1800 See Bewerley Liberty

Worked by: 1786 Busfield & Co.
1800 P.W. Overend & William Moorhouse

RAYGILL Lothersdale SD942453

Production: Lead Ore(tons) Lead (tons) Value (£)
1876-1900 No detailed returns

Production: Barytes Ore(tons) Value (£)
1856-1857 No detailed returns

Year	Ore(tons)	Value (£)
1876	2057.30	1547.00
1877	2722.80	4084.10
1878	2786.00	4179.00
1879	2245.00	1685.80
1880	2408.00	1683.00
1881	2017.00	1411.90
1882	2246.00	1505.00
1883	2313.00	1618.00
1884	2333.00	1670.00
1885	2577.00	1770.00
1886	2865.00	
1887	2733.00	1366.00
1888	2393.00	1189.00
1889	2083.00	947.00
1890	1204.00	542.00
1891	671.00	317.00
1892	812.00	385.00
1893	260.00	123.00
1894	146.00	58.00
1895	174.00	69.00

Comment: 1856-1857 See Laudersdale & Skipton
1888-1891 Including York & Lancaster United

Production: Fluorspar Ore(tons) Value (£)

Year	Ore(tons)	Value (£)
1878	23.00	15.00
1879	61.00	40.00
1880	84.00	21.00

Comment: 1880 Lothersdale

Worked by:	1876-1900	P.W. Spencer		
Agent:	1876-1881	Jonas Todd		
Employment:		Underground	Surface	Total
	1877	15	14	29
	1878	16	17	33
	1879	10	13	23
	1880	11	11	22
	1881	10	10	20
	1882	10	12	22
	1894	3	2	5
	1895-1896	1	1	2
	1900	16	17	33

RIDLEY OLD WORK Grassington SE031671

Production:	Lead	Ore(tons)	Lead (tons)	Value (£)
	1769		12.75	
	1770		12.00	
	1771		4.20	
	1772		4.09	
	1773		5.12	
	1774		12.16	
	1775		2.41	
	1778		5.25	
	1779		1.00	
	1782		5.33	
	1786		0.13	
	1789		0.44	
	1791		0.45	
	1792		4.75	
	1794		5.15	
	1795		4.25	
	1796		0.30	
	1798		0.80	
	1799		0.25	
	1802		2.65	
	1808		2.20	
	1809	5.15	2.35	
	1812	2.25	1.00	
	1813	5.35	2.50	
	1814	7.15	4.05	
	1817	0.65	0.35	
	1818	0.55	0.30	
	1819	1.40	0.75	
	1827	1.30	0.70	
	1838	2.43	1.45	
	1846	5.05	1.95	
	1850	5.55	2.40	

	1851	5.55	2.60	
	1852	3.65	1.65	
	1853	5.00	2.45	
Comment:	1839-1844	See Old Riddle		
Mineral Lord:	1809-1839	See under Grassington		

RIMINGTON		Rimington		SD814452
Production:	Lead	Ore(tons)	Lead (tons)	Value (£)
	1600-1822	No detailed returns		
	1878	5.00	3.00	31.20
	1879	1.20	0.90	12.80
	1885	8.00		52.00
Comment:	1600	Silver producer		
Production:	Zinc	Ore(tons)	Zinc (tons)	Value (£)
	1877	4.80		15.00
	1878	5.70		16.50
Comment:	1877-1879	Also called Skelhorn		
Production:	Barytes	Ore(tons)		Value (£)
	1879	10.00		7.50
	1880	331.00		219.10
	1882	1340.00		871.00
	1883	385.00		260.00
	1884	270.00		169.00
	1885	308.00		203.00
	1886-1891	No detailed returns		
	1923	100.00		
	1924	126.00		
	1925	155.00		
Comment:	1880-1891	Also called Yorkshire & Lancaster United		
	1885	December - For Sale		
	1888-1891	See Raygill		
	1923-1926	Also called Skeleron		
	1926	Standing		
Mineral Lord:	1600	William Pudsey		
	1764-1775	Richard Graham		
	1822-1844	George Lane-Fox		
Worked by:	1600	William Pudsey		
	1764	John Tongue		
	1775	Thomas Heelis & Co.		
	1822	Tomkinson & Co.		
	1876-1880	R. Baynes & Colville		
	1880-1885	York & Lancaster United Mining Co. Ltd		
	1923-1926	Skeleron Mining Co.		
Agent:	1876-1881	R. Baynes		
	1880-1884	John Borlase		
	1923-1926	J. Stanworth		

Employment:		Underground	Surface	Total
	1877	20	8	28
	1878	14	1	15
	1879	2	0	2
	1880	6	3	9
	1881	6	1	7
	1882	16	23	39
	1923	3	0	3
	1924	2	0	2
	1925	1	1	2

RIPLEY VEIN Grassington SE027669

Production:	Lead	Ore(tons)	Lead (tons)	Value (£)
	1754		6.00	
	1755		119.10	
	1765		0.50	
	1766		34.87	
	1767		53.80	
	1768		27.55	
	1769		46.91	
	1770		21.74	
	1771		18.34	
	1772		14.58	
	1773		14.50	
	1774		2.44	
	1775		5.13	
	1778		4.45	
	1779		3.78	
	1781		5.68	
	1782		1.37	
	1784		6.24	
	1785		1.89	
	1786		3.59	
	1787		0.61	
	1788		2.13	
	1789		14.26	
	1790		2.22	
	1791		0.09	
	1795		2.95	
	1796		1.65	
	1797		1.05	
	1798		1.30	
	1799		1.15	
	1800		3.50	
	1801		5.25	
	1802		2.85	
	1803		1.45	

	1804		0.90	
	1805		2.00	
	1806		1.15	
	1807		1.50	
	1808		1.65	
	1809	13.25	3.50	
	1810	19.05	8.15	
	1811	7.35	3.00	
	1812	7.60	3.35	
	1813	10.05	4.30	
	1814	4.83	1.60	
	1815	4.70	2.10	
	1816	2.85	1.40	
	1819	1.20	0.25	
	1820	3.35	1.20	
	1821	1.25	0.45	
	1822	1.10	0.50	
	1826	3.35	1.45	
	1827	2.10	0.90	
	1828	3.85	1.50	
	1829	4.15	1.95	
Mineral Lord:	1754-1829 See under Grassington			

RIPON END		Grassington		SE025669
Production:	Lead	Ore(tons)	Lead (tons)	Value (£)
	1776	No detailed returns		
Mineral Lord:	1776	See under Grassington		
Worked by:	1776	Stockdale & Co.		
Agent:	1776	Jacob Bailey		

RIPON, NEW		Grassington		SE025669
Production:	Lead	Ore(tons)	Lead (tons)	Value (£)
	1764		22.50	
	1765		14.75	
	1766		11.95	
	1767		17.37	
	1768		15.20	
	1769		23.90	
	1770		32.75	
	1771		47.24	
	1772		62.60	
	1773		0.70	
	1774		76.45	
	1775		102.45	
	1776		50.41	
	1777		60.61	
	1778		58.26	

	1779		89.66	
	1780		27.48	
	1781		52.98	
	1782		48.38	
	1783		56.15	
	1784		57.10	
	1785		58.46	
	1786		40.00	
	1787		33.53	
	1788		56.40	
	1789		65.70	
	1790		6.14	
	1791		17.82	
	1792		4.13	
	1793		8.90	
	1794		4.00	
	1795		8.60	
	1796		14.25	
	1797		4.10	
	1798		6.20	
	1799		6.80	
	1800		12.05	
	1801		11.85	
	1802		9.95	
	1803		5.80	
	1804		3.25	
	1805		5.55	
	1806		7.05	
	1807		4.30	
	1808		5.30	
	1809		0.35	
	1810		3.75	
	1811		2.15	
	1813		0.20	

Comment: 1764 May to June
1755-1765 See also Bacco Rake
Mineral Lord: 1735-1863 See under Grassington
Worked by: 1765-1779 Mr Shackleton & Co.
1774-1785 Robert Stockdale & Co.
1782-1803 Johnson Atkinson Busfield
Agent: 1782-1803 Christopher Lawson

RIPPON		Grassington		SE025669
Production:	Lead	Ore(tons)	Lead (tons)	Value (£)
	1766		1.00	
	1788		1.41	
	1789		0.50	

1809	29.93	14.55
1810	13.25	5.45
1811	12.90	6.05
1812	7.65	3.20
1813	7.35	3.10
1814	4.80	2.10
1815	2.25	0.90
1816	1.10	0.30
1817	14.25	7.60
1818	5.08	3.10
1820	1.95	0.85
1821	9.30	4.35
1822	0.50	0.25
1824	0.60	0.20
1825	5.04	2.70
1826	4.31	4.40
1827	2.60	1.30
1828	10.10	4.05
1829	6.05	2.20
1830	47.48	29.65
1831	3.00	1.75
1832	5.35	2.15
1833	4.43	1.80
1834	5.33	2.80
1835	3.08	1.40
1836	3.00	1.55
1838	3.28	1.35
1840	3.98	2.25
1841	18.13	8.90
1842	39.38	21.15
1843	48.55	25.45
1844	71.00	37.65
1845	80.88	39.10
1846	40.25	18.60
1847	45.10	21.35
1848	19.58	9.55
1849	4.40	1.75
1850	11.25	6.75
1852	1.70	0.80
1853	3.40	2.00

Mineral Lord: 1766-1853 See under Grassington
Worked by: 1766 Mr Braithwaite & Co.
1823-1834 Duke of Devonshire
Agent: 1823-1834 John Barratt

ROSEBERRY Great Ayton NZ583124

Production:	Iron	Ore(tons)		Value (£)
	1880-1926	No detailed returns		
Comments:	1881-1884	Standing		
	1887	Abandoned		
	1924-1929	Standing		
	1929	Abandoned		
Mineral Lord:	1880-1926	Staveley; Jackson		
Worked by:	1880-1883	Stevenson, Jaques & Co.		
	1884-1887	Roseberry Ironstone Co.		
	1906-1921	Tees Furnace Co. Ltd		
	1922-1925	Burton & Son		
	1926	Gribdale Mining Co. Ltd		
Agent:	1880	J.F. Lloyd & Hugh Chaytor		
	1881	William Walker		
	1907-1910	George A. Burton		
	1911	James Bell		
	1912	T. Eato		
	1913	A.H. Askew		
	1914-1917	James White		
	1918	D. Oakley		
	1919	J. Jefferson		
	1920-1925	D. Oakley		

Employment:		Underground	Surface	Total
	1883			37
	1907	70	21	91
	1908	194	34	228
	1909	160	42	202
	1910	166	50	216
	1911	234	54	288
	1912	227	53	280
	1913	229	54	283
	1914	222	80	302
	1915	188	47	235
	1916	182	50	232
	1917	205	54	259
	1918	187	69	256
	1919	308	78	386
	1920	197	74	271
	1921	163	57	220
	1922	145	55	200
	1923	125	50	175
	1924	119	45	164
	1925-1926	0	8	8

ROSEDALE ABBEY, SHERIFFS Rosedale West Side SE697962

Production:	Iron	Ore(tons)	Value (£)
	1875	12282.00	
	1876	13683.00	
	1882-1883	No detailed returns	
Comment:	1874	Sinking	
	1875-1876	Top Seam	
	1877-1881	Standing	
	1884-1885	Standing	
	1885	Abandoned	
	1874-1885	Part of Rosedale, West	
Mineral Lord:	1875-1885	H. Brewster Darley	
Worked by:	1875-1879	Rosedale & Ferryhill Iron Co. Ltd	
	1880-1885	West Rosedale Ironstone Co. Ltd	
Agent:	1876-1879	Mart. Morrison	
	1880	John Parkin	
	1880	C.N. Coates & Charles Parkin	
	1881	F.J.H. Lascelles	
	1881	Rob. Richards & Charles Parkin	
	1881-1883	J.H. Ward	
Employment:		Underground Surface Total	
	1883	Included with Rosedale, West	

ROSEDALE, EAST Rosedale Abbey SE706982

Production:	Iron	Ore(tons)	Value (£)
	1866	168739.00	75000.00
	1872	No detailed returns	
	1873	560668.40	168200.00
	1874	473140.00	141942.00
	1875	292326.00	
	1876	266422.80	
	1877	258801.60	
	1878	178905.00	
	1879	18718.70	
	1882-1925	No detailed returns	
Comment:	1866-1927	Top Seam	
	1866	Magnetic	
	1871	See Rosedale Abbey	
	1872	Magnetic	
	1873-1874	Including Rosedale Abbey West	
	1879-1881	Standing: Closed March	
	1912	Reopened January	
	1926-1927	Standing	
	1928	Abandoned	
Mineral Lord:	1866-1927	Vardon Estate	
Worked by:	1872-1874	Rosedale & Ferryhill Iron Co.	
	1875-1881	Rosedale & Ferryhill Iron Co. Ltd	

	1882-1911 Carlton Iron Co. Ltd			
	1912-1919 Lascelles & Shepherd			
	1920-1927 Shepherd & Pringle			
Agent:	1872-1874 John Parkin			
	1875-1881 John Roscamp			
	1876-1881 Mart. Morrison			
	1883-1898 F.J.H. Lascelles			
	1899-1900 Joseph Harle			
	1901-1910 R. Fishwick			
	1911-1914 F.J.H. Lascelles			
	1915-1919 John Wilson			
	1920-1927 F. Wells			
Employment:		Underground	Surface	Total
	1883			3
	1894	172	37	209
	1895	189	21	210
	1896	206	22	228
	1897	196	22	218
	1898	214	22	236
	1899	214	26	240
	1900	188	27	215
	1901	200	27	227
	1902	206	28	234
	1903	200	27	227
	1904	201	25	226
	1905	206	23	229
	1906	190	22	212
	1907	189	24	213
	1908	183	24	207
	1909	182	26	208
	1910	159	24	183
	1911	136	24	160
	1912	127	14	141
	1913	216	22	238
	1914	227	22	249
	1915	176	25	201
	1916	161	37	198
	1917	169	31	200
	1918	162	32	194
	1919	165	32	197
	1920	177	24	201
	1921	42	11	53
	1922	59	14	73
	1923	58	13	71
	1924	46	10	56
	1925	51	21	72
	1926	1	0	1

ROSEDALE, WEST Rosedale West Side SE727945

Production:	Iron	Ore(tons)	Value (£)
	1860	No detailed returns	
	1861	79786.00	11967.90
	1862	219123.00	32768.00
	1863	224889.00	
	1864	297579.70	66950.00
	1865	250000.00	62510.00
	1866	61643.00	
	1867	178227.50	49012.50
	1868	210082.00	57777.00
	1869	269595.50	67398.70
	1870	317060.00	79265.00
	1871	314394.80	78598.70
	1872-1874	No detailed returns	
	1875	79306.00	
	1876	103722.00	
	1877	85685.60	
	1878	55245.00	
	1879	6874.00	
	1880	6079.00	
	1889-1911	No detailed returns	
Comment:	1858	See Belmont	
	1860	Much raised - none sold	
	1863-1870	Magnetic	
	1879	Closed March	
	1881	Standing	
	1884-1887	Standing	
	1911	Abandoned	
Mineral Lord:	1875-1885	H. Brewster Darley	
Worked by:	1856-1868	George Leeman & Co.	
	1869-1874	Rosedale & Ferryhill Iron Co.	
	1875-1879	Rosedale & Ferryhill Iron Co. Ltd	
	1880-1885	West Rosedale Ironstone Co.	
	1886-1911	Carlton Iron Co. Ltd	
Agent:	1863	? Dixon	
	1864-1871	Jos. J. Forster	
	1872-1874	John Parkin	
	1875-1879	John Rosecamp	
	1876-1879	Mart. Morrison	
	1880	John Parker	
	1880	C.N. Coates & Charles Parkin	
	1881	F.J.H. Lascelles	
	1881	Rob. Richards & Charles Parkin	
	1881-1883	J.H. Ward	
	1887-1898	F.J.H. Lascelles	
	1899-1900	Joseph Harle	

	1901-1902	Joseph Elven		
	1904-1910	Thomas Pearson		
Employment:		Underground	Surface	Total
	1883			219
	1894	179	15	194
	1895	144	14	158
	1896	110	11	121
	1897	93	10	103
	1898	83	10	93
	1899	77	11	88
	1900	80	13	93
	1901	78	10	88
	1902	72	9	81
	1903	69	9	78
	1904	80	10	90
	1905	84	10	94
	1906	92	10	102
	1907	90	10	100
	1908	91	12	103
	1909	101	14	115
	1910	81	10	91
	1911	63	10	73
	1883 Includes Sheriffs Pit			

ROSEDALE ON COAST		Hinderwell	NZ798174
Production:	Iron	Ore(tons)	Value (£)
	1854-1876	No detailed returns	
Comment:	1854-1876	Top Seam	
	1863-1876	See Port Mulgrave	
Mineral Lord:	1854-1876	Scarth; Porritt; Brodrick	
Worked by:	1854-1862	Seymour & Partners	

ROUGH BOTTOM		Starbotton		SD961744
Production:	Lead	Ore(tons)	Lead (tons)	Value (£)
	1744		0.60	
Comment:	1744	Smelted at Buckden		
	1744	Location uncertain		
Mineral Lord:	1744	See under Grassington		
Worked by:	1744	Joseph Airey		

ROUGH INTAKE		Arkengarthdale		NY962049
Production:	Lead	Ore(tons)	Lead (tons)	Value (£)
	1790	49.10		
	1791	21.50		
Comment:	1790	June to November inclusive		
	1790-1791	December to May inclusive		
Mineral Lord:	1790-1791	See Arkengarthdale		

Worked by:	1790-1791	Charles Sleigh, William Hoar & Charles Foster		
Employment:		Underground	Surface	Total
	1790	8		
	1791	5		

ROUTH		Arkengarthdale		NY961044
Production:	Lead	Ore(tons)	Lead (tons)	Value (£)
	1907-1909	No detailed returns		
Comment:	1910-1916	Standing		
Mineral Lord:	1862	See Arkengarthdale		
Worked by:	1862	Arkendale Co.		
	1907-1916	"CB", Lead Mines Ltd		
Agent:	1907-1916	Thomas Harker		
Employment:		Underground	Surface	Total
	1862	4		
	1907-1916	No detailed returns		
Comment:	1907-1909	See Agnes		

ROYAL EXCHANGE		Conistone with Kilnsey		SE021701
Production:	Lead	Ore(tons)	Lead (tons)	Value (£)
	1831	8.38	5.93	
	1832	14.60	10.98	
	1833	7.28	5.55	
	1837	12.30	8.73	
	1838	9.78	7.03	
Comment:	1831-1838	Smelted at Grassington		
Worked by:	1831-1838	See Conistone Liberty		
Agent:	1831-1837	John Cockburn		
	1838	Joseph Kendal		

RUSHBOB		Grassington		SE029672
Production:	Lead	Ore(tons)	Lead (tons)	Value (£)
	1765		10.05	
	1766		8.55	
	1767		1.33	
	1768		50.00	
	1769		51.95	
	1770		75.35	
	1771		57.33	
	1772		35.88	
	1773		24.95	
	1774		17.30	
	1775		17.76	
	1779		38.06	
	1780		37.38	
	1781		32.42	
	1782		14.28	

	1783		42.55	
	1784		15.50	
	1785		21.02	
	1786		4.47	
	1787		2.85	
	1788		1.32	
	1789		4.53	
	1790		1.00	
	1791		0.10	
	1795		1.50	
	1796		1.70	
	1798		2.40	
	1800		5.10	
	1801		9.60	
	1802		1.95	
	1803		2.35	
	1804		2.40	
	1805		1.20	
	1806		0.40	
	1807		0.80	
	1809	2.05	1.05	
	1811	8.10	3.60	
	1812	3.10	1.35	
	1813	3.85	2.00	
	1814	9.68	5.35	
	1815	2.80	1.25	
	1817	3.15	1.85	
	1818	0.75	0.45	
	1819	0.60	0.35	
Mineral Lord:	1766-1819	See under Grassington		
Worked by:	1765	John Summers & Co.		

SARGILL		Abbotts Side		SD896929
Production:	Lead	Ore(tons)	Lead (tons)	Value (£)
	1864	11.90	8.30	
	1865-1866	No detailed returns		
	1867	15.00	12.00	
	1881	14.00	9.50	120.00
	1882	32.00	24.00	272.00
	1883	53.60	40.00	392.00
	1884	23.00		127.00
	1885	5.00		26.00
Coment:	1867	Including Thornton Moor, Virgin, Wet Groves		
Mineral Lord:	1860-1863	Lord Wharncliffe		
Worked by:	1860-1868	Sargill Mines Co.		
	1869-1880	Henry Pease		
	1881	Executors of Henry Pease		

	1882-1884	F.H. Pease			
Agent:	1864-1867	Messrs Winn			
	1868	Henry Pease & Co.			
	1869-1884	John Cain			
Secretary:	1860-1863	Messrs Winn			
Employment:		Underground	Surface	Total	
	1877	8		8	
	1878	7		7	
	1879	6		6	
	1880	8		8	

SATRON MOOR Muker SD941957

Production:	Lead	Ore(tons)	Lead (tons)	Value (£)
	1781-1806	No detailed returns		
	1842		11.76	
	1843		5.38	
	1844		1.55	
	1846		1.21	
	1847		6.35	
	1849		10.69	
	1918	No detailed returns		

Comment: 1781-1806 Includes Miles Pasture
1805-1806 Prospecting
1823 See Stotter Gill
1842-1849 Data from NYCRO ZLB 2/134 & 136
1919-1924 See Swaledale
Mineral Lord: 1781-1924 See AD Mines
Worked by: 1781-1806 Richard Metcalfe & Co.
1842-1849 Metcalfe & Co.
1918 Pickup & Fawcett

Employment:		Underground	Surface	Total
	1918	5		5

SATRON WALLS Muker SD944966

Production:	Lead	Ore(tons)	Lead (tons)	Value (£)
	1795	No detailed returns		
	1819		1.71	
	1820		1.55	
	1821		1.94	
	1824		0.68	
	1825		1.49	
	1826		2.12	
	1827		2.09	
	1831		1.71	
	1837		2.89	
	1842		0.70	
	1843		0.55	
	1845		0.30	

Comment:	1819-1845	Data from NYCRO ZLB 2/134 & 136		
Mineral Lord:	1819-1845	See AD Mines		
Worked by:	1819-1845	Thomas Calvert		
	1865-1870	South Swaledale Lead Mining Co. Ltd		

SCAR END Grassington

Production:	Lead	Ore(tons)	Lead (tons)	Value (£)
	1787		0.34	
	1788		0.06	
Mineral Lord:	1787-1788	See under Grassington		

SCAR FOOT Arkengarthdale NZ020031

Production:	Lead	Ore(tons)	Lead (tons)	Value (£)
Comment:	1748	See Scatter Scar		

SCARGILL Scargill NZ009091

Production:	Lead	Ore(tons)	Lead (tons)	Value (£)
	1802	No detailed return		
	1856	47.20	35.00	
	1857	60.00	44.50	
	1858	40.00	30.00	
	1859	No detailed return		
	1888	1.00		7.00
	1889	7.00	5.00	56.00
	1890	20.00	15.00	141.00
	1891	42.00	20.00	294.00
	1892	88.00	63.00	517.00
	1893	36.00	26.00	252.00
Comment:	1852-1863	See Spanham		
	1886	Prospecting		
	1894-1896	Standing		
	1895-1896	Winding up		
Mineral Lord:	1881-1882	Frederick A.T.C. Constable		
Worked by:	1802	London Lead Company		
	1881-1882	Scargill Mining Co. (J.P. Walton & Ptrs)		
	1882-1896	Scargill Lead Mining & Smelting Co. Ltd		
Agent:	1881-1890	John J. Millican		
	1891	Is. Walton		
	1892-1894	Thomas Harker		
Secretary:	1882-1890	John J. Millican		
	1891-1894	C.W. Harrison		

SCAR TOP Arkengarthdale NZ006032

Production:	Lead	Ore(tons)	Lead (tons)	Value (£)
	1872	34.45		
	1873	32.80		
	1874	21.75		
	1875	24.15		

	1876	0.60		
Mineral Lord:	1872-1876	See Arkengarthdale		
Worked by:	1872-1876	Arkendale Mining Co.		

SCATTER SCAR		Arkengarthdale		NZ019031
Production:	Lead	Ore(tons)	Lead (tons)	Value (£)
	1748	1.50		
	1749	2.00		
	1750	6.00		
	1787	2.00		
	1788	1.30		
	1789	5.50		
Comment:	1748	July to December inclusive		
	1750	January to June inclusive		
	1787-1788	December to May inclusive		
	1788	Standing - June to November inclusive		
	1788-1789	December to May inclusive		
	1789	Standing - June to November inclusive		
	1789-1790	December to May inclusive		
Mineral Lord:	1748-1790	See Arkengarthdale		
Worked by:	1748-1750	Charles Turner		
	1787-1790	Charles Sleigh, William Hoar & Charles Foster		
Employment:		Underground	Surface	Total
	1787-1788	1		
	1788-1789	1		
	1789-1790	2		

SETTLE LIBERTY		Settle		SD842643
Production:	Lead	Ore(tons)	Lead (tons)	Value (£)
	1731		0.40	
	1744		0.12	
	1778		0.24	
	1788		0.40	
Comment:	1731	Smelted at Kilnsey		
	1744-1788	Smelted at Grassington		
	1788	Stockdale Edge		
Mineral Lord:	1744-1873	See under Grassington		
Worked by:	1731	Thomas Waterhouse & Ptrs		
	1778	John Boskill & William Cleminson		
	1788	William Ibbotson		
	1869-1873	Settle Mining Co. Ltd		
Secretary:	1869-1873	John Cowburn		

SHARPER		Grassington		SE029679
Production:	Lead	Ore(tons)	Lead (tons)	Value (£)
	1807		1.65	
	1808		0.20	
Mineral Lord:	1807-1808	See under Grassington		

SILVERBAND Lunedale NY838271

Production:	Lead	Ore(tons)	Lead (tons)	Value (£)
	1833	6.60		
	1834	2.88		
	1835	1.80		
	1852	34.50	22.00	
	1853	15.20	11.20	
	1854-1855	No detailed returns		
	1880	24.10	18.00	228.00
	1882	7.70	4.80	48.00
	1889	3.00	2.00	25.00
	1895	4.00	2.50	24.00

Comment: 1838-1844 See Cronkley
Mineral Lord: 1833-1895 See Lunehead
Worked by: 1831 William Walton & Co.
1834 Silverband Company
1844 London Lead Company
1880-1883 Harry Shield & James Beadle Shield
1906 James B. Shield
Agent: 1880-1883 James B. Shield

Employment:	Underground	Surface	Total
1880	4		4

SILVERBAND, WEST Lunedale NY832268

Production:	Lead	Ore(tons)	Lead (tons)	Value (£)
	1897	3.00		13.00
	1900	3.00	2.00	22.00
	1911	2.00	1.00	16.00
	1912-1920	No detailed returns		

Comment: 1881-1883 Standing
1921-1922 Standing
Worked by: 1877-1883 London Lead Co.
1884-1901 Henry Shield & James Beadle Shield
1902-1912 James B. Shield
1913-1914 Alfred H. Shield
1915-1922 Randolph Shield
Agent: 1879-1883 Robert W. Bainbridge
1884-1912 James B. Shield
1913-1914 Alfred H. Shield
1915-1922 Randolph Shield

Employment:	Underground	Surface	Total
1898-1913	2	0	2
1914-1915	0	1	1
1916-1918	2	0	2
1919	0	2	2
1920	0	1	1

SILVER HILL Stonebeck Down SE103727

Production:	Lead	Ore(tons)	Lead (tons)	Value (£)
	1905-1906	No detailed returns		
Comment:	1906-1908	Standing		
Worked by:	1905-1908	Joseph Cradock		

Employment:		Underground	Surface	Total
	1905	6		6

SILVER RAKE Kettlewell SD986731

Production:	Lead	Ore(tons)	Lead (tons)	Value (£)
	1859		18.80	
	1860		26.75	
	1861		52.40	
	1862		17.70	
	1863		10.10	
	1864		33.45	
	1865		26.90	
	1866		23.80	
	1867		2.20	
	1868		0.35	
	1869		1.95	
	1870		7.35	
	1871		7.90	
	1872		1.60	
	1873		1.90	
	1874		2.05	
	1875		4.40	
	1876		3.80	
	1877		2.75	
	1878		5.10	
	1879		1.65	
	1859-1879	Smelted at Kettlewell		
	1862	28.70	16.40	
	1863	4.40	10.10	
	1864	60.10	39.10	
	1865	43.60	25.90	
	1866	37.90	23.80	
	1867	4.50	2.50	
	1868	0.90	0.50	
	1869	0.90	0.60	
	1870	18.00	11.10	
	1871	0.00	0.00	
	1872	1.00	0.70	
	1873	3.00	2.20	
	1900	3.00	2.00	22.00
	1874	10.10	7.50	95.20
	1875	3.40	1.60	30.30

	1876	3.20	1.70	
	1877	5.30	3.00	55.50
	1878	12.00	7.50	120.00
	1879	1.30	0.90	20.50

Comment: 1862-1879 Data from Hunt's Statistics
1852 Merged with Victoria
1863-1871 Includes Brackenthwaite
Mineral Lord: 1852-1879 See under Kettlewell Liberty
Worked by: 1852-1872 Silver Rake Mining Co.
1872-1883 Joseph Fallowfield Masser
Agent: 1862-1871 J. Vipond
1870-1880 John Ralph Place

Employment:		Underground	Surface	Total
	1862	7		
	1877	0	4	4
	1878	3		3

SIMON GROOVES Muker SD944954

Production:	Lead	Ore(tons)	Lead (tons)	Value (£)
	1865-1870	No detailed returns		

Mineral Lord: 1865-1870 See AD Mines
Worked by: 1865-1870 South Swaledale Lead Mining Co. Ltd

SIR FRANCIS LEVEL Melbecks NY940001

Production:	Lead	Ore(tons)	Lead (tons)	Value (£)
	1878	732.30		
	1879	766.70		
	1880	934.80		
	1881	577.90		
	1882	270.90		
	1883	159.15		
	1885	184.00		1084.00
	1886	85.00	65.00	605.00
	1887	4.00		
	1888	29.00		203.00
	1889	No detailed return		

Comment: 1864 Level begun in June as a joint venture
1877 Fryerfold Vein cut in March
1878-1883 Data from NYCRO ZLB 2/7
1878-1882 Sinking and working the Engine Sump
1885-1889 Standing
1889-1890 Preparing to sink the Engine Sump deeper
1894 Watersikes Vein cut in March
1895-1900 Standing
1904 Forehead stopped in January
1906 Men moved to Hard Level in February
1906 In liquidation from October

	1910-1912 Abandoned			
Worked by:	1864-1866 Blakethwaite Mining Company			
	1864-1887 Richard Machell Jaques & Co. (Old Gang Co.)			
	1867-1877 Sir George Denys			
	1878-1884 AD Lead Mining Co. Ltd			
	1889-1906 Old Gang Lead Mining Co. Ltd			
Agent:	1879-1883 Thomas Raw			
	1884-1897 John Reynoldson			
	1898-1901 Simon Cherry			
	1901-1912 Edward Cherry			
Employment:		Underground	Surface	Total
	1880	114	32	146
	1901-1909 No detailed returns			
Comment:	1901-1909 See Old Gang			

SIX MEERS Grassington SE029669

Production:	Lead	Ore(tons)	Lead (tons)	Value (£)
	1736		17.50	
	1740		0.67	
	1744		4.70	
	1745		0.24	
	1757		49.98	
	1760		158.69	
	1761		69.21	
	1763		64.78	
	1764		31.80	
	1765		43.70	
	1766		56.10	
	1767		21.17	
	1768		16.15	
	1769		15.63	
	1770		16.60	
	1771		20.65	
	1772		21.81	
	1773		7.18	
	1774		9.26	
	1775		0.25	
	1776		4.88	
	1778		2.37	
	1779		1.23	
	1780		11.63	
	1781		11.12	
	1782		23.28	
	1783		14.09	
	1784		46.07	
	1786		30.00	
	1787		35.54	

	1788		5.43	
	1789		9.85	
	1790		5.75	
	1794		0.45	
	1795		1.38	
	1796		3.10	
	1799		0.30	
	1800		0.65	
	1801		1.80	
	1802		2.20	
	1803		7.05	
	1804		6.80	
	1805		17.15	
	1806		4.35	
	1807		6.75	
	1808		6.35	
	1809	11.13	6.35	
	1810	25.30	11.05	
	1811	17.25	9.35	
	1812	6.90	2.85	
	1814	0.40	0.10	
	1815	3.10	1.75	
	1816	0.60	0.25	
	1817	4.93	1.20	
	1818	0.60	0.40	
	1819	1.65	0.65	
	1820	11.88	5.40	
Comment:	1820	See Friendship		
	1758-1759	Data missing		
Production:	Barytes	Ore(tons)		Value (£)
	1788	43.75		21.88
Comment:	1788	Barytes = Lead weight (2464 lbs/ton)		
Mineral Lord:	1736-1820	See under Grassington		
Worked by:	1756-1772	Thomas Smith & Co.		
	1772	Mr Shackleton		
	1782-1791	Mrs Wardle & Co.		
	1820	Joseph Constantine & Co.		
Agent:	1772-1791	Jacob Bailey		

SIXTY-NINE RUSHBOB Grassington SE029672

Production:	Lead	Ore(tons)	Lead (tons)	Value (£)
	1765-1819	No detailed returns		
Comment:	1765-1819	See under Rushbob		
Mineral Lord:	1765-1819	See under Grassington		

SKELERON Rimington SD814452

Production:	Lead	Ore(tons)	Lead (tons)	Value (£)
Comment:	1923-1926	See Rimington		

SKELTERTON Cracoe SD988602

Production:	Lead	Ore(tons)	Lead (tons)	Value (£)
	1739	No detailed return		
	1755		0.71	
Comment:	1739	Working		
	1755	Cracoe Green		
Mineral Lord:	1739-1755	See Cracoe Liberty		
Worked by:	1739	Joshua Stansfield		
	1755	Robert Bownas & Co.		

SKELTON Marske NZ078020

Production:	Lead	Ore(tons)	Lead (tons)	Value (£)
	1782-1874	No detailed returns		
Mineral Lord:	1782	John Hutton		
	1874	John Timothy Darcy Hutton		
Worked by:	1874	Robert Hirst & Company		

SKELTON Skelton NZ636168

Production:	Iron	Ore(tons)	Value (£)
	1860	10000.00	1500.00
	1861	9500.00	1475.00
	1862	No detailed return	
	1863	163933.50	
	1864	208038.30	
	1865	180753.10	54276.90
	1866	166161.00	41540.20
	1867	No detailed return	
	1868	155950.00	38987.50
	1869	No detailed return	
	1870	100182.00	25045.50
	1871	114076.20	28519.00
	1872	166419.40	
	1873	165279.60	49583.70
	1874	158636.00	47590.80
	1875	148776.00	
	1876	136448.20	
	1877	20549.50	
	1879	10029.30	
	1880	117182.90	
	1881	126480.40	
	1882-1922	No detailed returns	
	1935-1938	No detailed returns	
Comment:	1862	See Normanby	

	1867	See Normanby		
	1869	See Normanby		
	1877-1878	Standing		
	1923	Abandoned		
	1935	Developing		
	1938	Abandoned November		
Mineral Lord:	1858-1923	Wharton Estate		
	1923-1938	Bell Brothers		
Worked by:	1862-1873	Bell Brothers		
	1874-1922	Bell Brothers Ltd		
	1923	Dorman, Long & Co. Ltd		
	1935-1938	Dorman, Long & Co. Ltd		
Agent:	1862-1871	Addison L. Steavenson		
	1872	Mat. Hall		
	1873-1881	Addison L. Steavenson		
	1876-1877	Thomas Bell Jnr.		
	1878-1879	Thomas Bell & W. Moore		
	1880-1881	T. Bell & John Harbottle		
	1881-1921	Thomas Varty		
	1922-1923	J. Clement		
	1935-1938	J. Clement		
Employment:		Underground	Surface	Total
	1862	203		
	1883			187
	1894	172	30	205
	1895	199	33	232
	1896	203	34	237
	1897	176	32	208
	1898	171	34	205
	1899	161	31	192
	1900	176	33	209
	1901	172	37	209
	1902	172	41	213
	1903	173	37	210
	1904	701	139	840
	1905	672	133	805
	1906	670	138	808
	1907	154	29	183
	1908	644	139	783
	1909	647	144	791
	1910	163	37	200
	1911	161	35	196
	1912	154	29	183
	1913	152	28	180
	1914	149	29	178
	1915	106	26	132
	1916	104	25	129

	1917	107	26	133
	1918	106	31	137
	1919	110	37	147
	1920	120	29	149
	1921	111	25	136
	1922	80	23	103
	1923	107	25	132
	1935	4	12	16
	1936	54	12	66
	1937	77	14	91
	1938	67	14	81
Comment:	1904-1906 Includes Skelton Park			
	1908-1909 Includes Skelton Park			

SKELTON PARK Skelton NZ644180

Production:	Iron	Ore(tons)	Value (£)
	1868-1872	No detailed returns	
	1873	176238.00	52871.00
	1874	151572.50	45471.60
	1875	193790.00	
	1876	206003.80	
	1877	272018.00	
	1878	310757.40	
	1879	338731.00	
	1880	393787.30	
	1881	425379.30	
	1882-1838	No detailed returns	

Comment:	1874	Entry: 150,000 tons not included
	1925	Lower Pecten Seam abandoned
	1938	Abandoned April
Mineral Lord:	1868-1938	Wharton
Worked by:	1872-1873	Bell Bros.
	1874-1922	Bell Brothers Ltd
	1923-1938	Dorman, Long & Co. Ltd
Agent:	1872	John Corrie
	1873-1881	Addison L. Steavenson
	1876-1879	Thomas Bell
	1878-1879	W. Moore
	1880-1881	T. Bell & John Harbottle
	1882-1921	Thomas Varty
	1922-1935	J. Clement
	1936	M. Readman
	1937-1938	J. Clement

Employment:		Underground	Surface	Total
	1883			510
	1894	366	88	454
	1895	411	88	499

1896	428	90	518
1897	469	110	579
1898	468	109	577
1899	482	104	586
1900	482	109	591
1901	172	37	209
1902	469	102	571
1903	511	104	615
1907	471	106	577
1910	468	107	575
1911	444	102	546
1912	423	99	522
1913	409	92	501
1914	389	93	482
1915	287	76	363
1916	249	75	324
1917	266	83	349
1918	276	87	363
1919	261	96	357
1920	260	100	360
1921	256	100	356
1922	251	97	348
1923	297	93	390
1924	302	95	397
1925	245	72	317
1926	248	74	322
1927	253	80	333
1928	249	79	328
1929	249	81	330
1930	257	78	335
1931	264	71	335
1932	267	70	337
1933	262	73	335
1934	257	76	333
1935	249	72	321
1936	260	71	331
1937	172	67	239
1938	172	69	241

Comment: 1904-1906 Included with Skelton
1908-1909 Included with Skelton

SKELTON, NORTH North Skelton NZ675183

Production: Iron	Ore(tons)	Value (£)
1865-1871	No detailed returns	
1872	166419.00	
1873	165279.00	
1874	28421.80	8526.30

	1875	137133.00		
	1876	278697.00		
	1877	297193.00		
	1878	191732.00		
	1879	197965.00		
	1880	247735.10		
	1881	216278.00		
	1882-1919	No detailed returns		
	1935-1964	No detailed returns		
Comment:	1920-1934	Standing		
	1955-1958	Includes Lumpsey		
	1964	Abandoned		
Mineral Lord:	1865-1964	Wharton Estate		
	1865-1872	Bell Bros.		
	1873-1919	Bolckow, Vaughan & Co. Ltd		
	1935-1954	Dorman, Long & Co. Ltd		
	1955-1964	Dorman, Long (Steel) Ltd		
Agent:	1872	Thomas Lee		
	1873-1874	Mathew Hall		
	1875-1883	George Robinson		
	1884-1910	John Thomas		
	1911-1915	F.M. Robinson		
	1916	Robert Ransom		
	1917	F.M. Robinson		
	1919	H. Palmer		
	1935-1951	T.E. Slater		
	1954-1955	G.A. Roberts		
	1960-1964	G.W. Pearson		
Employment:		Underground	Surface	Total
	1883			297
	1894	184	60	244
	1895	235	54	289
	1896	266	54	320
	1897	268	59	327
	1898	273	52	325
	1899	258	57	315
	1900	257	55	312
	1901	246	45	301
	1902	269	52	321
	1903	257	55	312
	1904	269	59	328
	1905	278	63	341
	1906	297	44	341
	1907	315	60	375
	1908	351	55	386
	1909	355	61	416
	1910	378	60	438

1911	317	57	374
1912	317	60	377
1913	365	62	427
1914	370	65	435
1915	356	73	429
1916	351	70	421
1917	390	89	479
1918	393	93	486
1919	375	105	480
1935	443	99	542
1936	445	106	551
1937	483	110	593
1938	541	110	651
1940	634	122	756
1941	688	140	828
1942	671	137	808
1943	658	140	798
1944	576	137	813
1945	428	117	545
1948	299	93	392
1950	293	91	384
1951	272	82	354
1954	222	92	314
1955	243	94	337
1956	197	81	278
1957	183	82	265
1958	183	82	265
1959	170	75	245
1960	170	78	248
1961	127	68	195
1962	127	68	195
1963	125	62	187
1964	111	56	167

SKELTON, SOUTH Stanghow NZ655165

Production:	Iron	Ore(tons)	Value (£)
	1872	4034.00	
	1873	133492.80	40047.60
	1874	182253.00	54675.90
	1875	314237.00	
	1876	437872.90	
	1877	379112.60	
	1878	236582.00	
	1879	133403.20	
	1881	204996.00	
	1882-1927	No detailed returns	
	1929-1930	No detailed returns	

	1936-1954	No detailed returns
Comment:	1928	Standing
	1931-1935	Standing
Mineral Lord:	1870-1954	Wharton; Marley
	1872-1876	T. Vaughan & Co.
	1877-1878	Trustees of T. Vaughan & Co.
	1879-1881	Clay Lane Iron Works
	1882-1898	Clay Lane Iron Co. Ltd
	1899-1928	Bolckow, Vaughan & Co. Ltd
	1929-1954	Dorman, Long & Co. Ltd
Agent:	1872	M.W. Partington
	1873-1874	H. White
	1875	H. Ground
	1876-1880	John Thompson
	1881	E. Hamilton
	1881-1887	Jno. House
	1888-1910	Abraham Gray
	1911-1912	A.M. Hedley
	1913-1920	A. Gray
	1921-1923	R.W. Anderson
	1924-1926	H. Palmer
	1928-1929	J.R. Tomlinson
	1930	A.C. Thomson
	1931-1932	J.R. Tomlinson
	1933-1935	J. Clement
	1936	J. Crombie
	1937-1954	J. Clement

Employment:		Underground	Surface	Total
	1883			348
	1894	153	34	187
	1895	185	37	222
	1896	231	44	275
	1897	287	54	341
	1898	352	61	413
	1899	424	57	481
	1900	361	55	416
	1901	354	51	406
	1902	351	52	403
	1903	354	49	403
	1904	351	52	403
	1905	364	53	417
	1906	354	53	407
	1907	389	53	442
	1908	399	63	462
	1909	388	61	449
	1910	391	60	451
	1911	374	60	434

1912	360	66	426
1913	375	71	446
1914	369	67	436
1915	345	63	408
1916	343	61	404
1917	413	71	484
1918	362	75	437
1919	414	73	487
1920	379	59	438
1921	309	68	377
1922	58	24	82
1923	348	74	422
1924	275	68	343
1925	228	63	291
1926	37	21	58
1927	215	52	267
1928	10	8	18
1929	208	44	252
1930	235	43	278
1931	7	4	11
1932	4	5	9
1933	4	4	8
1934	5	14	19
1935	3	10	13
1936	173	65	238
1937	300	80	380
1938	498	109	607
1940	516	140	656
1941	465	143	608
1942	527	145	672
1943	509	131	640
1944	471	134	605
1945	358	86	444
1948	290	96	386
1950	275	89	364
1951	298	76	374
1954	225	68	293

SKINNINGROVE

		Skinningrove	
Production:	Iron	Ore(tons)	Value (£)
	1858	9485.00	1427.70
	1859	8206.00	1203.90
	1860	10231.80	1364.00
	1861	No detailed return	
Worked by:	1863-1865	Bell Bros. Losh, Wilson & Bell	
	1866	Henry Pease & Co.	
Agent:	1863-1865	Addison L. Steavenson	
	1866	William Cockburn	

SKIPTON PARK Skipton SE011528

Production:	Lead	Ore(tons)	Lead (tons)	Value (£)
	1852			54.25
	1852	Data from PRO BT31/164/495		
	1852	Precise location unknown		
	1852	See Yorkshire Mine		
Worked by:	1852	Yorkshire Mining Co. (Cost Book)		

SKIPTON ROCK Skipton SE007528

Production:	Lead	Ore(tons)	Lead (tons)	Value (£)
	1749		0.27	
	1778		0.15	
	1785		0.06	
Comment:	1749-1749	Smelted at Grassington		
Mineral Lord:	1749	Lord Thannet's Liberty		

SKYTHORNS PASTURE Threshfield SD975632

Production:	Lead	Ore(tons)	Lead (tons)	Value (£)
	1788		0.05	
Comment:	1788	Smelted at Grassington		
	1852	0.41	0.20	
Comment:	1852	Smelted at Starbotton		
	1866		0.98	
Comment:	1866	Smelted at Kettlewell		
Worked by:	1788	William Brown		
	1852	Christopher Paley		
	1866	William Paley & Co.		

SLACK Arkengarthdale NZ021040

Production:	Lead	Ore(tons)	Lead (tons)	Value (£)
	1782	6.00		
	1783	4.00		
	1784	3.70		
	1785	2.00		
	1786	7.20		
Comment:	1782-1783	November to November inclusive		
	1783-1784	December to May inclusive		
	1784	Standing - June to November inclusive		
	1784-1786	December to May inclusive		
	1786	Standing - June to November inclusive		
	1786-1787	December to May inclusive		
Mineral Lord:	1782-1787	See Arkengarthdale		
Worked by:	1782-1787	Charles Sleigh, William Hoar & Charles Foster		

Employment:		Underground	Surface	Total
	1782-1783	1		
	1783-1784	2		
	1784-1785	1		
	1785-1786	1		
	1786-1787	3		

SLANT GATE HEAD Buckden SD950771

Production:	Lead	Ore(tons)	Lead (tons)	Value (£)
	1777	No detailed return		
Mineral Lord:	1777	See under Grassington		
Worked by:	1777	John Tailforth & Ptrs		

SLAPEWATH Guisborough NZ646147

Production:	Iron	Ore(tons)		Value (£)
	1872	No detailed return		
	1873	52000.00		15600.00
	1874	25000.00		8579.00
	1875	51368.00		
	1876	73298.80		
	1877	78011.40		
	1878	80544.00		
	1879	26236.20		
	1880	47114.90		
	1881	172700.90		
	1882-1883	No detailed returns		
	1885-1905	No detailed returns		
Comment:	1864-1880	See Hollin Hill		
	1884	Standing		
	1906	Part of Spawood		
Worked by:	1872	T. Charlton		
	1873-1879	Trustees of the late T. Charlton		
	1880-1905	B. Samuelson & Co. Ltd		
Agent:	1872-1905	William Charlton		

Employment:		Underground	Surface	Total
	1883			156
	1894	189	39	219
	1895	177	29	206
	1896	159	35	194
	1897	267	52	317
	1898	311	74	385
	1899	336	70	406
Comment:	1900-1905	Included with Spa Wood		

SLEDDALE Muker SD833993

Production:	Lead	Ore(tons)	Lead (tons)	Value (£)
	1801-1802	No detailed returns		
Production:	Copper	Ore(tons)	Copper (tons)	Value (£)
	1907-1921	No detailed returns		
Comment:	1907-1921	See Great Sleddale		
Mineral Lord:	1801-1921	See AD Mines		
Worked by:	1801-1802	William Hillary & Co.		

SLEIGHTS BRIDGE		Sleights Bridge		NZ868083
Production:	Iron	Ore(tons)		Value (£)
	1856	11250.00		
	1857	No detailed return		
	1858	3823.00		
	1859	3823.00		675.00
Comment:	1856-1859	Pecten Seam		
	1858	For value see Grosmont		
Mineral Lord:	1856-1859	Yeoman		
Worked by:	1856-1859	Eskdale Iron Co.		

SLOPER		Grassington		SE020655
Production:	Lead	Ore(tons)	Lead (tons)	Value (£)
	1848	7.00	0.35	
	1849	24.00	1.15	
Mineral Lord:	1848-1849	See under Grassington		

SMILER		Grassington		SE022678
Production:	Lead	Ore(tons)	Lead (tons)	Value (£)
	1840	3.90	2.00	
	1845	3.00	1.85	
	1846	1.25	0.50	
	1849	2.05	0.80	
	1850	2.35	0.90	
Mineral Lord:	1840-1850	See under Grassington		

SMILING FANCY		Grassington		SE022678
Production:	Lead	Ore(tons)	Lead (tons)	Value (£)
	1753		3.65	
	1754		0.38	
	1762		0.15	
	1766		0.48	
	1767		0.24	
	1769		0.16	
	1771		0.31	
	1772		0.16	
	1773		0.05	
	1774		0.41	
	1775		0.52	
	1797		0.05	
	1798		0.85	
	1800		0.40	
	1802		0.20	
	1804		10.70	
	1805		10.60	
	1806		17.00	
	1807		12.00	

	1808		10.85
	1809	19.90	11.35
	1810	5.00	2.45
	1811	8.10	4.80
	1812	16.40	10.10
	1813	8.98	5.10
	1814	1.50	0.80
	1815	7.80	4.60
	1816	3.48	2.10
	1817	4.88	2.75
	1819	0.65	0.45
	1820	33.70	20.65
	1821	2.80	1.70
	1831	0.70	0.40
	1832	1.40	0.75

Comment: 1756-1761 Data missing
1763-1764 Data missing
Mineral Lord: 1753-1832 See under Grassington
Worked by: 1766 Ralph Summers & Co.

SMITHY WHIM Arkengarthdale NY976029

Production:	Lead	Ore(tons)	Lead (tons)	Value (£)
	1783	1.60		
	1785	115.20		
	1786	89.80		
	1787	10.70		
	1789	1.10		

Comment: 1783-1784 December to November inclusive
1784-1785 Standing: December to November
1785-1788 December to November inclusive
1788-1789 Standing: December to November
1789-1790 December to May inclusive
Mineral Lord: 1783-1790 See Arkengarthdale
Worked by: 1783-1790 Charles Sleigh, William Hoar & Charles Foster

Employment:		Underground	Surface	Total
	1783-1784	1		
	1785-1786	15		
	1786-1787	18		
	1787-1788	3		
	1789-1790	1		

SNATEY BEGGAR Grassington

Production:	Lead	Ore(tons)	Lead (tons)	Value (£)
	1815	0.10	0.04	

Mineral Lord: 1815 See under Grassington

SOUTH ALLOTMENT		Grassington		SE036669
Production:	Lead	Ore(tons)	Lead (tons)	Value (£)
	1793		24.50	
	1794		36.50	
	1795		14.45	
	1796		3.10	
	1814	0.83	0.45	
Mineral Lord:	1793-1814	See under Grassington		
Worked by:	1793-1795	John Barker		

SOUTH FIELDS		Middleton Tyas		NZ232044
Production:	Copper	Ore(tons)	Copper (tons)	Value (£)
	1891-1893	No detailed return		
Comment:	1894-1895	Standing		
Worked by:	1891-1895	Moulton Copper Mining Co.		
Agent:	1891-1895	Christopher Calvert		

SPA		Stanghow	NZ638158
Production:	Iron	Ore(tons)	Value (£)
	1864	15875.40	
	1865	9075.60	2722.50
	1866	53365.00	13341.20
	1870	109023.00	27255.70
	1871	128486.00	32121.20
	1872	35933.90	
	1873	109668.50	32900.40
	1875	111861.00	
	1876	91270.00	
	1877	75662.20	
	1878	60825.00	
	1879	64556.50	
	1880	108055.90	
	1881	115906.70	
	1882-1902	No detailed returns	
Comment:	1871	Or Margrave Park	
	1878	Standing June 1879	
	1903	Standing	
	1904	Abandoned	
Mineral Lord:	1864-1904	Lady Hewley Trust	
Worked by:	1864-1865	Bell Bros.	
	1872-1904	Gjers, Mills & Co. Ltd	
Agent:	1864-1865	Addison L. Steavenson	
	1872-1875	John Tate	
	1876	John Gjers	
	1881-1887	F. Tate	
	1888-1904	John Tate	

Employment:		Underground	Surface	Total
	1883			125
	1894	59	10	69
	1895	49	10	59
	1896	61	9	70
	1897	56	10	66
	1898	61	10	31
	1899	35	8	43
	1900	19	6	25
	1901	21	7	28
	1902	25	6	31
	1903	17	7	24
	1904		1	1

SPANHAM		Scargill		NZ009091
Production:	Lead	Ore(tons)	Lead (tons)	Value (£)
	1852-1863	No detailed return		
Comment:	1802-1896	See Scargill		
Worked by:	1852-1863	J. Leggett & Co.		
Agent:	1858	John Stoddart		
	1863	N. Hillary		

SPAWOOD		Guisborough	NZ638157
Production:	Iron	Ore(tons)	Value (£)
	1865	36694.50	9173.50
	1866	15726.00	3931.20
	1869	No detailed return	
	1870	35599.10	8899.70
	1871	59811.00	14952.70
	1872	63393.90	
	1873	77239.50	23171.80
	1874	No detailed return	
	1875	83536.00	
	1876	69301.20	
	1877	45302.90	
	1879	3698.40	
	1880	15271.40	
	1882-1886	No detailed returns	
	1889-1930	No detailed returns	
	1933	No detailed return	
Comment:	1866-1868	Spa	
	1869	See Belmont	
	1873-1874	See Belmont	
	1877-1878	Standing	
	1881	Standing	
	1887-1888	Standing	
	1890	Abandoned	

	1931-1932	Standing		
	1934	Abandoned April		
Mineral Lord:	1865-1934	Chaloner Estate		
Worked by:	1866-1869	Tow Law Coal & Iron Co.		
	1870-1872	Weardale Coal & Iron Co.		
	1875-1888	Weardale Iron & Coal Co. Ltd		
	1889-1922	B. Samuelson & Co. Ltd		
	1923-1934	Dorman, Long & Co. Ltd		
Agent:	1866-1871	Thomas Allison		
	1872	John Robinson		
	1875-1881	Thomas Allison		
	1878-1881	W. Robinson		
	1882-1888	J. Robinson		
	1889-1912	William Charlton		
	1913-1929	D.R. Brooks		
	1930-1934	M. Hedley		
Employment:		Underground	Surface	Total
	1883			112
	1900	409	74	483
	1901	280	64	344
	1902	409	73	482
	1903	462	89	551
	1904	520	119	639
	1905	564	126	690
	1906	602	131	733
	1907	594	134	728
	1908	601	127	728
	1909	618	139	757
	1910	617	143	760
	1911	642	154	796
	1912	628	157	785
	1913	651	166	817
	1914	655	170	825
	1915	450	143	593
	1916	459	146	605
	1917	529	149	678
	1918	524	154	678
	1919	516	172	688
	1920	498	174	672
	1921	133	70	203
	1922	24	35	59
	1923	265	171	436
	1924	323	133	456
	1925	348	131	479
	1926	405	138	543
	1927	397	135	532
	1928	290	135	425

	1929	455	147	602
	1930	418	142	560
	1931	7	6	13
	1932	7	8	15
	1933	30	24	54
	1934	44	24	68

Comment:	1894-1899	Included with Slapewath
	1901-1903	Includes Slapewath & Aysdalegate
	1904-1905	Includes Slapewath
	1906	Includes Slapewath & Aysdalegate

SPOUT GILL Muker SD937965

Production:	Lead	Ore(tons)	Lead (tons)	Value (£)
	1705	No detailed return		
	1750	31.20	20.68	
	1752	115.20	86.42	
	1753	57.60	38.68	
	1756	71.20	51.38	
	1817		2.31	
	1819		11.93	
	1820		22.66	
	1821		19.48	
	1822		4.76	
	1823		12.58	
	1824		12.52	
	1825		10.39	
	1826		2.91	
	1827		0.92	
	1835		1.52	

Comment:	1682	Includes Old & New Satron Walls Pastures
	1750	June to December
	1752-1753	December to June
	1817-1835	Data from NYCRO ZLB 2/134 & 136
Mineral Lord:	1682-1778	See AD Mines
Worked by:	1682	Edward Thompson & Co.
	1705	Thomas Wharton (5th Lord)
	1735-1753	Mine Adventurers of England
	1778	Thomas Simpson & Co.
	1814	Buxton & Co.
	1819-1827	James Brown
	1835	Thomas Calvert
Agent:	1740	James Harries

SPRINGS CAM Starbotton SD960743

Production:	Lead	Ore(tons)	Lead (tons)	Value (£)
	1856	6.70	4.20	
	1857	11.05	6.75	

Comment: 1856-1857 Smelted at Starbotton Cupola
Mineral Lord: 1856-1857 See under Grassington
Worked by: 1856-1857 John Siddle

STAGGS FELL High Abbotside SD865947

Production:	Lead	Ore(tons)	Lead (tons)	Value (£)
	1734-1741	No detailed returns		
	1813		2.23	

Comment: 1734-1813 Data from Sheffield Archives WHM 64 & 17
Mineral Lord: 1734 Edward Wortley
1813 James Archibald Stuart Wortley
Worked by: 1734-1741 London Lead Company
1813 R. Milner & Co.
Agent: 1735-1739 William Gorton
1739-1741 Thomas Westgarth

STAINTON MOOR Stainton SE082956

Production:	Lead	Ore(tons)	Lead (tons)	Value (£)
	1880-1881	No detailed returns		

Comment: 1882 Winding up
Worked by: 1880-1881 Stainton Moor Lead Mining Co. Ltd
Secretary: 1880-1881 George Nicholls

STAITHES Hinderwell NZ785188

Production:	Iron	Ore(tons)	Value (£)
	1838-1861	No detailed returns	

Comment: 1838-1861 See Belmont
Mineral Lord: 1838-1860 Marquis of Normanby
Worked by: 1838-1842 Wylam Iron Co.
1856-1860 Palmers Shipbuilding & Iron Co.

STANDARD Lunedale NY862230

Production:	Lead	Ore(tons)	Lead (tons)	Value (£)
	1741	9.40		
	1745	10.60		
	1746	14.90		
	1757	6.80		
	1758	12.60		
	1834	0.36		
	1835	0.44		
	1837	0.35		
	1838	1.70		
	1841	4.46		
	1842	1.65		

	1843	5.38		
	1844	2.71		
	1845	1.30		
Mineral Lord:	1741-1845	See Lunehead		
Worked by:	1771	London Lead Company		
	1831	James Ainsly & Co.		
	1835	James Shield		
	1844-1845	London Lead Company		

STANG		Arkengarthdale		NZ010059
Production:	Lead	Ore(tons)	Lead (tons)	Value (£)
	1871	29.15		
	1872	13.60		
	1873	1.15		
	1874	2.90		
	1875	0.60		
	1877	34.15		
	1878	606.70		
	1879	384.20		
	1880	282.25		
	1881	233.35		
	1882	407.05		
	1883	205.45		
	1884	134.15		
	1885	109.50		
	1886	43.95		
	1887	61.85		
	1888	157.75		
	1889	265.60		
	1890	259.20		
	1891	87.15		
Comment:	1871	Year ending June		
	1876	Standing		
	1891	Year ending May 21st		
	1907-1909	Stang Windegg		
	1907-1909	See Nuthole and Faggergill		
	1910	Standing		
	1911	Prospecting		
Mineral Lord:	1871-1916	See Arkengarthdale		
Worked by:	1871-1891	Arkendale Mining Co.		
	1907-1913	Stang and Cleasby Lead Mines Ltd		
Agent:	1907-1913	Thomas Harker		

Employment:		Underground	Surface	Total
	1862	33		
	1911	5		5

STANGHOW Boosbeck NZ654155

Production:	Iron	Ore(tons)		Value (£)
	1873	93013.60		27903.90
	1874	87167.90		26150.00
	1875	No detailed return		
	1880	29541.80		
	1885-1921	No detailed returns		
Comment:	1875	See Margrave Park?		
	1877-1879	Standing		
	1881-1884	Standing		
	1922-1927	Standing		
	1928	Abandoned		
Mineral Lord:	1872-1928	Wharton estate		
Worked by:	1881-1888	Stanghow Ironstone Co.		
	1889	Downey & Co.		
	1890-1891	Stanghow Ironstone Co. Ltd		
	1892-1993	Cochrane & Co.		
	1894-1928	Cochrane & Co. Ltd		
Agent:	1872-1876	William Walker		
	1877-1885	E. Hamilton		
	1886-1888	George Turbett		
	1889-1891	Robert Cutherbertson		
	1892-1908	William Walker		
	1909-1926	Thomas F. Snow		

Employment:		Underground	Surface	Total
	1883			112
	1900	409	74	483
	1894	188	66	254
	1895	208	76	284
	1896	226	87	313
	1897	238	88	326
	1898	243	91	334
	1899	235	27	262
	1900	233	80	313
	1901	180	99	279
	1902	196	86	282
	1903	205	88	293
	1904	217	81	298
	1905	237	84	321
	1906	270	94	364
	1907	286	96	382
	1908	278	94	372
	1909	263	89	352
	1910	303	94	397
	1911	354	99	443
	1912	310	96	406
	1913	298	92	390

1914	254	87	341
1915	234	81	315
1916	223	85	308
1917	249	85	334
1918	236	86	322
1919	264	93	357
1920	276	88	364
1921	276	89	365
1922	3	9	12
1923	9	9	18
1924	13	8	21
1925	5	6	11
1926	1	2	3

STANSFIELD MOOR		Blackshaw		SD921287
Production:	Lead	Ore(tons)	Lead (tons)	Value (£)
	1685	No detailed return		
Mineral Lord:	1685	Lord Halifax		
Worked by:	1685	Lord Halifax		

STARBOTTON CAM		Starbotton		SD961744
Production:	Lead	Ore(tons)	Lead (tons)	Value (£)
	1704		8.65	
	1705		49.00	
Comment:	1704-1705	Smelted at Buckden		
	1738-1744	See Cam Old Rake		
Worked by:	1704-1706	Mr Cooke		
	1738		1.95	
	1772		0.55	
	1815	16.05	10.05	
	1816		25.85	
	1817	4.93	3.20	
	1818	4.85	2.75	
	1819	4.45	2.65	
	1820	7.73	5.75	
Worked by:	1738	William Chapman		
	1772	George Hasleham & Robert Mitton		
	1815-1820	John Preston		
	1819	7.45	5.00	
	1820	7.30	5.45	
	1821	8.70	5.25	
	1822	11.90	6.95	
	1823	11.40	5.45	
	1824		7.30	
Worked by:	1819-1824	William Harrison		
	1824	37.20	15.90	
	1825	25.20	11.25	

	1826		16.25
	1828	4.25	1.35
	1849	3.30	1.80
Comment:	1738-1849	Smelted at Grassington	
	1826	Smelted at Kilnsey	
Worked by:	1824-1826	Christopher Harrison	
	1828	Joseph Harrison	
	1849	William Hillery	
	1827		16.95
	1828		13.60
	1829		3.70
	1830		6.20
	1831		4.00
	1838		3.45
	1841		1.65
Worked by:	1827-1841	Christopher Harrison	
	1829		0.45
	1830		0.30
Worked by:	1829-1830	William Harrison	
	1835		0.80
	1851		0.50
Worked by:	1835-1851	John Harrison	
	1835		1.55
	1837		1.25
Worked by:	1835-1837	John Sunter	
	1850		0.90
Worked by:	1850	John Siddle & Co.	
	1851		0.65
Worked by:	1851	William Hillery	
	1855		1.90
Worked by:	1855	Joseph Harrison	
	1857		2.40
Worked by:	1857	Robert Hancock	
Comment:	1827-1857	Smelted at Kettlewell	
	1840	Includes Cam Level	
	1841		0.10
	1845		2.90
	1846		1.15
	1847		3.75
	1848		1.45
Worked by:	1841-1848	James Hillery	
	1845-1848	William Hillery	
	1848		8.95
Worked by:	1848	John Hillery	
Comment:	1841	Smelted at Kettlewell	
	1842-1848	Smelted at Kettlewell or Starbotton	
	1850		4.00

	1851	6.60	4.95	
	1857	1.80	0.90	
	1859	3.65	1.90	
	1861	1.45	0.80	
	1862	0.90	0.55	
Worked by:	1850-1862	William Hillery		
	1855	8.45	6.60	
Worked by:	1855	Joseph Harrison		
	1856	0.65	0.20	
Worked by:	1856	John Harrison		
	1855		4.25	
	1856	6.70	4.20	
	1857	7.25	4.35	
Worked by:	1855-1857	John Siddle & Co.		
Agent:	1849-1868	William Craig		
	1857	4.20	2.65	
Worked by:	1857	Robert Hancock & Co.		
Comment:	1850-1862	Smelted at Starbotton Cupola		
	1860	1.50	0.80	
	1861	0.90	0.50	
	1863	4.50	2.80	
	1864	14.00	1.30	
	1865	1.60	0.90	
	1867	1.60	0.80	
	1869	16.00	8.50	
	1870-1871	No detailed returns		
	1872	4.20	3.10	
	1874	20.40	13.80	265.30
	1876	46.30	34.70	555.60
	1877	8.00	6.00	80.00
Comment:	1860-1877	Data from Hunt's Statistics		
	1865	Includes 1866		
	1867-1868	Not trading		
	1874-1877	Includes Buckden Gavel?		
	1876-1884	See Starbotton Gavel		
Mineral Lord:	1738-1877	See under Grassington		
Worked by:	1853-1867	Robert Wilkinson Farrow		
	1867-1868	United Cams Mining Co. Ltd		
	1876-1877	Gavel Mining Co.		
Agent:	1869-1877	Charles Lodge		
Secretary:	1867-1868	Joseph Garton Briggs		

STARBOTTON CUPOLA SMELT MILL SD955750

Production:	Lead	Ore(tons)	Lead (tons)	Value (£)
	1850		0.60	
	1852		2.05	
	1854		2.70	

	1855		3.35	
	1856		1.50	
	1857		13.00	
	1858		3.35	
	1859		3.40	
	1861		2.50	
	1862		0.40	

Comment: 1843-1862 Built c1842 and closed June 1862
1850-1862 Produced from lead fume

	1859	2.25	1.40	

Comment: 1859 Richard Bell - Plumber's ashes
Worked by: 1850-1862 Starbotton Smelting Co.
(Joseph Mason 1/3; Thomas Humphrey 1/3; Josiah Remfrey 1/6; Stephen Eddy 1/6)

STARBOTON GAVEL Starbotton SD960770

Production:	Lead	Ore(tons)	Lead (tons)	Value (£)
	1876	46.30	34.70	
	1877	34.80	24.70	
	1878	36.70	27.50	
	1881	37.00	26.00	
	1884	7.00	5.00	

Comment: 1866-1873 Gavel, Bishopdale
1874-1878 Gavel, Starbotton & Buckden Gavel
Mineral Lord: 1866-1890 See under Grassington
Worked by: 1866-1873 Henry Thomas Robinson
1874-1875 Gavel Mining Co.
1876 Bernard Lodge & Bowdin
1877-1890 Bernard Lodge, Marshall & Bowdin
Agent: 1874-1881 Bernard Lodge
Secretary: 1874-1875 Bernard Lodge

Employment:		Underground	Surface	Total
	1877	6	4	10
	1878	4	3	7
	1879	4	2	6
	1881	3	1	4

STARBOTTON LIBERTY Starbotton SD953748

Production:	Lead	Ore(tons)	Lead (tons)	Value (£)
	1739		0.75	
	1741		1.25	
	1744		0.70	

Comment: 1739-1744 Smelted at Buckden

	1715		18.82	
	1716		1.84	
	1727		3.01	
	1816	0.25	0.15	

	1817	1.25	0.85	
	1819	5.80	3.60	
	1823	4.15	1.80	
	1828	2.85	1.20	
	1849	0.80	0.45	
Worked by:	1816	Thomas Frost		
	1817	Christopher Joy		
	1819	Thomas Sidgwick		
	1823	Thomas Watson & Thomas Herey		
	1828	James Watson		
	1849	Matthew Bennett		
	1816	2.00	1.10	
	1817	2.75	1.65	
	1819	0.70	0.40	
Worked by:	1816	John Bennett		
	1817	John Wear		
	1819	Christopher Ash		
Comment:	1715-1849	Smelted at Grassington		
	1845		3.70	
	1846		1.15	
	1847		3.75	
	1849		8.95	
Comment:	1845-1849	Smelted at Starbotton Cupola		
	1877		4.45	
	1882		0.85	
	1883		4.70	
	1885		2.50	
Comment:	1877-1885	Smelted at Kettlewell		
	1874-1881	No detailed returns		
Comment:	1874-1881	Data from Hunt's Statistics		
	1874-1878	See Starbotton Gavel		
	1879-1881	Includes Buckden Gavel		
Mineral Lord:	1739-1882	See under Grassington		
Worked by:	1879-1881	Bernard Lodge & Bowdin		
Barmaster:	1705-1708	Stephen Peart		
	1708-1718	William Peart		
	1718-1743	Christopher Falshaw		
	1763-1800	Richard Falshaw		
	1815-1824	Joseph Mason		
Agent:	1879-1883	Bernard Lodge		
	1885	Mr Fawcett		

STEADY		Grassington		
Production:	Lead	Ore(tons)	Lead (tons)	Value (£)
	1805		0.40	
Mineral Lord:	1805	See under Grassington		

STEBDEN Thorpe SE002608

Production:	Lead	Ore(tons)	Lead (tons)	Value (£)
	1736		0.40	

Comment:	1736	Smelted at Grassington
Mineral Lord:	1736	See under Thorpe
Worked by:	1736	John Eckles & Co.

STEMPLE Arkengarthdale NY990025

Production:	Lead	Ore(tons)	Lead (tons)	Value (£)
	1782		2.50	
	1784		1.00	
	1785		2.20	
	1788		0.30	
	1789		7.30	
	1790		27.40	

Comment:	1782	November 1782 to November 1783 inclusive
	1783	Standing: December 1783 to November 1784
	1784	December 1784 to May 1785 inclusive
	1785	June 1785 to May 1786 inclusive
	1786-1788	Standing: December to November inclusive
	1788-1791	December to May inclusive
Mineral Lord:	1782-1791	See Arkengarthdale
Worked by:	1782-1791	Charles Sleigh, William Hoar & Charles Foster

Employment:		Underground	Surface	Total
	1782-1783	3		
	1784-1785	1		
	1785-1786	1		
	1788-1789	1		
	1789-1790	1		
	1790-1791	5		

STOCKDALE Muker SD865984

Production:	Lead	Ore(tons)	Lead (tons)	Value (£)
	1841		4.30	

Comment:	1841	Data from NYCRO ZLB 2/134 & 136
Mineral Lord:	1841	See AD Mines
Worked by:	1841	Thomas Hunter & Co.

STONEGILL 10 MEERS Carlton Highdale SD982768

Production:	Lead	Ore(tons)	Lead (tons)	Value (£)
	1774	No detailed return		

Comment:	1774	Data from *Leeds Mercury* 21/06/1774
Mineral Lord:	1774	Rev. Dr Marton

STONESDALE, WEST		Muker		NY886036
Production:	Lead	Ore(tons)	Lead (tons)	Value (£)
	1855		19.00	
	1856		475.00	
	1857		183.00	
	1858		13.19	
	1859		18.74	
	1860		15.00	
	1867-1871	No detailed returns		
Comment:	1867-1871	Data from Hunt's Statistics		
Mineral Lord:	1855-1871	See AD Mines		
Worked by:	1850-1860	Christopher Lonsdale Bradley		
	1867-1871	Stonesdale Company		
Agent:	1867-1870	Robert Lowes		

STONEY GROVES		Bewerley		SE097667
Production:	Lead	Ore(tons)	Lead (tons)	Value (£)
	1699-1841	No detailed returns		
	1861-1871	No detailed returns		
	1872	117.00	87.70	
	1873	17.40	17.00	
	1879	30.00	22.50	309.00
	1882	24.00	14.40	180.00
	1883	7.00	5.20	54.00
	1884	15.00	10.00	100.00
	1885	5.00	3.50	36.00
	1886	8.00	6.00	65.00
	1887	200.00		
	1888-1889	No detailed returns		
Comment:	1861-1871	See Prosperous & Providence		
	1874	Including part of Merryfield		
Production:	Barytes	Ore(tons)		Value (£)
	1887-1889	No detailed returns		
Mineral Lord:	1699-1889	See under Bewerley		
Worked by:	1803-1822	John Horner & Co.		
	1837-1841	William Watson & Co.		
	1841-1843	Cockerill & Yorkshire District Bank Co.		
	1853-1856	Prosperous & Stoney Grooves Mining Co.		
	1863-1863	Stoney Grooves Mining Co.		
	1863-1868	Nidderdale Lead Mining Co. Ltd		
	1869-1871	Stoney Groves Co.		
	1872-1873	Burnaby & Hutchinson		
	1874-1877	Ransgill Mining Co. Ltd		
	1879-1887	Stoney Groves Lead Mining Co.		
	1887-1889	Bewerley United Lead & Barytes Mining Co. Ltd		
	1894-1900	Hutchinson & Burnaby		
Agent:	1841-1843	John Ingleby		

	1863	William Newbould		
	1866	William Marshall		
	1867-1868	Matthew Newbould		
	1869-1873	William Newbould		
	1874	David Williams		
	1879-1881	David Williams		
	1892-1893	David Williams		
Secretary:	1866-1873	Thomas Sykes		
	1887-1889	John Prest Walker		
Employment:		Underground	Surface	Total
	1862	15		
	1879	7	3	10
	1882	5		5

STONEY GROVES SYNDICATE Bewerley SE094667

Production:	Lead	Ore(tons)	Lead (tons)	Value (£)
	1886	10.00	7.00	70.00

STONEY RAKE Kettlewell SD968735

Production:	Lead	Ore(tons)	Lead (tons)	Value (£)
	1859		4.95	
	1860		1.50	
	1863		0.40	
Comment:	1859-1863	Smelted at Kettlewell		
	1859	Including Gentlewoman Mine		
	1860	Merged with Cam Scar in the summer		
Mineral Lord:	1859-1863	Trust Lords of Kettlewell		
Worked by:	1859	John Tattersall & Co.		
	1859-1860	Stoney Rake Mining Co.		
	1863	Simon Brown & Partner		

STONEY RAKE Starbotton SD962744

Production:	Lead	Ore(tons)	Lead (tons)	Value (£)
	1737		7.39	
	1738		7.35	
	1739		2.50	
	1740		2.40	
Comment:	1737-1740	Smelted at Grassington		
	1740		3.10	
	1741		1.35	
	1744		1.50	
Comment:	1740-1744	Smelted at Buckden		
Mineral Lord:	1737-1738	See under Grassington		
Worked by:	1737-1744	John Airey		

STOOL Grassington SE015677

Production:	Lead	Ore(tons)	Lead (tons)	Value (£)
	1800		7.70	
	1801		22.95	
	1802		15.15	
	1804		6.95	
	1805		18.20	
	1806		0.90	
	1807		0.75	
	1808		21.00	
	1826	2.45	1.60	
	1827	11.53	7.45	
	1828	11.43	8.00	
	1829	6.53	3.90	
	1830	0.85	0.40	
	1836	1.63	0.85	
	1838	4.10	1.90	
	1841	3.00	0.95	
	1843	0.95	0.60	
	1844	12.13	7.65	
	1845	3.15	2.15	
	1846	1.60	1.05	
	1847	16.18	10.05	
	1848	5.03	2.85	
	1851	0.90	0.40	
	1853	0.80	0.45	

Mineral Lord: 1800-1853 See under Grassington

STOTTERGILL Muker SD941957

Production:	Lead	Ore(tons)	Lead (tons)	Value (£)
	1823	No detailed return		

Comment:	1781-1918	See Satron Moor
	1918	Prospecting
Mineral Lord:	1781-1918	See AD Mines
Worked by:	1814	John Rider Wood & Co.
	1823	William Metcalfe & Co.
	1865-1870	South Swaledale Lead Mining Co. Ltd
	1918	Fawcett & Pickup

SUMMER LODGE No.1 Grinton SD948954

Production:	Lead	Ore(tons)	Lead (tons)	Value (£)
	1774	No detailed return		
	1775		4.46	
	1777		1.13	
	1783		5.59	

Comment:	1774	10 Meers granted on February 10th
	1775	Standing - Ownership in dispute
Mineral Lord:	1774-1783	See under Grinton
Worked by:	1774-1775	Thomas Cowling & Co.

SUMMER LODGE No.2 Grinton SD965950

Production:	Lead	Ore(tons)	Lead (tons)	Value (£)
	1809		1.23	
	1810		117.07	
	1811		351.78	
	1812		636.82	
	1813		594.15	
	1814		249.92	
	1815		453.53	
	1816		577.06	
	1817		118.75	
	1848		2.29	
	1854-1893	No detailed returns		

Comment:	1809-1817	Data from PRO CREST 2/1390
	1817	To June 28th
	1854-1857	Standing
	1877-1887	Standing
	1894-1897	Standing
Mineral Lord:	1809-1897	See under Grinton
Worked by:	1809-1817	See under Grinton
	1848	Thomas Calvert
	1851-1857	Whitaside Mining Co.
	1862-1867	Summerlodge Mining Co.
	1877-1886	J.C.D. Charlesworth
	1887	Swaledale Mining Association Ltd
	1888-1897	Grinton Mining & Smelting Co. Ltd
Agent:	1861	Ralph Milner
	1862-1867	Adam Barker
	1887-1893	John Ascough Rodwell
	1894	F. Rodwell
	1895-1897	J. Barker

Employment:		Underground	Surface	Total
	1862	7		

SUMMER LODGE, WEST Grinton SD952952

Production:	Lead	Ore(tons)	Lead (tons)	Value (£)
	1774	No detailed return		

Comment:	1774	8 Meers granted on February 10th
	1775	Standing - ownership in dispute
Mineral Lord:	1774-1775	See under Grinton
Worked by:	1774-1775	Joseph Cowling & Co.

SUMMER'S SHAFT Grassington SE027668

Production:	Lead	Ore(tons)	Lead (tons)	Value (£)
	1824	2.35	1.40	
	1825	4.75	2.55	

Comment:	1824-1825	Part of Coalgrovebeck
Mineral Lord:	1824-1825	See under Grassington

SUN HUSH Melbecks NY935014

Production:	Lead	Ore(tons)	Lead (tons)	Value (£)
	1873	1.53		
	1874-1912	No detailed return		
Comment:	1894-1902	Standing		
	1906	In liquidation		
	1910-1912	Abandoned		
Mineral Lord:	1873-1912	See AD Mines		
Worked by:	1873	A.D. Lead Mining Co.		
	1874-1886	A.D. Lead Mining Co. Ltd		
	1889-1906	Old Gang Lead Mining Co. Ltd		
Agent:	1879-1883	Thomas Raw		
	1884-1896	John Reynoldson		
	1897-1909	Simon Cherry		
	1910-1912	Edward Cherry		
Secretary:	1898-1912	Edward Cherry		
Employment:		Underground	Surface	Total
	1903-1909	See Old Gang		

SUNSIDE Bewerley SE115640

Production:	Lead	Ore(tons)	Lead (tons)	Value (£)
	1760-1814	No detailed returns		
Mineral Lord:	1760-1814	See under Bewerley		
Worked by:	1760-1782	Thornhill & Co.		
	1782-1790	P.W. Overend & Co.		
	1800-1814	Edward Cleaver & Co.		

SUNSIDE Bewerley SE123656

Production:	Lead	Ore(tons)	Lead (tons)	Value (£)
	1845-1898	No detailed returns		
Comment:	1845-1860	See Pateley District		
	1863-1871	See Nidderdale		
	1871-1874	Including Nidderdale & Merryfield		
Mineral Lord:	1845-1898	See Bewerley Liberty		
Worked by:	1863-1871	Nidderdale Lead Mining Co. Ltd		
	1872-1876	Sunside & Merryfield Lead Mining Co. Ltd		
	1877-1898	Burnaby & Hutchinson		
Agent:	1871-1874	William Marshall		
Secretary:	1859-1876	Thomas Sykes		
Employment:		Underground	Surface	Total
	1877	4	1	5
	1878	6	2	8
	1879	4	3	7

SUNSIDE-COCKHILL		Bewerley		SE114648
Production:	Lead	Ore(tons)	Lead (tons)	Value (£)
	1829	626.92		
	1830	540.02		
	1831	64.95		
	1839		318.74	
	1840		273.20	
	1841		218.58	
	1842		259.55	
	1843		402.23	
	1844		282.32	
Comment:	1829	March to December		
	1831	January to February		
	1844	January to June		
	1829		86.78	
	1830		74.25	
	1831		6.30	
Comment:	1829-1831	Slag lead		
	1795-1804	Driving Joint Level to Craven Cross Mine		
	1800	Includes Sunside		
	1808	Driving Low Crosscut to Thornhill Meers		
	1824	Merged with North Coldstones Mine		
	1855	274.00	182.10	
	1856-1860	No detailed returns		
	1861	367.80	239.00	
	1862	458.90	291.40	
	1863	423.60	309.60	
	1864	462.30	300.50	
	1865	199.90	134.00	
	1866	197.30	128.30	
	1867	204.00	153.00	
	1868	292.30	190.00	
	1869	277.40	180.30	
	1870	180.30	140.50	
	1871	128.50	92.00	
	1872	131.00	97.70	
	1873	92.60	69.40	
	1875	78.10	51.00	1071.10
	1876	77.20	56.90	1173.60
	1877	157.00	111.00	2078.90
	1878	324.00	220.70	3413.70
	1879	371.00	227.00	3004.00
	1880	238.00	178.70	2285.00
	1881	100.00	72.00	860.00
	1882	50.00	37.50	425.00
	1883	50.00	37.50	387.00
	1884	40.00	30.00	250.00

	1885	20.00	15.00	130.00
	1886	20.00	14.00	140.00
	1887	50.00		
	1888-1893	No detailed returns		

Comment: 1845-1860 See Pateley District
1861-1900 Data from Hunt's Statistics
1875-1879 Includes Eagle & Perseverance Levels
1881-1905 In liquidation
1922-1938 See Cockhill

Mineral Lord: 1800-1900 See Bewerley Liberty

Worked by: 1800-1814 Edward Cleaver & Co.
1824-1866 Sunside Mining Co.
1845-1866 H. & J. Hutchinson, John Barratt & Joseph Mason
1866-1875 Hutchinson, Burnaby, Heaps & Co.
1875-1879 Pateley Bridge Lead Mines & Smelting Co. Ltd
1879-1883 Pateley Bridge Company Ltd
1887-1893 David Williams
1894-1900 T. Hutchinson & David Williams

Agent: 1824-1836 Nathan Newbould
1836-1868 Matthew Newbould
1869-1873 William Newbould
1874-1878 T. Hutchinson
1875-1880 Charles Williams
1877-1878 James Blenkiron
1879-1881 T.H. Hutchinson
1881 David Williams

Secretary: 1875-1881 William John Lavington

Employment:		Underground	Surface	Total
	1862	73		
	1877	44	14	58
	1878	40	14	54
	1879	55	9	64
	1880	37		37
	1881	7	2	9
	1882	8		8

SUN VEIN Arkengarthdale NY985024

Production:	Lead	Ore(tons)	Lead (tons)	Value (£)
	1749	22.20		
	1750	3.00		
	1782	21.50		
	1783	7.80		
	1784	7.50		
	1785	4.10		
	1786	10.80		

Comment: 1749-1750 Sun Shaft
1750 January to March inclusive

	1782	November 1782 to November 1783 inclusive
	1783-1786	December to May inclusive
	1786	Standing - June to November inclusive
	1786	December 1786 to November 1787 inclusive
Mineral Lord:	1749-1787	See Arkengarthdale
Worked by:	1749-1750	Charles Turner
	1782-1787	Charles Sleigh, William Hoar & Charles Foster

Employment:		Underground	Surface	Total
	1782-1783	5		
	1783-1784	2		
	1784-1785	2		
	1785-1786	2		
	1786-1787	3		

SURRENDER Reeth NY974025

Production:	Lead	Ore(tons)	Lead (tons)	Value (£)
	1797		6.14	
	1798		33.48	
	1799		407.08	
	1800		530.33	
	1801		1020.00	
	1802		441.00	
	1803		425.00	
	1804		703.00	
	1805		776.00	
	1806		538.00	
	1807		1315.00	
	1808		1348.00	
	1809		1096.00	
	1811		864.00	
	1812-1815	No detailed returns		
	1816		286.92	
	1817		518.35	
	1818		1010.63	
	1819		983.96	
	1820		488.55	
	1821		343.68	
	1822		235.74	
	1823		341.68	
	1824		314.03	
	1825		257.07	
	1826		227.19	
	1827		303.86	
	1828		368.99	
	1829		346.43	
	1830		454.48	
	1831		242.50	

	1832		184.74	
	1833		146.43	
	1834		135.35	
	1835		116.01	
	1836		212.72	
	1837		294.59	
	1838		224.22	
	1839		58.68	
	1840		104.60	
	1841		53.67	
	1842		148.96	
	1843		304.93	
	1844		473.42	
	1845		349.84	
	1846		340.17	
	1847		342.38	
	1848		354.78	
	1849		418.49	
	1850		436.00	
	1851		371.00	
	1852		649.00	
	1853		425.00	
	1854		462.00	
	1855		425.00	
	1856		402.00	
	1857		481.00	
	1858		493.00	
	1859		386.00	
	1860		292.00	
	1861		174.00	
Comment:	1797-1800 Data from WRO CR1248/21/R16			
	1801-1815 Data from Jennings Thesis			
	1816-1849 Data from NYCRO ZLB 2/134 & 138			
	1850-1861 Data from Jennings Thesis			
	1862	536.80	331.40	
	1863	No detailed return		
	1868	57.20	42.90	
	1869	No detailed return		
	1870	94.50	70.80	
	1871	118.10	88.50	
	1872	68.20	51.10	
	1873	74.10	55.50	
	1874	31.00	23.20	
	1875	88.00	66.00	1056.00
	1876	110.00	68.70	1320.00
	1877	90.70	56.00	972.20
	1878	28.00	19.50	280.00

	1879	47.50	36.00	403.70
	1880	108.00	81.00	982.80
	1881	103.00	73.50	872.90
	1882	45.50	28.40	376.00
	1883	7.50	4.70	53.00
	1884	19.00		131.00
	1885	14.00	9.00	84.00
Comment:	1862-1885	Data from Hunt's Statistics		
	1863	See Swaledale and Arkendale		
	1875	Includes Swinnergill		
	1879	Ore raised not weighed or sold		
	1885-1887	Standing		
	1894-1902	Standing		
	1906	In liquidation		
	1910-1912	Abandoned		
	1873	10.80		
	1874	29.80		
	1875	62.50		
	1876	97.30		
	1877	91.25		
	1878	41.55		
	1879	38.75		
	1880	107.35		
	1881	83.65		
	1882	46.10		
Comment:	1873-1882	Data from NYCRO ZLB 2/7		
Mineral Lord:	1797-1912	See AD Mines		
Worked by:	1797-1819	AD Lessors & William Chaytor & Co.		
	1819-1836	William Chaytor & Co.		
	1836-1848	George Chaytor & Co.		
	1860-1873	Surrender Mining Co.		
	1873-1880	AD Lead Mining Co. Ltd		
	1881-1884	Sir Francis Denys		
	1885-1887	Surrender Mining Co.		
	1889-1906	Old Gang Lead Mining Co. Ltd		
Agent:	1801-1802	Thomas Raw		
	1805-1807	John Gill		
	1805	George Hutchinson		
	1826	James Spensley		
	1861-1863	Thomas Raw		
	1864-1867	Emerson Alderson		
	1868-1871	John Ralph Place		
	1872-1882	Thomas Raw		
	1877	Robert Wharton		
	1883-1885	Richard Cherry		
	1886-1887	Simon Cherry		
	1888-1896	John Reynoldson		

	1897-1909	Simon Cherry		
	1910-1912	Edward Cherry		
Secretary:	1860-1863	G. Robinson & Co.		
	1874-1880	W.S. Cooper		
	1891-1912	Edward Cherry		
Employment:		Underground	Surface	Total
	1862	99		
	1877	24	4	28
	1878	6		6
	1879	26		26
	1880	22		22
Comment:	1903-1909	See Old Gang		

SWAINBY		Whorlton	NZ479006
Production:	Iron	Ore(tons)	Value (£)
	1858	50000.00	7500.00
	1859	59750.00	9500.00
	1860	46066.00	6142.00
	1861	No detailed return	
Mineral Lord:	1856-1868	Marquis of Ailesbury	
Worked by:	1856-1865	Holdsworth, Bennington, Byers & Co.	
	1866-1868	Stockton Rail Mill Co.	
Agent:	1863-1868	J. Hall	

SWALEDALE		Muker			SD911992
Production:	Lead	Ore(tons)	Lead (tons)		Value (£)
	1919-1924	No detailed returns			
Comment:	1918	See Satron Moor			
	1921-1924	Standing			
Mineral Lord:	1919-1924	See A.D. Mines			
Worked by:	1919-1922	Pickup & Fawcett			
	1923-1924	A.D. Office			
Agent:	1923-1924	Edward Cherry			
Employment:		Underground	Surface	Total	
	1920	8	1	9	

SWALEDALE AND ARKENDALE			Swaledale	
Production:	Lead	Ore(tons)	Lead (tons)	Value (£)
	1845	4257.00	3275.00	
	1847	4200.00	3200.00	
	1848	4053.00	3040.00	
	1849	4954.00	3648.00	
	1850	5110.30	3475.00	
	1851	5000.00	3472.00	
	1852	4765.00	3240.00	
	1853	4947.30	3364.00	
	1854	4817.00	3276.00	

	1855	4345.00	2956.00	
	1856	5371.30	4278.70	
	1857	6326.00	3722.00	
	1858	5517.00	3478.00	
	1859	4720.00	2976.00	
	1860	4410.00	2780.00	
	1861	3032.00	2274.00	
	1862	2460.00	1640.00	
	1863	2874.00	2156.00	
	1864	2964.00	2224.00	
	1865	2887.00	2165.60	
	1866	4565.00	3652.70	
	1867	2345.40	1759.00	
	1868	No detailed return		
Comment:	1845	Includes 1846		
	1850-1851	Includes Hurst		
	1863-1867	Including six other mines		
	1868	See individual mines		

SWALEDALE, EAST Marrick NZ045023

Production:	Lead	Ore(tons)	Lead (tons)	Value (£)
	1864-1872	No detailed returns		
Comment:	1864-1872	See Hurst		

SWALEDALE, SOUTH Muker SD888966

Production:	Lead	Ore(tons)	Lead (tons)	Value (£)
	1865-1873	No detailed returns		
	1867-1869		420.50	
Comment:	1828-1861	See Muker Edge		
	1865-1873	Data from Hunt's Statistics		
	1867-1869	Data from NYCRO ZLB		
	1867-1873	Including Muker Side & Lover (Glover) Gill		
Mineral Lord:	1865-1873	See AD Mines		
Worked by:	1865-1871	South Swaledale Lead Mining Co. Ltd		
Agent:	1869-1871	John Ralph Place		

SWALEDALE, WEST Muker NY868014

Production:	Lead	Ore(tons)	Lead (tons)	Value (£)
	1750-1870	No detailed returns		
Comment:	1750-1870	See Lane End & Keldside		
	1861-1862	Standing		
Mineral Lord:	1860-1866	See AD Mines		
Worked by:	1862-1866	West Swaledale Company		
Agent:	1843-1866	Robert Lowes		
	1861-1866	John Lowes		
Secretary:	1860-1863	Christopher Lonsdale Bradley & Co.		

SWINDEN Linton in Craven SD981618

Production:	Lead	Ore(tons)	Lead (tons)	Value (£)
	1736		0.38	
	1749		0.05	
	1795		0.18	
	1803		0.30	
	1810	0.40	0.25	
Mineral Lord:	1736-1810	See under Grassington		
Worked by:	1736	John Spencer & Ptrs		
	1749	William Ellis		
	1795	John Gill		
	1803	Thomas Marshall		
	1810	John Lupton		
Production:	Zinc	Ore(tons)	Zinc (tons)	Value (£)
	1796	35.00		
	1797	3.66		
Comment:	1736-1810	Lead smelted at Grassington		

SWINNERGILL Muker NY914013

Production:	Lead	Ore(tons)	Lead (tons)	Value (£)
	1705	No detailed return		
	1751		74.00	
	1752		163.10	
	1753		95.80	
	1755		25.90	
	1756		9.70	
Comment:	1752-1753	December to June		
	1755	June to December		
	1755-1756	December to June		
	1804-1805	No detailed returns		
	1806		18.18	
	1807		40.14	
	1808		53.14	
	1809		41.96	
	1810		58.74	
	1811		30.91	
	1812		19.58	
	1813		19.58	
	1814		13.57	
	1815		16.50	
	1816		3.15	
	1817		54.28	
	1818		19.90	
	1819		61.44	
	1820		55.83	
	1821		152.07	
	1822		91.85	

	1823		67.00
	1824		117.73
	1825		155.01
	1826		129.78
	1827		163.33
	1828		232.93
	1829		215.34
	1830		92.62
	1831		27.89
	1832		11.13
	1834		1.96
	1835		9.33
	1836		2.36
	1837-1861	No detailed returns	
	1862	19.00	
	1863	77.60	
	1864	86.70	
	1865	176.95	
	1866	2.75	
	1867	1.00	
	1868-1872	No detailed returns	
	1873	1.00	
	1874	36.25	
	1875	12.85	
	1876	86.85	
	1877	41.90	
	1878	732.30	
	1879	766.70	
	1880	934.80	
	1881	577.90	
	1882	270.90	
	1883	159.15	
Comment:	1806-1814	Data from NYCRO ZLB 2/11	
	1815-1836	Data from NYCRO ZLB 2/134	
	1873-1883	Data from NYCRO ZLB 2/7	
	1806	Smelted at Beldi Hill	
	1806-1814	Estimated from pieces weighing 156.637 lbs	
	1807-1814	Smelted at Swinnergill	
	1815-1819	Smelted at Swinnergill & elsewhere	
	1832	January to July	
	1837-1872	See Blakethwaite	

Production:	Lead	Ore(tons)	Lead (tons)	Value (£)
	1874	36.20	27.10	470.00
	1875	No detailed return		
	1876	86.80	54.40	1042.20
	1877	48.00	30.00	531.60
	1878	700.00	455.00	7402.50
	1879	824.00	618.00	7211.00

	1880	954.00	715.50	8812.90
	1881	629.00	440.00	5332.00
	1882	313.50	185.70	2586.00
	1883	163.70	98.20	1269.00
	1884	96.00		525.00

Comment:	1874-1884	Data from Hunt's Statistics
	1875	See Surrender
	1876-1878	Including Blakethwaite
	1879-1881	Swinnergill A.D. Sir Francis
	1894-1902	Standing
	1906	In liquidation
	1910-1912	Abandoned
Mineral Lord:	1705-1912	See AD Mines
Worked by:	1705	Thomas Wharton (5th Lord)
	1751-1756	Trustees of the Duke of Wharton
	1787	Captain Metcalfe & Co.
	1804-1812	Thomas Hopper & Co.
	1812-1832	Anthony Hopper & Co.
	1834-1836	Sundry waste workers
	1836-1847	Ottiwell Tomlin & Co.
	1848-1859	Thomas Bradley & Co.
	1860-1866	Blakethwaite Co.
	1867-1872	Sir George Denys
	1873-1887	A.D. Lead Mining Co. Ltd
	1889-1906	Old Gang Lead Mining Co. Ltd
Agent:	1873-1882	Thomas Raw
	1874-1877	Robert Wharton
	1883-1896	John Reynoldson
	1897-1909	Simon Cherry
	1910-1912	Edward Cherry
Secretary:	1873-1881	W.S. Cooper
	1898-1912	Edward Cherry

Employment:		Underground	Surface	Total
	1877	36	6	42
	1878	100	36	136
	1879	107	47	154

Comment: 1903-1909 See Old Gang

SWORD & PISTOL Grassington SE021671

Production:	Lead	Ore(tons)	Lead (tons)	Value (£)
	1776		5.84	
	1800		3.10	
	1801		0.45	
	1802		5.40	
	1803		3.45	
	1804		1.25	
	1815	0.50	0.25	

Mineral Lord: 1776-1815 See under Grassington

SYKES Bowland Forest High SD628519

Production:	Lead	Ore(tons)	Lead (tons)	Value (£)
	1575	No detailed return		
	1767		0.60	
Comment:	1575	Silver producer		
	1575	NB Bulmer's date is approximate.		
	1866-1881	See Whitewell		
Mineral Lord:	1575	The Crown		
Worked by:	1575	Bevis Bulmer		
	1767	James Swale		

TANNER RAKE Arkengarthdale NZ015031

Production:	Lead	Ore(tons)	Lead (tons)	Value (£)
	1748	20.60		
	1749	40.20		
	1750	20.60		
	1782	19.60		
	1783	8.60		
	1784	126.40		
	1785	117.20		
	1786	27.90		
	1787	28.50		
	1788	23.60		
	1789	39.80		
	1790	22.40		
	1871	9.60		
	1872	13.70		
	1874	11.30		
	1875	1.75		
	1876	0.25		
	1878	1.40		
	1879	0.55		
	1891	0.45		
Comment:	1748	July to December inclusive		
	1750	January to June inclusive		
	1782	November 1782 to November 1783 inclusive		
	1783-1790	December to November inclusive		
	1790	December 1790 to May 1791 inclusive		
	1871	Year ending June		
	1873	Standing		
	1877	Standing		
	1880-1890	Standing		
	1891	Year ending May 21st		
Mineral Lord:	1748-1891	See Arkengarthdale		
Worked by:	1748-1750	Charles Turner		
	1782-1791	Charles Sleigh, William Hoar & Charles Foster		
	1871-1891	Arkendale Mining Co.		

Employment:		Underground	Surface	Total
	1782-1783	6		
	1783-1784	4		
	1784-1785	11		
	1785-1786	23		
	1786-1787	8		
	1787-1788	12		
	1788-1789	3		
	1789-1790	1		
	1790-1791	2		

TAYLOR RAKE		Buckden		SD958793
Production:	Lead	Ore(tons)	Lead (tons)	Value (£)
	1777	No detailed return		
Comment:	1777	See Buckden Gavel No.1		
Mineral Lord:	1777	See under Grassington		
Worked by:	1777	George Tennant		

TAYLOR'S SHAFT		Grassington		SE027669
Production:	Lead	Ore(tons)	Lead (tons)	Value (£)
	1823	64.65	37.35	
	1824	170.68	101.85	
	1825	93.45	52.05	
	1826	46.38	27.95	
	1827	27.38	13.35	
	1828	2.10	0.75	
	1835	4.45	2.00	
	1837	1.48	0.30	
	1842	1.75	0.80	
Mineral Lord:	1823-1842	See under Grassington		
Worked by:	1823-1842	Duke of Devonshire		
Agent:	1823-1834	John Barratt		
	1834-1842	Stephen Eddy		

TEN MEERS, WEST		Thornthwaite with Padside		SE111632
Production:	Lead	Ore(tons)	Lead (tons)	Value (£)
	1804		14.65	
	1826		12.05	
	1827		7.37	
	1828		9.01	
	1830		17.91	
	1831		7.01	
	1832		7.09	
	1833		5.52	
	1834		5.26	
	1835		3.68	
	1836		7.53	

	1837		6.39	
	1838		3.08	
	1839		5.12	
Comment:	1805-1825	Included with East & West 10 Meers		
	1804-1825	Smelted at Grassington		
	1826-1839	Smelted at Greenhow		
Mineral Lord:	1804-1839	See under Grassington		
Worked by:	1804	Robert Birch & Co.		
	1805-1839	Thomas Stoney		

TENNANT'S PASTURE		Grassington		
Production:	Lead	Ore(tons)	Lead (tons)	Value (£)
	1843	4.30	1.70	
Mineral Lord:	1843	See under Grassington		

THIEVELEY		Holme Chapel		SD873278
Production:	Lead	Ore(tons)	Lead (tons)	Value (£)
	1629	8.80		
	1630	36.97		
Comment:	1629-1630	Smelted at Thieveley		
	1630	0.22	0.15	
Comment:	1630	Smelted at Grassington		
	1631	40.40		
	1632	17.49		
	1633	6.00		
	1634	11.28		
Comment:	1632-1634	Smelted at Holme Chapel		
Mineral Lord:	1629-1635	King Charles I		
Worked by:	1628-1629	Highley & Co.		
	1629-1635	King Charles I		
Agent:	1629-1635	Roger Kenyon (Commissioner)		
	1629-1633	Edward Talbot (Overseer)		
	1633-1635	William Harrison (Overseer)		

THORNHILL MEERS		Bewerley		SE112635
Production:	Lead	Ore(tons)	Lead (tons)	Value (£)
	1800-1824	No detailed returns		
Comment:	1808	Connected with Cockhill Level		
	1824	Merged with Sunside-Cockhill Mine		
Mineral Lord:	1800-1824	See under Bewerley		
Worked by:	1800	Stoney & Crossby		
	1814	John Holmes & Co. (Lease expired 1827)		
	1824	Richard Ward & Co.		

THORNTON MOOR Thornton Rust SD965885

Production:	Lead	Ore(tons)	Lead (tons)	Value (£)
	1850		0.20	
	1851		0.25	
	1853		2.80	
	1856		1.20	
	1858		2.00	
	1861		1.35	
	1866		0.70	
Comment:	1850-1866	Data from Lord Bolton's Lead Book		
	1867	See Sargill		
	1873	Suspended		
Mineral Lord:	1845-1877	See under Keld Heads		
Worked by:	1845-1877	James Percival & Co.		

THORNTREE Preston under Scar SE063929

Production:	Lead	Ore(tons)	Lead (tons)	Value (£)
	1841-1849	No detailed returns		
	1855-1856	No detailed returns		
Comment:	1850-1866	Data from Lord Bolton's Lead Book		
Mineral Lord:	1841-1856	See under Keld Heads		
Worked by:	1841-1849	William Davidson		
	1855	Peter Buck & Co.		
	1856	Keld Heads Mining Co.		

THORPE EDGE Hudswell NZ124004

Production:	Lead	Ore(tons)	Lead (tons)	Value (£)
	1675-1687	No detailed returns		
	1865	No detailed return		
Mineral Lord:	1675-1684	Thomas Wharton		
	1684-1685	Philip Wharton		
	1685-1687	Angelica (Pellisary) Wharton		
	1782	John Hutton		
	1865	John Timothy Darcy Hutton		
Worked by:	1675-1681	Philip Swale & Robert Barker		
	1681-1687	Philip Swale & Adam Barker		
	1865	William Richardson & Company		

THORPE LIBERTY Thorpe SE007615

Production:	Lead	Ore(tons)	Lead (tons)	Value (£)
	1509	No detailed return		
	1739		0.21	
Worked by:	1739	Anthony Medcalf		
	1746		0.58	
Worked by:	1746	Robert Harrison		
	1749		3.45	
	1750		0.77	

Worked by:	1749-1750	Mr Morley	
	1767		0.05
Worked by:	1767	Robert Birch	
	1767		0.35
Worked by:	1767	William Rodgers	
	1768		0.20
Worked by:	1768	John Herd	
	1768		0.75
Worked by:	1768	Thomas Paley	
	1773		0.08
Worked by:	1773	William Buck	
	1774		0.25
	1775		0.15
Worked by:	1774-1775	Thomas Ripley	
	1775		0.74
Worked by:	1775	Richard Ducket	
	1776		0.08
	1778		1.65
	1782		0.25
	1789		1.05
	1790		5.40
	1791		0.25
	1792		0.10
Worked by:	1776-1792	Mr Tempest	
	1788		0.08
Worked by:	1788	William Pickersgill	
	1838	0.88	0.60
Worked by:	1838	Thomas Atkinson	
Comment:	1739-1838	Smelted at Grassington	
	1736	See Stebden	
	1850-1898	See Elbolton	
Mineral Lord:	1509	Roger Tempest	
	1717	Stephen Tempest	
	1739-1853	Mr Tempest	

THREE FOOTED STOOL Grassington SE015677

Production:	Lead	Ore(tons)	Lead (tons)	Value (£)
	1792		108.30	
	1793		203.70	
	1795		210.10	
	1796		70.70	
	1797		61.05	
	1798		73.30	
	1799		6.45	
	1800		41.70	
	1809	33.70	17.50	
	1810	23.33	11.30	

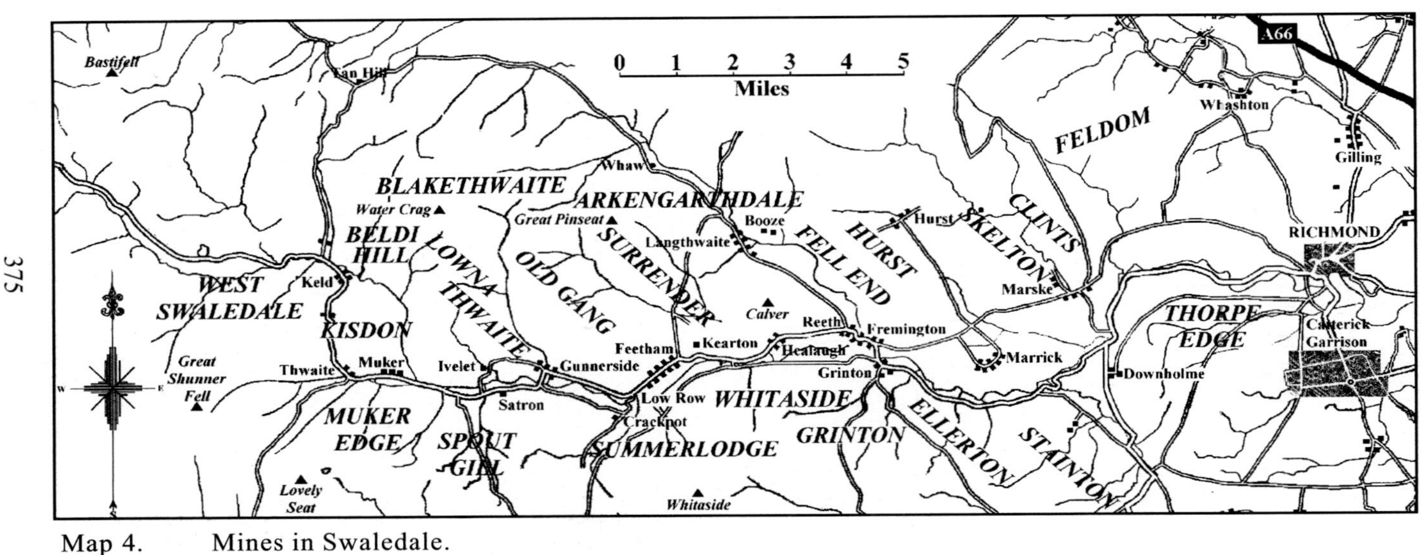

Map 4. Mines in Swaledale.

	1811	28.73	17.05
	1812	1.65	0.90
	1813	30.55	19.30
	1815	31.35	14.70
	1816	2.15	1.15
	1817	16.88	10.35
	1818	15.20	9.05
	1819	1.25	0.65
	1821	1.30	0.80
	1824	3.80	2.30

Mineral Lord: 1792-1824 See under Grassington

Worked by: 1792 John Stott & Co.

1812 Jacob Ragg & Co.

THREE MEERS Grassington SE028670

Production:	Lead	Ore(tons)	Lead (tons)	Value (£)
	1762		60.60	
	1765		56.80	
	1766		26.85	
	1767		76.75	
	1768		68.58	
	1769		75.00	
	1770		48.85	
	1771		41.80	
	1773		91.70	
	1774		63.80	
	1775		32.15	
	1776		28.30	
	1777		22.39	
	1778		39.23	
	1779		22.40	
	1780		33.63	
	1782		42.45	
	1783		34.76	
	1785		25.68	
	1786		13.29	
	1787		7.66	
	1789		14.29	
	1790		6.03	
	1791		2.08	
	1795		1.35	
	1796		2.85	
	1797		0.75	
	1798		0.70	
	1799		0.50	
	1800		0.80	
	1801		5.70	

	1802		6.53	
	1803		9.15	
	1804		4.55	
	1805		2.50	
	1806		8.65	
	1807		6.70	
	1808		4.75	
	1809	15.10	6.95	
	1810	1.80	0.80	
	1811	20.03	9.70	
	1812	6.95	3.15	
	1813	7.83	4.25	
	1814	8.18	3.40	
	1815	1.35	0.55	
	1816	0.45	0.15	
	1818	1.45	0.55	
	1819	2.90	1.15	
	1820	2.50	1.00	
	1843	1.55	0.65	

Comment: 1821-1842 See under Friendship
Mineral Lord: 1762-1843 See under Grassington
Worked by: 1756-1769 Mr Shackleton & Co.
1769-1782 Mrs Shackleton & Co.
1782-1784 Mrs Wardle & Co.
1820 Joseph Constantine
Agent: 1759-1788 Jacob Bailey
1766 Ralph Summers

THRESHFIELD PASTURE Threshfield SD976631

Production:	Lead	Ore(tons)	Lead (tons)	Value (£)
	1791		0.10	

TOBACCO RAKE Grassington SE024669

Production:	Lead	Ore(tons)	Lead (tons)	Value (£)

1755-1765 No detailed returns
Comment: 1755-1765 Part of New Ripon
Mineral Lord: 1755-1765 See under Grassington

TINKER RAKE Starbotton SD961744

Production:	Lead	Ore(tons)	Lead (tons)	Value (£)
	1739		0.75	
	1740		1.05	

Comment: 1739-1740 Smelted at Buckden
Mineral Lord: 1739-1740 See under Grassington
Worked by: 1739-1740 William Chapman

TOCKETTS Tocketts NZ620179

Production:	Iron	Ore(tons)		Value (£)
	1875	3992.00		
	1876	151996.00		
	1877	121551.70		

Comment:	1877-1880	Standing
	1880	Abandoned
Mineral Lord:	1874-1880	Admiral Chaloner
Worked by:	1874	J. Pease & Jos. W. Pease
	1875-1880	J.W. Pease & Co.
Agent:	1875-1878	Christopher Heslop
	1879-1880	William Walton

TOFT RIGG ALLOTMENT Bewerley SE136648

Production:	Lead	Ore(tons)	Lead (tons)	Value (£)
	1792-1824	No detailed returns		

Comment:	1792-1824	See Bale Bank
Mineral Lord:	1792-1824	See under Bewerley
Worked by:	1800	Sir John Ingilby & Co.

TOPSETT Arkengarthdale

Production:	Lead	Ore(tons)	Lead (tons)	Value (£)
	1782	9.04		
	1783	1.79		
	1784	0.07		
	1785	0.11		
	1786	0.15		
	1787	0.25		
	1788	0.30		

Comment:	1782	November 1782 to November 1783 inclusive
	1783-1785	December to May inclusive
	1785	Standing - June 1785 to May 1786
	1786	June 1786 to November 1787 inclusive
	1787	Standing - May 1787 to November 1788
	1788	December 1788 to November 1789 inclusive
Mineral Lord:	1782-1789	See Arkengarthdale
Worked by:	1782-1789	Charles Sleigh, William Hoar & Charles Foster

Employment:		Underground	Surface	Total
	1782-1783	10		
	1783-1784	6		
	1784-1785	1		
	1786	1		
	1787	1		
	1787-1788	3		
	1788-1789	1		

TOTTER GILL Arkengarthdale NY992024

Production:	Lead	Ore(tons)	Lead (tons)	Value (£)
	1784	0.50		

Comment:	1784	June to November inclusive
	1784-1790	Standing - December to May inclusive
	1790	June to November inclusive
Mineral Lord:	1784-1790	See Arkengarthdale
Worked by:	1784-1790	Charles Sleigh, William Hoar & Charles Foster

Employment:		Underground	Surface	Total
	1784	1		
	1790	1		

TROUT BECK Grassington SD992646

Production:	Lead	Ore(tons)	Lead (tons)	Value (£)
	1826	7.15	4.15	
	1827	1.38	0.90	

Mineral Lord:	1826-1827	See under Grassington
Worked by:	1826	William Bell & James Parkin

TURF MOOR Arkengarthdale NY994021

Production:	Lead	Ore(tons)	Lead (tons)	Value (£)
	1871	5.95		
	1872	10.25		
	1873	5.35		
	1874	5.70		
	1875	1.70		
	1876	0.30		
	1877	0.90		
	1881	12.95		
	1882	5.30		
	1883	2.35		
	1884	2.95		
	1885	1.05		
	1886	0.45		
	1887	0.35		
	1888	2.00		
	1889	1.45		

Comment:	1871	Year ending June
	1878-1880	Standing
Mineral Lord:	1871-1889	See Arkengarthdale
Worked by:	1871-1889	Arkendale Mining Co.

TURF PITS Grassington SE028675

Production:	Lead	Ore(tons)	Lead (tons)	Value (£)
	1776		43.50	
	1777		44.10	
	1778		36.00	

1779		50.70
1780		58.61
1781		49.35
1782		72.28
1783		22.27
1784		7.88
1785		7.50
1786		10.51
1787		9.74
1788		8.54
1789		2.24
1790		2.40
1791		1.40
1792		0.45
1793		0.44
1794		0.40
1795		0.65
1796		2.13
1797		0.45
1799		3.55
1800		2.65
1801		2.40
1802		0.85
1803		1.35
1804		0.20
1805		0.30
1806		7.15
1807		3.90
1808		3.15
1809	5.40	3.15
1810	1.10	0.60
1811	26.35	16.70
1812	30.85	20.05
1813	27.15	17.05
1814	17.90	10.55
1815	47.68	28.80
1816	36.55	22.90
1817	39.00	22.20
1818	9.33	5.70
1819	3.75	1.45
1820	12.15	7.05
1821	3.30	1.80
1822	10.05	6.10
1823	0.60	0.35
1824	0.35	0.20
1826	3.88	1.80
1827	2.73	1.40

	1828	2.30	1.35	
	1829	12.30	8.50	
	1830	9.13	6.05	
	1833	0.25	0.10	
	1840	1.90	1.05	
	1841	6.98	3.00	
	1842	4.95	2.10	
	1844	4.75	2.35	
	1845	0.75	0.35	
	1848	2.25	1.35	
	1849	0.68	0.40	
	1850	4.55	2.05	
	1853	2.25	0.95	

Mineral Lord: 1776-1853 See under Grassington

TWENTY MEERS Conistone with Kilnsey SE015703

Production:	Lead	Ore(tons)	Lead (tons)	Value (£)
	1768		4.33	

Comment: 1768 Smelted at Grassington
Mineral Lord: 1768 See Conistone Liberty
Worked by: 1768 James Bell & Mr Holme

UNDEREDGE Arkengarthdale NY991030

Production:	Lead	Ore(tons)	Lead (tons)	Value (£)
	1783	2.00		
	1786	0.40		

Comment: 1783 May to November inclusive
1783-1786 Standing: December to November inclusive
1786 December 1786 to May 1787 inclusive
Mineral Lord: 1784-1787 See Arkengarthdale
Worked by: 1784-1787 Charles Sleigh, William Hoar & Charles Foster

Employment:		Underground	Surface	Total
	1783	1		
	1786-1787	1		

UNION Grassington SE020657

Production:	Lead	Ore(tons)	Lead (tons)	Value (£)
	1779		2.03	
	1789		0.10	

Mineral Lord: 1779-1789 See under Grassington

UPLEATHAM Marske NZ625204

Production:	Iron	Ore(tons)	Value (£)
	1856	171360.00	
	1857	171366.00	
	1858	190306.00	28595.90
	1859	265524.90	39829.50

1860	391410.00	58711.50
1861	288191.40	43228.60
1862	433139.30	64970.00
1863	573613.30	
1864	689940.40	
1865	717998.00	215399.00
1866	568758.00	142189.50
1867	597995.00	164448.60
1868	573566.00	143391.20
1869	573655.80	143413.70
1870	578820.00	144705.00
1871	607234.70	151808.60
1872	588031.00	
1873	550930.00	165279.00
1874	505470.00	151641.00
1875	640905.00	
1876	662200.00	
1877	613744.80	
1878	732139.00	
1879	714075.20	
1880	794886.70	
1881	770807.80	
1882-1923	No detailed returns	

Comment: 1851-1923 Main and Pecten Seams
1923 Abandoned

Mineral Lord: 1862-1924 Lord Zetland

Worked by: 1851-1857 Derwent Iron Co.
1857-1880 Joseph Whitwell Pease & Co.
1881-1924 Pease and Partners Ltd

Agent: 1863-1874 William Cockburn
1875 Christopher Heslop
1876-1879 William Walton
1880-1881 William Moore
1882-1917 Christopher Heslop
1919-1923 George C. Heslop

Employment:

	Underground	Surface	Total
1862	343		
1883			718
1894	349	94	443
1895	355	100	455
1896	361	103	464
1897	376	107	483
1898	385	114	499
1899	386	125	511
1900	399	136	535
1901	384	130	514
1902	385	113	498

1903	382	120	502
1904	384	119	503
1905	387	121	508
1906	349	124	473
1907	345	116	461
1908	323	113	336
1909	270	104	374
1910	266	92	358
1911	269	103	372
1912	259	102	361
1913	273	108	381
1914	262	100	362
1915	200	108	308
1916	249	98	347
1917	232	109	341
1918	182	98	280
1919	188	124	312
1920	183	107	290
1921	181	70	251
1922	189	68	257
1923	159	65	224

UPSALL Upsall NZ573173

Production: Iron Ore(tons) Value (£)
1866-1927 No detailed returns

Comment: 1866-1927 See Eston
1878-1881 Standing
1891-1893 Standing

Mineral Lord: 1866-1945 Greenwood family

Worked by: 1866-1927 Bolckow, Vaughan & Co. Ltd
1929-1945 Dorman, Long & Co. Ltd

Agent: 1878-1879 Thomas Lee
1880-1910 John Thompson
1911-1912 A.M. Hedley
1913-1925 W.G. Grace
1926-1927 T.E. Slater

Employment: Underground Surface Total

Comment: 1894-1927 Included with Eston

VENTURE Grassington

Production:	Lead	Ore(tons)	Lead (tons)	Value (£)
	1802		0.35	
	1807		0.30	

Comment: 1807 Mary's Venture

Mineral Lord: 1802-1807 See under Grassington

VICTORIA		Bolton by Bowland		SD760504
Production:	Lead	Ore(tons)	Lead (tons)	Value (£)
	1869-1871	No detailed returns		
Comment:	1869-1873	Data from PRO BT31/1470/4469		
	1872-1873	In liquidation		
Worked by:	1869-1871	Victoria Mining Company Ltd		
Agent:	1869-1871	Robert Wilson		
Secretary:	1869-1871	John Southworth		

VICTORIA		Kettlewell		SD982733
Production:	Lead	Ore(tons)	Lead (tons)	Value (£)
	1850-1852	No detailed returns		
Comment:	1852	Merged with Silver Rake		
	1853-1879	See Silver Rake		
Mineral Lord:	1850-1852	See under Kettlewell		
Worked by:	1850-1852	Victoria Mining Company		

VIRGIN		Castle Bolton		SE003933
Production:	Lead	Ore(tons)	Lead (tons)	Value (£)
	1850		3.30	
	1851		6.10	
	1852		10.45	
	1853		17.65	
	1854		9.25	
	1855		8.00	
	1856		7.30	
	1857		9.40	
	1858		11.85	
	1859		20.65	
	1860		12.15	
	1861		12.15	
	1862		36.70	
	1863		36.40	
	1864		53.40	
	1865		25.65	
	1866		16.40	
	1867		9.20	
	1869		6.75	
	1871		1.20	
Comment:	1850-1871	Data from Lord Bolton's Lead Book		
	1864-1865	No detailed returns		
	1866	5.00	3.20	
	1867	No detailed return		
Comment:	1864-1865	See Keld Head		
	1867	See Sargill		
Production:	Barytes	Ore(tons)		Value (£)
	1887	8.00		
	1888-1891	No detailed returns		

Comment:	1864-1897	Data from Hunt's Statistics		
	1888-1889	See Lunehead		
	1891-1897	Standing		
Mineral Lord:	1833-1897	See under Keld Heads		
Worked by:	1833	J. Burnett & Co.		
	1850-1863	John Calvert & Co.		
	1862-1865	George Harker		
	1866-1878	Virgin Mines Co.		
	1886-1897	Virgin Moss Mining Co.		
Agent:	1866	William Sigston Winn		
	1867-1878	George Harker		
	1886-1893	John Ascough Rodwell		
	1894-1897	F. Rodwell		

WALDEN HEAD		Burton cum Walden		SE016817
Production:	Lead	Ore(tons)	Lead (tons)	Value (£)
	1862-1881	No detailed returns		
Comment:	1862-1881	Including Wasset Fell		
	1873	Suspended		
Mineral Lord:	1862-1881	Henry Thomas Robinson		
Worked by:	1862-1881	Thwaite & Co.		

WARREN MOOR		Kildale		NZ625089
Production:	Iron	Ore(tons)		Value (£)
	1864-1874	No detailed returns		
Comment:	1864-1874	Top Seam		
	1872-1874	Called Leven Vale		
Mineral Lord:	1864-1874	Trustees of R.B. Livesey		
Worked by:	1864-1867	Watson & Murray		
	1872-1874	Leven Vale Co. Ltd		

WASH (HOUSE) VEIN		Grassington		SE023668
Production:	Lead	Ore(tons)	Lead (tons)	Value (£)
	1739		0.25	
	1743		2.78	
	1744		0.90	
	1748		0.75	
	1750		0.34	
	1762		0.70	
	1767		0.86	
	1774		0.22	
	1776		0.10	
	1781		0.34	
	1782		0.51	
	1789		0.21	
	1790		0.20	
	1791		0.35	

	1800		0.30
	1802		0.25
	1804		1.65
	1805		0.25
	1806		0.20
	1807		1.90
	1808		3.00
	1809	10.18	4.45
	1810	1.55	0.75
	1811	0.60	5.00
	1812	1.15	0.45
	1820	5.85	2.05
	1822	14.05	5.90
	1823	3.00	1.00
	1824	24.35	9.20
	1825	2.20	0.90
	1826	14.30	6.05
	1827	6.23	1.80
	1829	4.28	2.00
	1830	2.80	0.90
	1831	1.03	0.40
	1832	3.35	1.60
Comment:	1756-1761	Data missing	
	1763-1764	Data missing	
	1810	Waste ore	
Mineral Lord:	1739-1832	See under Grassington	

WASSET FELL Burton cum Walden SD992833

Production:	Lead	Ore(tons)	Lead (tons)	Value (£)
	1862-1881	No detailed returns		
Comment:	1862-1881	See Walden Head		

WATERFALL Tocketts NZ626172

Production:	Iron	Ore(tons)	Value (£)
	1892-1901	No detailed returns	
Comment:	1901	Abandoned	
Mineral Lord:	1892-1901	Trustees of Admiral Chaloner	
Worked by:	1892-1901	Cargo Fleet Iron Co. Ltd	
Agent:	1892-1893	John Cowie	
	1894-1901	Thomas Saunders	

Employment:		Underground	Surface	Total
	1894	31	33	64
	1895	11	52	63
	1896	21	36	57
	1897	15	35	50
	1898	19	30	49
	1899	22	28	50
	1900	27	29	56

WAYWORTH Kildale NZ652097

Production:	Iron	Ore(tons)		Value (£)
	1866-1867	No detailed returns		
Comment:	1866-1867	Sinking		
	1866-1867	Top Seam		
Worked by:	1866-1867	Dr Loy		
Agent:	1866-1867	John Watson		

WEATHER GLEAM Grassington SE031672

Production:	Lead	Ore(tons)	Lead (tons)	Value (£)
	1796		1.60	
	1797		1.95	
	1798		5.70	
	1811	4.80	2.80	
	1813	1.40	0.65	
Mineral Lord:	1796-1813	See under Grassington		
Worked by:	1796	John Bagshaw		

WEMMERGILL BECK HEAD Lunedale NY895239

Production:	Lead	Ore(tons)	Lead (tons)	Value (£)
	1831	No detailed returns		
Mineral Lord:	1831	See Lunehead		
Worked by:	1831	John Barker & Co.		

WENSLEYDALE Bainbridge SD902898

Production:	Lead	Ore(tons)	Lead (tons)	Value (£)
	1855	19.35	14.05	
Comment:	1855	Smelted at Starbotton Cupola		
	1862	51.80	37.60	
Comment:	1862	Data from Hunt's Statistics		
	1872		0.05	
Comment:	1872	Smelted at Kettlewell		
	1862-1871	See Raigill		
Mineral Lord:	1854-1871	Trust Lords of Bainbridge		
Worked by:	1854-1858	Wensleydale Mining Co. (Cost Book)		
	1858-1866	Wensleydale Mining Co. Ltd		
Agent:	1854-1862	William Craig		
Secretary:	1866	C.E. Bolton		

WENSLEYDALE Wensleydale

Production:	Lead	Ore(tons)	Lead (tons)	Value (£)
	1850	No detailed return		
	1851	696.00	500.00	
	1852	2670.00	1386.00	
	1853	1185.00	615.00	
	1854	910.30	682.00	
	1855	1864.00	1200.00	

1856	2800.00	1806.00	
1857	2550.00	1643.00	
1858	2421.00	1599.90	
1859	1585.00	1047.00	
1860	2815.00	1872.00	
1861	2550.00	1605.00	
1862	2024.00	1418.80	
1863	2234.00	1413.00	

WEST BURTON LIBERTY Burton Cum Walden SE019868

Production:	Lead	Ore(tons)	Lead (tons)	Value (£)
	1684-1703	No detailed returns		
Comment:	1684-1685	Smelting ore from the AD Mines Swaledale		
	1702-1703	Smelting at Marrick Cupola		
	1850-1861	See Bishopdale Gavel		
Mineral Lord:	1667-1718	Benjamin Purchas		
Worked by:	1684-1685	Benjamin Purchas		

WEST BURTON Burton Cum Walden SE019868

Production:	Lead	Ore(tons)	Lead (tons)	Value (£)
	1864	400.00	280.00	
	1865	99.00	70.30	
	1866	94.00	63.00	
	1867	50.00	33.00	
	1876	7.90	5.80	
	1877	21.50	15.30	242.40
	1880	31.00	23.20	335.20
	1881	28.90	20.50	234.00
Comment:	1881	Now abandoned February 1882		
Worked by:	1862-1869	John Tattersall & Co.		
	1876-1880	Henry Pease		
	1881	Executors of Henry Pease		
Agent:	1876-1881	John Cain		

Employment:		Underground	Surface	Total
	1863	20		
	1877	12	6	18
	1878	21		21
	1879	9	1	10
	1880	7	0	7

WET GROOVES Carperby cum Thoresby SD986903

Production:	Lead	Ore(tons)	Lead (tons)	Value (£)
	1569	No detailed return		
	1850		7.30	
	1851		19.15	
	1852		23.50	
	1853		30.85	

	1854		26.80	
	1855		7.45	
	1856		5.10	
	1857		7.90	
	1858		54.65	
	1859		69.05	
	1860		56.75	
	1861		7.85	
	1862		2.80	
	1863		1.20	
	1865		3.60	
	1866		2.70	
	1867		0.40	
Comment:	1848-1867	Data from Lord Bolton's Lead Book		
Production:	Lead	Ore(tons)	Lead (tons)	Value (£)
	1862	3.70	2.70	
	1864	6.00	3.60	
	1866-1867	No detailed returns		
	1872	4.70	3.50	
	1873	No detailed return		
	1875	27.10	20.00	668.80
	1876	74.70	55.00	958.80
	1879	20.00	15.00	206.00
Comment:	1862-1879	Data from Hunt's Statistics		
	1867	See Sargill		
	1870-1871	See How Bank		
	1879	Standing		
Production:	Fluorspar	Ore(tons)		Value (£)
	1946-1970	No detailed returns		
Mineral Lord:	1848-1970	See under Keld Heads		
Worked by:	1569	Henry Earl of Cumberland		
	1848-1867	Craig, Longbottom & Co.		
	1872-1879	John Bowman & Son		
	1946-1970	Edwin Drake & William Taylor		
Agent:	1862-1879	John Tattersall		

Employment:		Underground	Surface	Total
	1862	4		
	1877	8	2	10
	1878	8		8

WETSHAW		Arkengarthdale		NY980027
Production:	Lead	Ore(tons)	Lead (tons)	Value (£)
	1790	4.10		
	1876	84.90		
	1877	1.65		
	1878	80.20		
Comment:	1790	December 1789 to November 1790 inclusive		

Mineral Lord:	1789-1878	See Arkengarthdale		
Worked by:	1789-1790	Charles Sleigh, William Hoar & Charles Foster		
	1876-1878	Arkendale Mining Co.		
Employment:		Underground	Surface	Total
	1789-1790	1		

WHARFEDALE		Starbotton		SD951727
Production:	Lead	Ore(tons)	Lead (tons)	Value (£)
	1857-1859	No detailed returns		
	1860	47.70	27.40	
	1861	40.90	25.10	
	1862	17.10	10.00	
	1863	40.10	21.80	
	1864	49.10	24.10	
	1865	73.80	41.70	
	1866	35.00	18.30	
	1867	13.30	6.60	
	1868	02.80	1.30	
	1869	13.20	10.00	
	1870	18.50	10.50	
	1871	11.50	6.30	
	1872	15.20	11.40	
	1873	47.20	35.40	
	1874	40.90	30.60	476.40
	1875	46.50	25.50	
	1876	30.60	18.30	
	1877	35.80	17.80	329.30
	1878	41.20	26.50	412.00
	1879	19.70	15.00	203.30
	1859-1879	Data from Hunt's Statistics		
	1870		3.75	
	1871		0.10	
Comment:	1870-1871	Smelted at Kettlewell		
	1876		10.60	
	1877		10.00	
	1879		44.55	
	1880		1.80	
Comment:	1876-1880	Smelted at Grassington		
	1821-1828	See Moor End		
	1879-1880	In liquidation		
Mineral Lord:	1857-1880	See under Starbotton Liberty		
Worked by:	1857-1880	Wharfdale [sic] Mining Co. Ltd		
Agent:	1862-1868	Robert Place		
	1869-1880	John Ralph Place		
Secretary:	1857-1878	William Henry Burrell		

Employment:		Underground	Surface	Total
	1862	5		
	1878	7		7

WHARFEDALE Kettlewell SD955725

Production:	Lead	Ore(tons)	Lead (tons)	Value (£)
	1860-1880	No detailed returns		
Comment:	1860-1879	See Moor End, Starbotton		
	1869-1880	Wayleave for Charlton's Level £10/year		
Mineral Lord:	1860-1880	Trust Lords of Kettlewell		
Worked by:	1869-1880	Wharfdale [sic] Mining Co. Ltd		

WHIRLER RAKE Grassington SE022682

Production:	Lead	Ore(tons)	Lead (tons)	Value (£)
	1752		0.50	
	1753		1.36	
	1769		0.55	
	1800		0.20	
Comment:	1800	At east end of Green Bycliffe		
Mineral Lord:	1752-1800	See under Grassington		

WHICKHAM Grassington SE034669

Production:	Lead	Ore(tons)	Lead (tons)	Value (£)
	1805		3.70	
	1806		2.45	
	1807		1.25	
	1808		0.85	
	1809	0.13	0.05	
	1812	3.20	1.25	
Comment:	1778-1804	See under Cottingley		
Mineral Lord:	1805-1812	See under Grassington		
Worked by:	1805-1812	Colonel Henry Wickham		

WHIM SHAFT, WEST Arkengarthdale NY974030

Production:	Lead	Ore(tons)	Lead (tons)	Value (£)
	1784	430.30		
	1785	316.70		
	1786	80.10		
	1787	11.40		
	1789	1.80		
Comment:	1784-1788	December to November inclusive		
	1788	Standing: December 1788 to November 1789		
	1789-1790	December 1789 to November 1790 inclusive		
Mineral Lord:	1784-1790	See Arkengarthdale		
Worked by:	1784-1790	Charles Sleigh, William Hoar & Charles Foster		

Employment:		Underground	Surface	Total
	1784	14		
	1784-1785	43		
	1785-1786	27		
	1786-1787	8		
	1787-1788	4		
	1789-1790	2		

WHITASIDE		Grinton		SD990956
Production:	Lead	Ore(tons)	Lead (tons)	Value (£)
	1767	2582.40	2028.65	
	1768-1772	No detailed returns		
	1772	342.64	136.73	
	1773	379.39	248.09	
	1774	43.46	23.55	
	1775		98.81	
	1776		99.23	
	1777		134.02	
	1778		99.30	
	1779		107.04	
	1780		119.45	
	1781		87.86	
	1782		90.02	
	1783		835.27	
	1785		140.10	
	1786		28.05	
	1787		35.24	
	1788		15.25	
	1790		69.84	
	1792		37.28	
	1793		70.42	
	1794		35.69	
	1795		8.86	
	1796		34.88	
	1797		70.83	
	1798		177.14	
	1799		142.30	
	1800		316.48	
	1801		140.44	
	1802		225.81	
	1803		252.91	
	1804		150.30	
	1805		10.14	
	1806		49.13	
	1807		91.03	
	1810		114.43	
	1811		343.23	
	1812		675.01	
	1813		495.39	
	1814		292.20	
	1848		1070.20	
	1850		1612.70	
	1862	47.00	30.00	
	1872	12.90	9.70	
	1873	No detailed return		

	1888	3.00			20.00
	1889	No detailed return			
Comment:	1805-1814	Data from PRO LLRO 3/86			
	1848-1850	Data from DRO D/HH 6/4/30 & 31			
	1862-1889	Data from Hunt's Statistics			
	1767	From 1761 to November 1767 inclusive			
	1772	From September 17th			
	1774	To March 12th			
	1785	Includes 1784			
	1792	Includes 1791			
	1795	Includes part 1796			
	1798	Includes part 1799			
	1799	Includes part 1800			
	1877-1886	Standing			
	1894-1897	Standing			
Mineral Lord:	1541-1889	See under Grinton			
Worked by:	1761-1774	John Harker & Co.			
	1774-1775	Thomas Simpson & Co.			
	1848-1875	Whitaside Mining Co.			
	1877-1886	J.C.D. Charlesworth			
	1887	Swaledale Mining Association Ltd			
	1888-1897	Grinton Mining & Smelting Co. Ltd			
Agent:	1848-1853	Robert Banson			
	1861	Ralph Milner			
	1862-1870	Adam Barker			
	1871-1875	Francis Garth			
	1887-1893	John Ascough Rodwell			
	1894-1896	F. Rodwell			
	1897	J. Barker			
Employment:		Underground	Surface	Total	
	1768			400	
	1775			80	
	1862	9			

WHITBY IRON MINES North Riding

Production:	Iron	Ore(tons)	Value (£)
	1867	2522.40	630.60

WHITECLIFFE Loftus NZ711188

Production:	Iron	Ore(tons)	Value (£)
	1872	No detailed return	
	1873	72885.00	21865.50
	1874	98478.00	29543.40
	1875	110091.00	
	1876	159060.00	
	1877	143056.60	
	1878	112263.00	

	1879	6928.90
	1880	No detailed return
Comment:	1855	Abandoned
	1876	Transferred to J.W. Pease & Co. November 1876
	1878-1884	Standing
	1884	Abandoned
Mineral Lord:	1872-1884	Lord Zetland
Worked by:	1871-1872	North Cleveland Ironstone Co.
	1872-1876	Swan, Coates & Co.
	1877-1880	J.W. Pease & Co.
	1881-1884	Pease and Partners Ltd
Agent:	1872-1875	Thomas Hodgson
	1876	John G. Swan
	1877-1884	William France

WHITCLIFFE PASTURE Richmond NZ162021

Production:	Lead	Ore(tons)	Lead (tons)	Value (£)
	1668-1792	No detailed returns		
Production:	Copper	Ore(tons)	Copper (tons)	Value (£)
	1668-1792	No detailed returns		
Comment:	1763	5 Meers Richmond Out Moor		
Mineral Lord:	1668-1792	Corporation of Richmond		
Worked by:	1668	Charles Lord St John		
	1697	Thomas Yorke & Company		
	1718	Thomas Davile & Company		
	1750-1754	Ralph Close		
	1758	William Chaytor		
	1763	Robert Colling		
	1764	Cuthbert Readshaw		
	1792	William Chaytor		

WHITE EARTH Downholme SE015984

Production:	Lead	Ore(tons)	Lead (tons)	Value (£)
	1803-1805	No detailed returns		
Comment:	1803-1805	See Also Downholme & High Rock		
Mineral Lord:	1803-1990	See under Downholme		
Worked by:	1803-1805	David Bradbury & John Berwick		
	1856-1857	Thomas Siddale		
	1864	William Alderson		

WHITEWELL Forest of Bowland SD646543

Production:	Lead	Ore(tons)	Lead(tons)	Silver(ozs)	Value(£)
	1866	250.00	190.00	750.00	
	1867	690.00	489.50	2060.00	
	1868	441.00	326.50	1530.00	
	1869	300.00	225.00	999.00	
	1870	200.00	144.00	620.00	

	1871	80.00	62.00	308.00	
	1872	8.00	6.00		
	1873	No detailed return			
	1874	1.50	1.10		17.70

Comment:	1866-1877	Data from Hunt & PRO BT31/1205/2731C
	1866	Ore 200 corrected from 69 stats
	1867	Ore 630 corrected from 69 stats
	1868	Ore 550 corrected from 69 stats
	1874-1877	In liquidation
Worked by:	1865	Colonel Townley & Co.
	1866-1877	Whitewell Mining Co. Ltd
Agent:	1865	T. Ware
	1865-1867	William Hill
	1867-1868	M. Harpur
	1869-1877	William Hoyle
Secretary:	1866	Thomas Hughes
	1867	T. Ware
	1869-1871	John Lewis
	1871-1877	John Fowler

WHITHAM PASTURE Grassington

Production:	Lead	Ore(tons)	Lead (tons)	Value (£)
	1812	1.90	0.80	
	1815	1.05	0.45	
	1821	3.00	1.45	

Mineral Lord: 1812-1821 See under Grassington

WILKINSON PITS Grassington SE034671

Production:	Lead	Ore(tons)	Lead (tons)	Value (£)
	1774		48.00	
	1775		212.00	
	1776		223.00	
	1777		64.75	
	1778		168.00	
	1779		120.00	
	1780		96.00	
	1781		76.84	
	1782		24.35	
	1783		24.00	
	1784		30.30	
	1785		28.00	
	1787		48.00	
	1789		24.00	
	1790		48.00	
	1791		24.00	
	1792		48.00	
	1795		11.75	

	1796		2.30	
	1797		6.45	
	1798		5.50	
	1801		0.45	
	1802		3.00	
Comment:	1774	The rights to use Pit Moss Shaft were purchased from Shackleton & Co. in April		
Mineral Lord:	1774-1802	See under Grassington		
Worked by:	1774-1802	Messrs Wilkinson		

WILTON		Middlesbrough		
Production:	Iron	Ore(tons)		Value (£)
	1885-1927	No detailed returns		
Comment:	1885-1927	See Eston		
Worked by:	1885-1927	Bolckow, Vaughan & Co. Ltd		
Agent:	1885-1910	John Thompson		
	1911-1912	A.M. Hedley		
	1913-1925	W.G. Grace		
	1926-1927	T.E. Slater		
Employment:		Underground Surface Total		
	1893-1927	Included with Eston		

WINDEGG		Arkengarthdale		NZ012052
Production:	Lead	Ore(tons)	Lead (tons)	Value (£)
	1657	18.15		
	1658	29.20		
	1748	25.90		
	1749	55.70		
	1750	21.00		
	1782	117.20		
	1783	87.80		
	1784	33.70		
	1785	4.20		
	1786	10.10		
	1787	0.20		
	1788	6.90		
	1789	20.20		
	1790	33.00		
	1891	7.80		
Comment:	1657-1658	Including Eastfield, Eeastmist, Lowfield Groves, White Gang 1st & 2nd Shafts		
	1782	November 1782 to November 1783 inclusive		
	1783-1788	December to May inclusive		
	1788	Standing - June 1788 to May 1789		
	1789-1791	June to May inclusive		
Mineral Lord:	1657-1891	See Arkengarthdale		
Worked by:	1657-1658	John Bathurst		

	1748-1750	Charles Turner		
	1782-1791	Charles Sleigh, William Hoar & Charles Foster		
	1891	Arkendale Mining Co.		
Employment:		Underground	Surface	Total
	1782-1783	23		
	1783-1784	14		
	1784-1785	6		
	1785-1786	2		
	1786-1787	6		
	1787-1788	1		
	1788-1789	2		
	1789-1790	3		
	1790-1791	4		
	1862	7		

WINNS LEVEL		Appletreewick			SE066621
Production:	Lead	Ore(tons)	Lead (tons)		Value (£)
	1877-1890	No detailed returns			
Comment:	1877-1879	See Appletreewick Gill Head			
Mineral Lord:	1877-1890	See Appletreewick Liberty			
Worked by:	1877-1890	Samuel Pullan			
Employment:		Underground	Surface	Total	
	1877	4	2	6	
	1878	4	0	4	
	1879	3	1	4	

WINTERBURN LIBERTY		Winterburn		SD934569
Production:	Lead	Ore(tons)	Lead (tons)	Value (£)
	1773		0.14	
	1789		0.50	
	1790		0.35	
Comment:	1773-1790	Smelted at Grassington		
	1773-1790	May include Brockabank		
Worked by:	1773-1790	Mr Wilkinson		

WINTERGILL		Egton	NZ759018
Production:	Iron	Ore(tons)	Value (£)
	1878-1879	No detailed returns	
Comment:	1878-1883	Working Ellerbeck Bed	
	1879-1883	Standing	
Mineral Lord:	1878-1883	John Foster & Son	
Worked by:	1871	M. Snowdon	
	1878-1880	Lovel & Roseby	
	1882-1883	Thomas Evans	
Agent:	1878-1883	Thomas Evans	

WOODALE Carlton Highdale SE020781

Production:	Lead	Ore(tons)	Lead (tons)	Value (£)
	1873		1.54	
Comment:	1873	From Woodale Cow Side		
Worked by:	1873	Horner & Co.		

WOODHALL Arkengarthdale

Production:	Lead	Ore(tons)	Lead (tons)	Value (£)
	1785	3.80		
	1786	9.70		
	1787	9.80		
	1788	4.70		
Comment:	1785-1788	December to May inclusive		
	1788	Standing - June to November inclusive		
	1788	December 1788 to November 1789 inclusive		
Mineral Lord:	1782-1791	See Arkengarthdale		
Worked by:	1782-1791	Charles Sleigh, William Hoar & Charles Foster		
Employment:		Underground	Surface	Total
	1785-1786	1		
	1786-1787	2		
	1787-1788	2		
	1788-1789	2		

WOODHALL Carperby cum Thoresby SD975910

Production:	Lead	Ore(tons)	Lead (tons)	Value (£)
	1702-1703	No detailed returns		
	1868	6.50	4.80	
	1869	No detailed return		
	1870	4.10	3.10	
	1871	2.30	1.70	
Comment:	1703	Smelting at Marrick Cupola		
	1873	Suspended		
Mineral Lord:	1702-1877	See under Keld Heads		
Worked by:	1702-1703	Mr Thompson		
	1862-1870	Lightfoot's Devisees		
	1871-1877	Woodhall Mining Co.		
Agent:	1862	William Craig		
	1862-1870	Messrs J. Winn		
	1871-1877	J. Raisbeck		

WORSAW Worston SD777435

Production:	Lead	Ore(tons)	Lead (tons)	Value (£)
	1593	No detailed return		
	1668	No detailed return		
Mineral Lord:	1668	Duke of Albermarle		
Worked by:	1668	George Lascelles & Co.		

WORTON Bainbridge SD958901

Production:	Lead	Ore(tons)	Lead(tons)	Silver(ozs)	Value(£)
	1871-1874	No detailed return			
	1875	108.00	81.00	240.00	1561.00
	1876	117.30	88.00		
	1877	38.20	28.50		478.10
	1879	10.00	7.50		103.00
	1880	23.60	17.70		224.00
	1881	34.00	23.60		306.00
	1882	22.50	15.50		202.00

Worked by: 1877-1883 Worton Mining Co.
Agent: 1879-1881 John Tattersall
1880-1881 Jos. Hopper
1882 C. Rodwell
1883 J. Raw

Employment:		Underground	Surface	Total
	1877-1878	28	2	10
	1879	8	0	8
	1880	13	1	14

WRECKHILLS Hinderwell NZ810166

Production: Iron Ore(tons) Value (£)
1856-1864 No detailed returns
Comment: 1856-1864 Main and Top Seams
Mineral Lord: 1856-1864 Addison Brown
Worked by: 1856-1859 Victoria Iron & Cement Co.
1859-1864 Albert Iron & Cement Co.

WYNCH BRIDGE TRIAL Holwick NY956276

Production: Zinc Ore(tons) Zinc (tons) Value (£)
1941-1942 No detailed returns
Comment: 1941-1942 Prospecting for zinc
1942 Discontinued
1943 Abandoned
Worked by: 1941-1943 Metallic Ores Committee

YARNBURY Grassington SE016659

Production:	Lead	Ore(tons)	Lead (tons)	Value (£)
	1735		1.88	
	1736		5.47	
	1737		15.02	
	1738		36.86	
	1739		30.96	
	1740		26.19	
	1741		63.08	
	1742		67.64	
	1743		8.48	

1744	53.45
1745	35.34
1746	13.32
1747	45.51
1748	17.58
1749	7.21
1750	1.67
1751	16.93
1752	10.63
1753	5.48
1754	3.93
1755	3.94
1765	3.26
1766	8.97
1767	16.19
1768	6.28
1769	6.17
1770	1.83
1771	2.06
1772	1.80
1774	1.46
1776	0.29
1777	0.28
1778	0.82
1779	0.53
1780	10.26
1781	1.35
1782	17.79
1783	1.46
1784	1.61
1785	4.47
1786	21.32
1787	39.52
1788	17.73
1789	6.76
1790	9.80
1791	8.45
1792	4.09
1793	2.96
1794	4.85
1795	4.00
1796	1.45
1798	0.70
1799	7.05
1800	13.05
1801	7.30
1802	13.85

1803		7.05
1804		0.75
1808		0.35
1809	1.80	0.85
1810	0.80	0.45
1811	2.10	0.90
1812	49.48	27.00
1813	36.05	20.25
1814	24.73	13.50
1815	16.25	8.35
1816	7.13	3.55
1817	6.70	3.60
1818	3.85	1.95
1819	11.05	5.55
1820	38.90	22.05
1821	30.75	15.75
1822	63.73	30.30
1823	154.60	84.70
1824	251.50	128.60
1825	467.80	236.00
1826	605.95	339.75
1827	701.62	453.25
1828	544.14	347.20
1829	387.40	220.30
1830	446.18	245.50
1831	281.55	159.35
1832	332.53	196.55
1833	285.78	161.40
1834	194.45	101.40
1835	161.10	85.10
1836	125.35	71.15
1840	3.60	1.25
1841	6.58	3.10
1842	4.95	2.25
1843	6.80	3.20
1844	16.65	8.10
1845	11.75	6.55
1846	11.38	5.35
1848	1.10	0.55

Comment: 1756-1764 Data missing
1828-1829 See Coalgrovebeck & Yarnbury
1836-1839 See Coalgrovebeck & Yarnbury

Mineral Lord: 1735-1848 See under Grassington

Worked by: 1821-1848 Duke of Devonshire

YORKSHIRE & LANCASTER UNITED Rimington SD814452

Production:	Lead	Ore(tons)	Lead (tons)	Value (£)
	1880-1891	No detailed returns		
Comment:	1880-1891	See Rimington Mine		

YORKSHIRE Appletreewick SE069644

Production:	Lead	Ore(tons)	Lead (tons)	Value (£)
	1852-1860	No detailed returns		
	1861	12.40	8.10	
	1863	22.20	10.30	
	1864	137.20	89.20	
	1865	231.20	154.90	
	1866	290.00	191.20	
	1867	198.60	149.20	
	1868	90.70	59.00	
	1869	23.20	17.40	
	1874	4.40	3.10	108.00
	1880	2.60	1.30	15.90

Comment: 1852-1874 Working at Nussey Knott
1879-1881 Driving level nearly 1 mile long
Mineral Lord: 1852-1881 See Appletreewick Liberty
Worked by: 1852-1856 Yorkshire Mining Co. (Cost Book)
1856-1881 Yorkshire Mining Co. Ltd
Agent: 1862-1868 Matthew Newbould
1869-1875 William Newbould
1876-1880 Samuel Simpson
Secretary: 1857-1862 Edward Bolton
1862-1881 John Gledhill

Employment:		Underground	Surface	Total
	1862	10		

YORKSHIRE MINES (LLC) Teesdale

Production:	Lead	Ore(tons)	Lead(tons)	Silver(ozs)	Value(£)
	1855	13.60	8.50		
	1856	No detailed returns			
	1857	14.50	10.80		
	1858	40.10	28.50		
	1859	No detailed return			
	1860	65.80	42.20	215.00	
	1861	162.90	105.30	526.00	
	1862	242.00	157.30		
	1863	176.10	118.00		
	1864	174.90	117.20		
	1865	No detailed return			
	1866	102.20	71.40		
	1867	No detailed return			

Comment: 1855-1879 See Lunehead

	1863-1864	Governor & Company's mines in Teesdale		
	1877-1879	Governor & Company's mines in Teesdale		
Worked by:	1860-1879	London Lead Company		
Employment:		Underground	Surface	Total
	1877	28	12	40
	1878	22	16	38
	1879	20	10	30

ZZ - SUNDRIES

Production:	Lead	Ore(tons)	Lead(tons)	Silver(ozs)	Value(£)
	1858			1570.00	
	1859			1000.00	
	1860			2500.00	
	1861			2750.00	
	1862	9.10	4.80	3000.00	
	1863	11.40	7.60	3080.00	
	1864	131.90	37.10	2992.00	
	1865	11.70	6.20	2247.00	
	1866	31.50	21.20	1500.00	
	1867	25.00	19.00	3000.00	
	1868	25.20	16.40		
	1869	17.00	12.00		
	1870	20.00	15.00		
	1873			1500.00	
	1874			1000.00	
	1875			1000.00	
	1876			2250.00	
Comment:	1858-1859	Chiefly from white lead manufacturers			
Production:	Barytes	Ore(tons)			Value (£)
	1860	1750.00			
	1861	795.00			
	1862	500.00			
Production:	Iron	Ore(tons)			Value (£)
	1858-1859	No detailed return			
	1860	10000.00			1000.00
	1861	No detailed return			
	1876	168371.00			
	1877	143805.00			
	1878	225000.00			
	1879	15723.30			
	1880	282826.60			
	1881	92839.00			
Comment:	1858-1859	See Grosmont Cleveland			
	1860	Cleveland			
	1861	See Grosmont Cleveland			
	1876-1878	Cleveland			
	1879-1881	Est. Cleveland			

Index to personal names

C

I

J

T

U

V

W

Y

Z